introduction to

STATISTICAL THERMODYNAMICS

introduction to statistical thermodynamics

ELDON L. KNUTH
Chemical, Nuclear, Thermal Division
Department of Engineering
University of California
Los Angeles

McGRAW-HILL BOOK COMPANY
New York San Francisco St. Louis
London Toronto Sydney

INTRODUCTION TO STATISTICAL THERMODYNAMICS

Printed in the United States of America

Library of Congress catalog card number: 66-20005

1234567890 PE 721069876

35262

preface

The motivation for writing this book was the need for an undergraduate statistical-thermodynamics text to supplement the several available excellent undergraduate classical-thermodynamics texts. In particular, the need exists for a supplement which is arranged such that no "picking and piecing" is required in order to devote as little as one-third semester or as much as one semester to an introduction to statistical thermodynamics. The (relatively few) existing undergraduate statistical-thermodynamics texts appear to be arranged for a course of study requiring a minimum of one semester. If it is desired to use one of them for less than a semester, one is compelled to "pick and piece" in order to reach, in the allotted time, the applications required for student motivation. Such "picking and piecing" may lead to the omission, in the skipped chapters, of material relevant to the assigned chapters. Even if such an omission does not occur, the student may suspect that it has occurred.

This book is designed for use by students who have studied previously the fundamentals of classical thermodynamics but who have had no introduction to statistical thermodynamics. I am aware that different teachers have different opinions concerning the order in which classical and statistical thermodynamics are to be introduced to the student. My decision to introduce statistical thermodynamics after the students have studied the fundamentals of classical thermodynamics was based, in part, upon a two-semester study (in 1961-1962) of the effects of the order of presentation. In one phase of the study, one group of junior-level students studied statistical thermodynamics first, whereas another group of students with similar backgrounds studied classical thermodynamics first. In order to minimize the teacher variable, the teachers exchanged classes at the end of the first semester. Students in the group taught classical thermodynamics followed by statistical thermodynamics did significantly better on a comprehensive final examination than did the students in the group taught statistical thermodynamics followed by classical thermodynamics. Since this study was limited to (1) a particular institution, (2) only two teachers, (3) only two textbooks, and (4) the academic year 1961-1962, caution must be used when extrapolating these results to other institutions, other teachers, other textbooks, and other times. Nevertheless, these results have encouraged me to commit myself to an undergraduate statistical-thermodynamics book which presupposes a knowledge of the fundamentals of classical thermodynamics.

Although the notes upon which this book is based were written primarily for use at the junior level, the book is applicable at whatever level statistical thermodynamics is introduced for the first time. Depending upon the school, the introduction may occur at junior, senior, or first-year-graduate levels.

Several alternative viewpoints and methods are available when setting up a course of study in statistical thermodynamics. Some of these alternatives are listed here in order to place the viewpoints and methods of the present book in better perspective. (Lettered entries are alternatives.)

1. Model used when averaging
   a. A large number of identical models of the system under consideration (the method of Gibbs)
   b. A system consisting of a large number of identical elementary particles or subsystems (the method of Maxwell and Boltzmann)
2. Procedures used when averaging
   a. Average over the most probable distribution
   b. Average over all possible distributions
3. Interpretation of probabilities
   a. Fraction of a large number of systems in a given state (or range of states)
   b. Fraction of a long period of time that a single system spends in a given state (or range of states)
4. Mechanics used to predict possible states
   a. Quantum mechanics
   b. Classical mechanics
5. Boundary conditions on system
   a. Impervious to neither energy nor matter; volume fixed
   b. Impervious to matter but not energy; volume fixed
   c. Impervious to energy and matter; volume fixed
6. Relationship between classical and statistical thermodynamics
   a. They are equally fundamental
   b. Classical thermodynamics is more fundamental
   c. Statistical thermodynamics is more fundamental

The viewpoints and methods which I adopted are listed as alternative *a* in each category. Whenever two methods appeared to be equally simple, I chose the more general method.

Regarding the model used when averaging, Schrödinger (see Bibliography) writes:

> The older and more naive application is to *N* actually existing physical systems in actual physical interaction with each other, e.g., gas molecules or electrons or Planck oscillators or degrees of freedom ("ether oscillators") of a "hohlraum." The *N* of them together represent the actual physical system under consideration. This original point of view is associated with the names of Maxwell, Boltzmann, and others.
>
> But it suffices only for dealing with a very restricted class of physical systems – virtually only with gases. It is not applicable to a system which does not consist of a great number of identical constituents with "private" energies. . . .
>
> Hence a second point of view (or, rather, a different application of the same mathematical results), which we owe to Willard Gibbs, has been developed. It has a particular beauty of its own, is applicable quite generally to every physical system, and has some advantages to be mentioned forthwith. Here the *N* identical systems are mental copies of the one system under consideration – of the one macroscopic device that is actually erected on our laboratory table. . . . The advantage consists not only in the general applicability, but also in the following two points:
>
> (*i*) *N* can be made arbitrarily large. . . . Hence the applicability, for example, of Stirling's formula . . . need never be questioned.
>
> (*ii*) No question about the individuality of the members of the assembly can ever arise – as it does, according to the "new statistics," with particles. Our systems are macroscopic systems, which we could, in principle, furnish with labels.

As a final point in his comparison of the method of Maxwell and Boltzmann to the method of Gibbs, Schrödinger notes that "the fluctuations of a system in a heat-bath at constant temperature are much more easily obtained directly from the Gibbs point of view." (I believe that if Schrödinger had had a greater interest in chemistry, he would have extended this statement to include also the fluctuations of an open system in contact with a reservoir at constant chemical potential.) Considering all these points, I agree with Schrödinger that "there is no point in following up the more complicated device" (the method of Maxwell and Boltzmann). I believe that the ensemble of independent members which I use erases the objection that the ensemble method is more abstract than is the method of Maxwell and Boltzmann. For the convenience of the reader, an annotated Selected Bibliography of Works using the Ensemble Method is included on page xiv.

Regarding the procedure used when averaging, since the number of members of the ensemble may be increased indefinitely, the use of the most probable distribution is just as rigorous (although not as elegant) as the use of all possible distributions. The principal advantage of using the most probable distribution is that it requires much less sophisticated mathematics.

The choice of interpretation of probabilities was motivated in part by the fact that, for a macroscopic system, the time required for the system to pass, at least once, through all allowed system quantum states is much larger than the time over which one averages when one makes measurements. Hence measurements on macroscopic systems are to be interpreted as averages over relatively short periods of time. These measurements are reproducible because a great majority of the allowed quantum states of a macroscopic system have macroscopic properties which are indistinguishable with the instruments used.

Fortunately, all major factors relevant to the choice between classical and quantum mechanics support the use of quantum mechanics. Not only is it more simple in many respects, both in concept and in practice, to apply probability theory to systems with discrete allowable energy levels than to systems with continuously variable energies, but also quantum mechanics provides the most general description of a mechanical system — and includes, as a special case, classical mechanics. Furthermore, in a quantum-mechanical treatment, Planck's constant *h* and the concept of indistinguishable particles are an integral part of the mechanics and do not have to be introduced artifically. Finally, numerous phenomena (including thermal radiation at intermediate wavelengths, variation of heat capacities with temperature, and the contribution of the electron gas to the heat capacity of a metal) are described inadequately by classical mechanics. The objection that the required introduction to quantum mechanics is beyond the reach of upper-division students has been erased by the strengthened backgrounds of the students and by the appearance of upper-division texts such as that by Sherwin.[1] The present book requires no background in quantum mechanics.

The three tabulated alternative combinations of system boundary conditions (corresponding respectively to the grand canonical, the canonical, and the microcanonical ensembles) are, of the many possible combinations, the three which are used most frequently. The grand canonical ensemble is, simultaneously, the most general ensemble, the ensemble with the least mathematical difficulties, and the ensemble which is related most easily to thermodynamics. Regarding its generality, Fowler and Guggenheim[2] write, " . . . a more general and powerful statistical method than any we have explicitly used hitherto . . . is the quantal analog of Gibbs' use of the *grand canonical ensemble*. . . . " and Münster (see Bibliography) writes, on page 187, "The method of the grand canonical ensemble is, due to its generality and adaptability, one of the most important tools of statistical thermodynamics." Regarding its mathematical advantages, Reif (see Bibliography) writes on page 227, ". . . where the constraint of a fixed number of particles is cumbersome, one can . . . readily circumvent the complication by approxi-

[1]C. W. Sherwin, "Introduction to Quantum Mechanics," Henry Holt and Company, New York, 1959.

[2]R. H. Fowler and E. A. Guggenheim, "Statistical Thermodynamics," p. 231, The University Press, Cambridge, 1939.

mating the actual situation with one where only the mean number of particles is fixed, i.e., by using the grand canonical distribution." Hence, since most results of interest to thermodynamicists are independent of the nature of the ensemble which is used, I use the grand canonical ensemble frequently, the canonical ensemble sometimes, and the microcanonical ensemble seldom.

In the spirit of developing a treatment which is brief, suitable for use at the upper-division level, and yet rigorous, several additional (relatively minor) innovations have been introduced. For example, the identification of the most probable distribution of ensemble members has been simplified by identifying it directly with that distribution for which the number of possible quantum states of the ensemble and reservoir is a maximum; a greater similarity in the treatments of the discrete nature of matter and the discrete nature of energy has been achieved by considering the number of particles in an open system to be a function of the quantum state of the system; and the correspondence between classical and statistical thermodynamics has been established relatively simply by comparing two equations from classical thermodynamics with two equations from statistical thermodynamics.

I have attempted to unify the methods as much as possible without introducing the unnecessary mathematical complications. Typical results of this effort are treatment of the Maxwell-Boltzmann system as a limiting case of Fermi-Dirac and Bose-Einstein systems and assignment of a central role to the partition function in each of the seven applications (Chapters 8 to 14).

The first seven chapters are devoted to the fundamentals, the next seven chapters contain applications of the fundamentals to a series of relatively simple examples, and the last chapter is devoted to a summary and comparisons of the essential features of the preceding chapters. The applications (Chapters 8 to 14) are an essential part of the book; they simultaneously clarify the fundamentals and illustrate the capability of statistical thermodynamics to provide physical interpretations and numerical values of thermodynamic properties. Examples serve both to clarify the main text and to provide detailed applications. The approximately one hundred problems are an important part of the book; they include simple derivations omitted in the text, typical applications of the fundamentals, and questions designed to stimulate independent thinking.

The notes upon which this book is based evolved as I taught the second-semester junior-level course in thermodynamics ten times during the past eight years. An average of five weeks (15 contact hours) of the semester was spent on statistical thermodynamics, covering the first seven chapters and two of the next seven chapters (that is, the fundamentals and two applications). In a typical schedule, approximately one hour was spent on each of the first four chapters, approximately two hours on each of the next five chapters, and one hour on a quiz. In 10 weeks (30 contact hours), one might cover nearly all of the 15 chapters; in a full semester (45 contact hours), one might cover all 15 chapters and all the appendixes. An attempt has been made to include a sufficiently wide range of topics so that the book might be useful to engineers, chemists, and physicists.

Questions concerning the appropriate level of generality arose at several points in the writing of the book. Should I specialize, thereby gaining simplicity? Or should I generalize, thereby facilitating more extensive applications? In several instances, I found that a specialized discussion in the classroom accompanied by a generalized description in the printed notes (book) provided an excellent solution. The teachers using this book may wish to specialize in the classroom, replacing the generalized displacements (for example, Chapter 3) by the volume, the mixture of particles of several types (for example, Chapter 3) by a pure substance, and the generalized coordinates (for example, Chapter 7) by rectangular coordinates. In these cases, the specialization of a generalized expression appears to be more simple than the generalization of a specialized expression.

To the many people who have influenced, wittingly or unwittingly, this book, I am indebted. Of my teachers, I wish to single out Professor W. D. Rannie, who aroused an interest in the methods of J. Willard Gibbs. Professor Myron Tribus (always ready to discuss viewpoints and methods of thermodynamics) stimulated me, in my early days at UCLA, to consider alternative approaches in the teaching of statistical thermodynamics. As my interest in statistical thermodynamics became more serious, I found the writings of Professor T. L. Hill to be more and more valuable; in fact, Chapter 12, "Perfect Adsorbed Gas," is based directly upon his treatment. (The weaknesses which might be found in my treatment are not his responsibility, of course.) During my two weeks at M.I.T. during July, 1965, Professors J. H. Keenan, G. N. Hatsopoulos, and R. A. Gaggioli contributed significantly by their critical reviews of the manuscript – particularly of the first several chapters. Dean L. M. K. Boelter provided the atmosphere of freedom which is essential to the exploration of new ideas. Of the many students who have uncovered weaknesses and deficiencies in the manuscript, I would like to single out for special thanks Mr. N. El-Ramly. By inviting me to participate in the UCLA Modern Engineering for Engineering Executives course, Professor J. M. English (in 1961) and Professor R. L. Perrine (in 1965) encouraged and facilitated the preparation of preliminary versions of the manuscript. Members of the Reports Group converted, with relatively few typographical errors, my long-hand version of the manuscript into legible typed copy. My wife has provided not only an atmosphere in which it is easy for me to devote time to writing but also invaluable assistance in proofreading.

ELDON L. KNUTH

contents

appendixes

selected bibliography of works using the ensemble method

1. **Boltzmann, L.**: *"Lectures on Gas Theory," University of California Press, Berkeley, Calif., 1964.*

Although Boltzmann did not use ensembles extensively in his analyses, he did refer in these Lectures to the concept of the ensemble we call microcanonical–particularly in Chapter III, "Principles of General Mechanics Needed for Gas Theory," of Part II, published originally in 1898. (Gibbs acknowledged that the first explicit consideration of the distribution of a large number of members of an ensemble was by Boltzmann in a paper titled "Zusammenhang zwischen den Sätzen über das Verhalten mehratomiger Gasmoleküle mit Jacobi's Princip des letzten Multiplicators," published in 1871.) The Translator's Introduction is recommended highly for students at all levels; the Lectures are recommended for serious graduate students.

2. **Gibbs, J. W.**: *Elementary Principles in Statistical Mechanics, in H. A. Bumstead and R. G. Van Name, "The Collected Works of J. Willard Gibbs," vol. II, pp. 1-207, Yale University Press, New Haven, Conn., 1948.*

This masterpiece, written in 1901, established the discipline of statistical thermodynamics and introduced (in addition to the microcanonical ensemble) the canonical and grand canonical ensembles. This rigorous exposition is recommended to serious graduate students but would be difficult reading for undergraduates.

3. **Tolman, R. C.:** *"The Principles of Statistical Mechanics," Oxford University Press, Fair Lawn, N.J., 1938.*

This 661-page treatise applies the ensemble method, used so effectively by Gibbs in his treatments of classical-mechanical systems, to quantum-mechanical systems. Every serious student of statistical thermodynamics should study, eventually, this careful treatment.

4. **Slater, J. C.:** *"Introduction to Chemical Physics," McGraw-Hill Book Company, New York, 1939.*

The content and style of this book have contributed to the reduction of the barriers separating physics and chemistry. The student may wish to consider this book for supplementary reading.

5. **Schrödinger, E.:** *"Statistical Thermodynamics," Cambridge University Press, New York, 1946.*

This stimulating 95-page course of seminar lectures appears to have influenced, more than any other single publication, the trend toward the use of the ensemble method which has occurred during the past decade. Although written clearly, its conciseness may deter students from reading it until after completing introductory studies of the subject.

6. **ter Haar, D.:** *"Elements of Statistical Mechanics," Holt, Rinehart and Winston, Inc., New York, 1954.*

The ensemble method is used extensively in the latter three-fourths of the book. It is recommended to graduate students.

7. **Becker, R.:** *"Theorie der Wärme," Springer-Verlag OHG, Berlin, 1955.*

Written by a physicist, this volume provides a good introduction to classical thermodynamics, statistical thermodynamics, and irreversible thermodynamics. In German.

8. **Denbigh, K.:** *"The Principles of Chemical Equilibrium," Cambridge University Press, New York, 1955.*

Part III, "Thermodynamics in Relation to the Existence of Molecules," provides a brief treatment of statistical thermodynamics which emphasizes chemical-engineering applications. Chemical engineers and chemists may wish to consider this book for supplementary reading.

9. **Münster, A.**: *"Statistische Thermodynamik," Springer-Verlag OHG, Berlin, 1956.*

This 852-page treatise includes, particularly in Chapter VII, discussions and applications of the grand canonical ensemble. In German.

10. **Hill, T. L.**: *"Statistical Mechanics," McGraw-Hill Book Company, New York, 1956.*

This advanced treatment, emphasizing developments in physical chemistry and chemical physics since about 1940, also includes discussions and applications of the grand canonical ensemble. Chemists might consider this book for an advanced course.

11. **Landau, L. D.: and E. M. Lifshitz**: *"Statistical Physics," Addison-Wesley Publishing Company, Inc., Reading, Mass., 1958.*

The first edition of this book, published in 1938, was among the first books using the powerful methods of Gibbs. Physicists might consider this book for an advanced course.

12. **Kittel, C.**: *"Elementary Statistical Physics," John Wiley & Sons, Inc., New York, 1958.*

The author discusses irreversible thermodynamics and transport theory as well as equilibrium statistical thermodynamics. The level is suitable for first-year graduate students.

13. **Chisholm, J. S. R., and A. H. de Borde**: *"An Introduction to Statistical Mechanics," Pergamon Press, London, 1958.*

The authors "aimed at producing a concise introduction to statistical mechanics suitable for students pursuing an Honours course in Physics or Mathematics." Most upper-division students might find it too difficult.

14. **Hill, T. L.**: *"Introduction to Statistical Thermodynamics," Addison-Wesley Publishing Company, Inc., Reading, Mass., 1960.*

Since my viewpoints and methods are similar to those used by Hill, I have adopted some of the nomenclature used in this book in order to facilitate its use by the student in later studies. This text, covering a wide range of topics, is intermediate in difficulty to the present book and to Hill's "Statistical Mechanics."

15. Tribus, M.: *"Thermostatics and Thermodynamics," D. Van Nostrand Company, Inc., Princeton, N.J., 1961.*

Combining information theory, statistical thermodynamics, and classical thermodynamics, the author departed from tradition by introducing, in a first course in thermodynamics, concepts of statistical thermodynamics before concepts of classical thermodynamics. This book was intended for use by upper-division students in engineering.

16. Andrews, F. C.: *"Equilibrium Statistical Mechanics," John Wiley & Sons, Inc., New York, 1963.*

This brief (206 page) volume was written by a chemist for use at the upper-division level. It is recommended for supplementary reading.

17. Huang, K.: *"Statistical Mechanics," John Wiley & Sons, Inc., New York, 1963.*

Classical thermodynamics, kinetic theory, and statistical mechanics (with applications to modern topics of interest to physicists) are covered. The level and coverage are suitable for a graduate course in physics.

18. Hatsopoulos, G. N., and J. H. Keenan: *"Principles of General Thermodynamics," John Wiley & Sons, Inc., New York, 1965.*

In Part II, General Thermodynamics, the authors approach the perennial problem of reconciling classical and statistical thermodynamics by defining a thermodynamic system as "an entity which is representative of a Gibbs ensemble and whose state is an average of the states of the members of the ensemble." The emphasis on rigor and generality (at the expense of brevity) makes this book particularly suitable for graduate-level use.

19. Reif, F.: *"Fundamentals of Statistical and Thermal Physics," McGraw-Hill Book Company, New York, 1965.*

The author presents a unified treatment of classical thermodynamics, statistical thermodynamics, and kinetic theory. Although written primarily for use by upper-division physics students, the encyclopedic contents and the advanced level of certain topics make the book suitable also for a first-year graduate course.

***chapter* 1**

viewpoints and methods

A theory is the more impressive the greater the simplicity of its premises is, the more different kinds of things it relates, and the more extended is its area of applicability. Therefore the deep impression which classical thermodynamics made upon me. It is the only physical theory of universal content which I am convinced that, within the framework of the applicability of its basic concepts, it will never be overthrown (for the special attention of those who are skeptics on principle).

A. Einstein, 1946 †

Classical thermodynamics (that is, nonstatistical thermodynamics of macroscopic systems) is perhaps the most general discipline developed for direct application to physical systems. It is founded upon a small number of axioms and is applicable to many different types of systems; its principles are independent of physical models of matter. Hence the results of classical thermodynamics are relatively permanent.

The inventions of useful molecular models of matter created, however, a need for a discipline which supplements classical thermodynamics by using to the fullest possible extent these useful (although sometimes crude) molecular models in order to provide physical interpretations (that is, explanations) of the macroscopic behavior of matter and numerical values of the thermodynamic properties of matter. (Classical thermodynamics is not concerned, for example, with the origins of equations of state, but considers them to be available from measurements.) Consequently, a discipline was developed which applies a relatively small number of fundamental postulates, the methods of probability theory, and the laws of mechanics to either (1) system models involving large numbers of microscopic particles (or subsystems) or (2) ensembles of large numbers of system models in order to

† A. Einstein, Autobiographical Notes, in P. A. Schilpp (ed.), "Albert Einstein: Philosopher-Scientist," Tudor Publishing Company, New York, 1951.

predict the macroscopic behavior of these systems. This discipline provides statistical and mechanical interpretations of thermodynamic properties (for example, entropy, temperature, and chemical potential) and of thermodynamic processes (for example, processes involving work interactions and heat interactions). To the approximations required in practice for applying the laws of mechanics to systems that are of interest to engineers and scientists, it provides procedures for predicting numerical values of thermodynamic properties from given molecular properties, such as a procedure for predicting heat capacities of polyatomic gases from molecular properties deduced from spectroscopic measurements. It is frequently called **statistical thermodynamics** and is used in studies in such diverse fields as biology, metallurgy, chemistry, solid-state physics, nuclear physics, astrophysics, communications, energy conversion, gas dynamics, and electronics.

Questions concerning the relative positions of classical thermodynamics and statistical thermodynamics are raised sometimes. Since classical thermodynamics does not involve physical models of matter, is it the more fundamental discipline? Or is statistical thermodynamics, since it provides physical interpretations and numerical values, the more fundamental discipline? Is one of these disciplines the "correct" discipline and the other only an approximation? A reasonable attitude might be to consider these two disciplines to be equally fundamental and equally valid, and to require that when they describe the same phenomena, their descriptions be in agreement. This attitude is taken here; some aspects of classical thermodynamics and statistical thermodynamics are placed in correspondence, whereas other aspects are considered to be complementary.

As an introduction to the differences and analogies between these two disciplines, consider energy. According to the **first law of thermodynamics**, energy is a function of the state of a system; changes in **energy** may be associated with adiabatic work effects according to

$$dE = -đW_{\text{ad}}$$

where E is the energy of the system, $đW_{\text{ad}}$ is the work done adiabatically by the system, and the bar through the differential indicates that the work done is a function of the process involved, that is, it is not a unique function of the final and initial states of the system. (The **work** done adiabatically by a system may be determined by repeating adiabatically the changes undergone by the system and observing the distance that a given weight external to the system is raised while no other permanent changes are produced in its environment.) This definition of energy does not depend upon a physical model of matter and does not provide physical interpretations; the given equation implies that, using the methods of classical thermodynamics, changes in energy may be computed from measurements of work done but that numerical values of energy cannot be established. In statistical thermodynamics, on the other hand, although changes in energy still may be computed from work done, energy is interpreted as the expected value of the sum of the kinetic and potential energies of the microscopic particles or subsystems of the system; to the approximations required to apply the laws of mechanics to systems of interest to engineers and scientists, numerical values of energy may be established.

The discussion of statistical thermodynamics presented here uses quantum-mechanical (rather than classical-mechanical) concepts and language. The reader who has some acquaintance with the several texts dealing with statistical thermodynamics notes, perhaps, that many of these texts introduce first a statistics of classical mechanics and discuss later (if at all) a statistics of quantum mechanics. Introducing the statistics of classical mechanics first is in agreement with the order in which the discipline of statistical thermodynamics evolved. Here, however, the statistics of quantum mechanics is used from the beginning. It is more simple in many respects, both in concept and in practice, to apply probability theory to systems with discrete allowable energy levels than to systems with continuously variable energies. In a quantum-mechanical treatment, Planck's constant h and the concept of indistinguishable particles are an integral part of the mechanics and do not have to be introduced artificially. Furthermore, quantum mechanics provides the most general description of a mechanical system—and includes, as a special case, classical mechanics. Fortunately, only a modest number of concepts and principles from quantum mechanics are required. In the first five chapters, the only quantum-mechanical concepts required are those of discrete quantum states, discrete energy levels, and discrete mass quantities; in Chapter 6 the Pauli exclusion principle must be added; in Chapters 8 to 14 the allowed quantum states of several simple mechanical models are required.

The **probability** used, for example, in Chapter 2 is interpreted as the fraction of a large number of systems which are in a given quantum state. Some authors state that this probability is the fraction of a long period of time that a single system spends in a given quantum state. For a macroscopic system, however, this "long period of time" is much longer than the period of time over which one averages when one makes measurements. Hence measurements on macroscopic systems are to be interpreted as averages over relatively short periods of time. These measurements are reproducible because a great majority of the allowed quantum states of a macroscopic system have macroscopic properties which are indistinguishable with the instruments used. Fortunately, calculations involving averages of stationary states of a large number of systems are more simple than calculations involving averages over time of nonstationary states of a single system.

In the discussions of probabilities, and in the calculations of expected values from these probabilities, the concept of an ensemble of members will be found useful. As used in the present text, an **ensemble of members** is defined to be a large number n of independent members in contact with a **reservoir** (i.e., environment) under the following conditions (see Figure 1-1):

1. The reservoir is so large that its intensive properties are not affected by interactions with the members of the ensemble,
2. Each **ensemble member** is a model of the system under consideration and all members are identical (they have the same *possible* quantum states but are not necessarily in the same quantum state),
3. The ensemble of members and reservoir are isolated from the rest of the universe, and

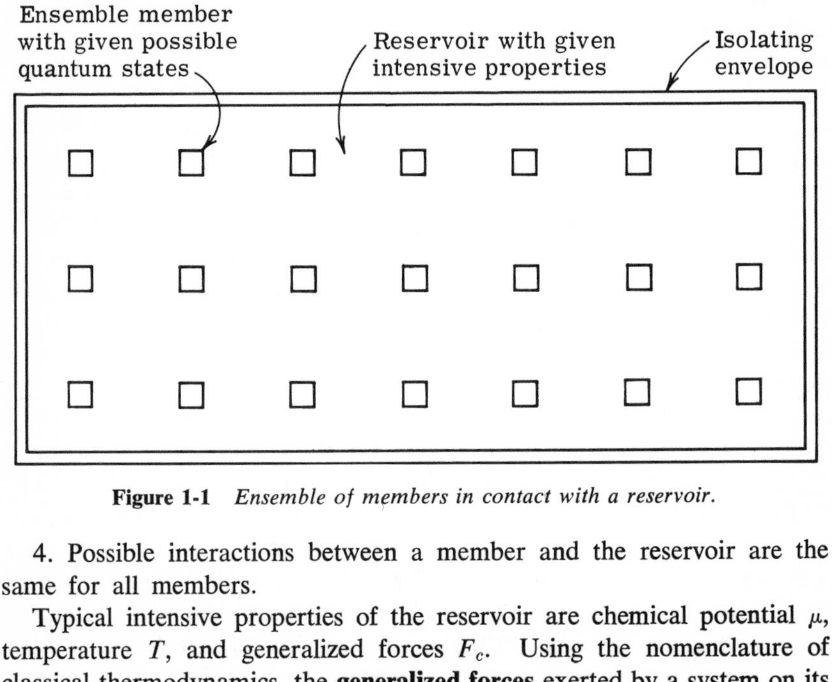

Figure 1-1 *Ensemble of members in contact with a reservoir.*

4. Possible interactions between a member and the reservoir are the same for all members.

Typical intensive properties of the reservoir are chemical potential μ, temperature T, and generalized forces F_c. Using the nomenclature of classical thermodynamics, the **generalized forces** exerted by a system on its surroundings may be identified by writing the work done by the system in the form

$$\text{đ}W_r = \sum_c F_c \, dX_c$$

where the subscript r refers to a reversible process and the X_c's are the **generalized displacements**. Since the work done adiabatically by a system equals the decrease in the energy of the system, one may write alternatively

$$F_c = -\left(\frac{\partial E}{\partial X_c}\right)_{X_c', S}$$

where the subscripts X_c' and S indicate respectively that all generalized displacements except X_c are held constant and that entropy is held constant. (Holding the entropy constant does not ensure that the process is reversible and adiabatic, but it does ensure that the effect on the system is the same as it would be if the process were reversible and adiabatic.) Since the X_c's are extensive, they are called "extensive quantities" in some texts; since they may be interpreted as parameters of the environment of the system, they are called "external parameters" in other texts. Typical examples of generalized forces and displacements are given in Table 1-1.

Table 1-1 Examples of generalized forces and displacements

Generalized force	*Generalized displacement*
Force	Length
Surface tension	Area
Pressure	Volume
Electrostatic field intensity	Volume × electric displacement
Magnetic field intensity	Volume × magnetic induction

NOTE: Electric displacement and magnetic induction are intensive properties.

The generalized force and the generalized displacement used most frequently in thermodynamics are pressure p and volume V.

Example

As an example of the concept of an ensemble in contact with a reservoir, consider the ensemble and reservoir which correspond to a mole of argon in a 1-liter closed container in thermal contact with air which surrounds it. The ensemble members would be a large number of 1-mole quantities of argon in 1-liter closed containers. The reservoir might be air which fills all space interior to some large isolating envelope but exterior to the members. Since the ensemble corresponds to a closed container in thermal contact with its surroundings, the container walls permit transfer of energy but not mass. As a consequence of these energy transfers, the energies of the several members of the ensemble may differ. However, as a consequence of the relatively large size of the reservoir (the body of air surrounding the containers of argon), the temperature and pressure of the reservoir are affected negligibly by these energy transfers.

After a brief discussion (Chapter 2) of the postulated analogy between the mechanical properties of a system described by classical thermodynamics and the expected values of the mechanical quantities of an ensemble described by statistical thermodynamics, it is shown (Chapter 3) that use of a sum known as the **partition function** facilitates the application of the fundamental postulates of statistical thermodynamics and the methods of probability theory to results provided by the discipline of quantum mechanics. Next, procedures for calculating expected values of mechanical quantities are established (Chapter 4). These expected values are brought into correspondence with the mechanical properties of classical thermodynamics (Chapter 5), and statistical-thermodynamical analogs of the nonmechanical properties of classical thermodynamics are established. After a discussion of systems of particles with negligible effects of interparticle forces (Chapter 6), the methods of quantum mechanics are introduced briefly (Chapter 7) in order to provide a background for use of results of quantum mechanics in the applications which follow (Chapters 8 to 14). These applications (namely, the perfect monatomic gas, Einstein monatomic crystal, blackbody radiation, perfect electron gas, perfect adsorbed gas, perfect diatomic gas, and Debye monatomic crystal), although relatively simple, illustrate the capability of statistical thermodynamics to provide physical interpretations and numerical values of thermodynamic properties.

PROBLEM

1-1 Examine the proposal that a macroscopic measurement corresponds to an average over all possible system quantum states. As will be shown in Appendix E, the number of allowed system quantum states is of order e^N, where N is the number of particles in the system. For definiteness, consider a crystal. In order to obtain a very conservative lower limit to the time required for the system to pass through all possible system quantum states, consider the (highly improbable) case in which (*a*) The system passes through all possible system quantum states before passing through a given system quantum state twice, and (*b*) The system passes through system quantum states with frequency $N\nu$, where ν is the characteristic frequency of vibration of the crystal. For a typical crystal, ν is of order 6×10^{12} cycles/sec; N is of the order of Avogadro's number. Compare the value of time calculated for this case with the age of the universe. Does a macroscopic measurement correspond to an average over all possible system quantum states?

chapter **2**

fundamental postulates

The only error into which one can fall, is the want of agreement between the premises and the conclusions, and this, with care, one may hope, in the main, to avoid.
J. W. Gibbs, 1901 †

Within the discipline of statistical thermodynamics, several alternative paths (of various lengths) lead essentially to the same procedure for calculating property values of interest to thermodynamicists. The shortest path known to the author (excluding the zero-length path which is realized when beginning with the desired result!) is marked by the following two fundamental postulates:

> *Postulate* 1: The classical value of a mechanical-thermodynamic property of a system in equilibrium is analogous to the expected value computed from the most probable distribution of ensemble members among the possible ensemble-member quantum states.
>
> *Postulate* 2: The most probable distribution of ensemble members among possible ensemble-member quantum states is that distribution for which the number of possible quantum states of the ensemble and reservoir is a maximum.

The present chapter is devoted to clarifying the terms used in these postulates and reviewing the procedures used when calculating most probable distributions and expected values.

By **classical value** of a thermodynamic property is meant the value obtained from **macroscopic measurements** (measurements which cannot detect the presence of or the effects of individual molecules) in typical

† H. A. Bumstead and R. G. Van Name (eds.), "The Collected Works of J. Willard Gibbs," vol. II, p. x, Yale University Press, New Haven, Conn., 1948.

laboratory experiments and used in classical thermodynamics. Some of these values may be measured directly (e.g., pressure, volume, temperature, and mass), whereas others are measured indirectly (e.g., entropy, internal energy, enthalpy, Helmholtz function, and Gibbs function). Since some of these values are given relative to some arbitrary reference state, one must use this reference state consistently in a comparison of the results of macroscopic measurements with the predictions of statistical thermodynamics.

By **mechanical-thermodynamic property** is meant a macroscopic quantity (such as pressure, volume, energy, and mass) which has a well-defined value when a member is in a given quantum state. **Nonmechanical-thermodynamic properties** (such as temperature, chemical potential, and entropy) are not mentioned in Postulate 1 because their expected values cannot be computed directly from a distribution of ensemble members among the possible ensemble-member quantum states. Their statistical-thermodynamical analogs can be evaluated only after they have been identified in a comparison of results of statistical thermodynamics with results of classical thermodynamics.

The word "system" (sometimes, "thermodynamic system") is used when applying the language of classical thermodynamics; the statistical-thermodynamical analog of a system is a body with its state defined by expected values computed for the ensemble. (Since the state of a single member of an ensemble differs, in general, from the state defined by expected values computed for the ensemble, a single member of an ensemble is not an analog of a system.) The definition of either a system or an ensemble member must include (either explicitly or implicitly) specifications of the possible states and the possible processes for changing the state. Note that although the possible states of a system and the possible states of a member of an ensemble corresponding to this system are related, they differ sometimes. For example, a system corresponding to an ensemble of members, each member containing only one particle, will have states of uniform density, whereas the member of the ensemble will not.

By **ensemble-member quantum state** is meant a stationary state of a finite ensemble member, which state is described by (discrete) quantum numbers equal in number to the number of degrees of freedom of the member, and with which state is associated a discrete energy level and a discrete mass quantity. (A **stationary state** is a state for which the methods of quantum mechanics predict values of mechanical quantities which are time independent.) In the following paragraphs, the member quantum state will be indicated by the subscript j. If the given member has ϕ degrees of freedom, then the subscript j stands for ϕ quantum numbers. Specifying the quantum state (that is, assigning a value to each of the quantum numbers) fixes uniquely the energy level and the mass quantity. However, specifying the energy level and the mass quantity does not fix the quantum state; in general, more than one quantum state may have the same energy level and the same mass quantity. The prediction of possible quantum states (and associated energy levels and mass quantities) is the purpose of the discipline of quantum mechanics. (The reader may be aware that, in a typical application, the methods of quantum mechanics are applied to a system with specified mass quantity in order to predict possible system quantum states and associated energy levels. If possible system quantum states and associated energy levels are predicted for a large number of different mass quantities, then one may catalog these predictions by listing, as the independent parameter, the system quantum states and tabulating, as dependent quantities, the associated mass quantities and energy levels.)

By **distribution of ensemble members** is meant a specification of the number of members in each possible member quantum state—with no concern for the quantum state of a given member. On the other hand, the **ensemble quantum state** used in Postulate 2 is fixed by specifying the quantum state of each member of the ensemble. (When counting ensemble quantum states, each member of the ensemble is considered to be distinguishable by virtue of its location.) Hence specifying an ensemble quantum state fixes the distribution of ensemble members, whereas specifying a distribution of ensemble members does not fix, in general, the ensemble quantum state. Specifying the distribution does fix, however, a set of possible ensemble quantum states. (In the language of probability theory, an ensemble quantum state is a permutation, whereas the distribution of ensemble members is a combination.)

The significance of the two stated postulates is clarified perhaps by Figure 2-1, where the number of possible ensemble quantum states is indicated schematically as a function of some index of the distribution of ensemble members among possible ensemble-member quantum states. (The vertical line in this figure represents an extremely narrow gaussian curve.) Postulate 2 states that the most probable distribution of ensemble members coincides with that distribution for which the number of possible quantum states of the ensemble and reservoir is a maximum; Postulate 1 states that although the most probable distribution is not the only distribution, it dominates all possible distributions.

According to Postulate 1, the expected value of a mechanical quantity may be computed "from the most probable distribution of ensemble members." In order to place this statement in convenient mathematical language, represent a "distribution of ensemble members" by the set of numbers n_j, where n_j is the number of members in their jth quantum state. Since, at any given time, each ensemble member must be in one (and in only one) member quantum state, the set n_j must satisfy

$$\sum_j n_j = n$$

where n is the total number of members in the ensemble. Of all the possible distributions of ensemble members, one distribution is, in general, more probable than any other distribution. (See Postulate 2.) Identify this distribution by placing an asterisk on the appropriate set of numbers n_j. Then the **expected value** of a mechanical quantity may be calculated, according to Postulate 1, from

$$\langle A \rangle = \frac{1}{n} \sum_j n_j^* A_j$$

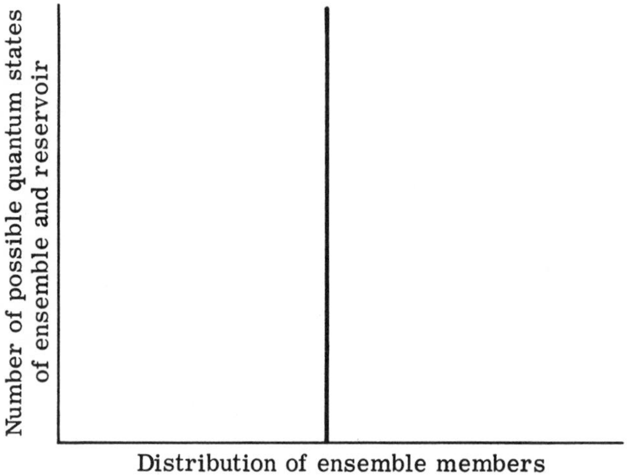

Figure 2-1 *Schematic diagram of the number of possible quantum states of ensemble and reservoir as a function of distribution of ensemble members for an ensemble of a large number of members.*

where n_j^* is the most probable number of members in their jth quantum state and A_j is the value of the mechanical quantity A when the member is in member quantum state j. Since the ratio n_j^*/n is used frequently, it is given a special symbol and name. In this book, it is represented by the symbol P_j and is called either the probability of member quantum state j or, more briefly, the probability. Then the expected value of a mechanical quantity may be computed from

$$\langle A \rangle = \sum_j P_j A_j \tag{2-1}$$

Values of P_j are predicted by statistical thermodynamics; values of A_j by quantum mechanics.

It is to be kept in mind that the procedure outlined here for calculating expected values yields values which are analogous to the classical values of mechanical-thermodynamic properties for a system in equilibrium. If a system is not in equilibrium, an equation similar to Equation (2-1) can be used nevertheless—provided, however, that one has information sufficient to replace P_j by the (nonequilibrium) number of members in member quantum state j divided by the total number of members in the ensemble.

Postulate 2 emphasizes that the laws of mechanics and probability are insufficient for the establishment of an analog of classical thermodynamics. Although, without Postulate 2 (or its equivalent), one can identify the distribution of ensemble members for which the number of possible quantum states of the ensemble and reservoir is a maximum, one cannot establish analogs of the second law of classical thermodynamics and its consequences.

Application of Postulate 2 requires an expression for the number of possible quantum states of the ensemble and reservoir as a function of the distribution of ensemble members. For a given distribution of the ensemble members among the possible ensemble-member quantum states (i.e., for a given set of values of the n_j's), the generalized displacements and energy of all ensemble members taken together, and consequently the generalized displacements and energy of the reservoir, are fixed. Hence, from the state principle of classical thermodynamics, the thermodynamic state of the reservoir is fixed. (The quantum state of neither the reservoir nor the ensemble of members is fixed, however. Specification of the quantum state of the reservoir requires more information than does specification of the thermodynamic state of the reservoir; specification of the quantum state of the ensemble requires more information than does specification of the distribution of ensemble members.) For a fixed thermodynamic state of the reservoir (i.e., for fixed generalized displacements and energy of the reservoir, and consequently for fixed generalized displacements and energy of all ensemble members taken together), the number of possible quantum states of the ensemble is independent of the quantum state of the reservoir. For a fixed distribution of ensemble members (i.e., for fixed generalized displacements and energy of all ensemble members taken together, and consequently for fixed generalized displacements and energy of the reservoir), the number of possible quantum states of the reservoir is independent of the quantum state of the ensemble. Hence one may write, for a given distribution,

$$\Omega_t = \Omega_R \Omega$$

where Ω_t is the total number of possible quantum states of the ensemble of members and the reservoir, Ω_R is the number of possible quantum states of the reservoir, and Ω is the number of possible quantum states of the ensemble of members.

Example

As an example of the use of products of independent numbers of possibilities (permutations), consider the offer of a building contractor to provide a choice of three alternative floor plans, three alternative exterior finishes, and two alternative garage locations for a house. If the floor plans, exterior finishes, and garage locations can be chosen independently of each other, then the total number of possible permutations (house appearances) is

$$\Omega_t = \Omega_1\Omega_2\Omega_3$$

where Ω_1 = number of different floor plans

Ω_2 = number of different exterior finishes

Ω_3 = number of different garage locations

Using the given numbers, one finds that $\Omega_t = 3 \times 3 \times 2 = 18$ different house appearances are possible.

Since information concerning the reservoir is not sought, a more explicit form of Ω_R is not required; one needs to know only that it is a function of the generalized displacements, the energy, and the number of particles of type i of the reservoir. However, since information concerning the distribution of ensemble members is sought, a more explicit form of Ω is required. Hence consider the number of different ways (permutations) in which n members in a given distribution (combination) of quantum states may be arranged. For convenience, examine the combination of n numbers

$$6 \quad 3 \quad 1 \quad 37 \quad 86 \quad 2 \quad 137 \quad 1 \quad 4 \quad 43 \quad 5 \quad \cdots$$

where each member is represented by the value of j which indicates its quantum state. If all n numbers are different, then the first number in this combination may be chosen from n different numbers, the second number from $(n - 1)$ different numbers, the third number from $(n - 2)$ different numbers, and so on. Hence if all n numbers are different, this combination may be written in $n! \equiv n(n-1)(n-2) \cdots 1$ different ways. However, if n_j members are in their jth quantum state, the number of different ways in which this combination may be written is reduced by the factor $n_j!$. Hence the number of possible quantum states of the ensemble of members is given by the **combinatorial formula**

$$\Omega = \frac{n!}{\prod_j n_j!}$$

where $\pi_j n_j!$ is a convenient symbol for the continued product $(n_1!) \times (n_2!) \times (n_3!) \times \cdots \times (n_j!) \times \cdots$. The total number of possible quantum states of the ensemble of members and the reservoir may be written

$$\Omega_t = \Omega_R \frac{n!}{\prod_j n_j!} \tag{2-2}$$

The analysis of the next chapter will substantiate that the only information concerning Ω_R which is required is the quantum-mechanical result that it is some function of the energy, the number of particles of type i, and the generalized displacements (e.g., volume) of the reservoir.

Example

In an application of the aforementioned combinatorial formula, consider the number of possible ways (permutations) in which 10 horses can be divided into "money horses" (the first three horses to come in) and "also-rans" if one is not interested in the order in which either the money horses or the also-rans come in. Let n represent the total number of horses, n_1 the number of money horses, and n_2 the number of also-rans. If the order in which the horses came in were of interest, then $n!$ permutations would be possible. Since permutations of the first three horses and of the last seven horses are not of interest, the number must be divided by the number of uninteresting permutations; that is, it must be divided by $(n_1!) \times (n_2!)$. Hence the number of possible ways in which 10 horses can be divided into money horses and also-rans is given by

$$\Omega = \frac{n!}{(n_1!) \times (n_2!)} = \frac{10!}{(3!) \times (7!)} = 120$$

In the absence of useful prior information concerning the relative abilities of the horses and jockeys, one might expect to guess correctly the money horses (irrespective of the order in which they came in) in only 1 out of 120 ten-horse races.

Now a procedure for maximizing Ω_t is required. (Which set of n_j's gives, subject to constraints which may be imposed upon the members, the largest value of Ω_t?) This procedure is simplified if one takes advantage of the fact that Ω_t is a monotonic function of $\ln \Omega_t$, so that if $\ln \Omega_t$ is maximized, then Ω_t is maximized. Hence write Equation (2-2) in the form

$$\ln \Omega_t = \ln \Omega_R + \ln (n!) - \sum_j \ln (n_j!) \tag{2-3}$$

Since the ensemble contains a large number of members, one may use **Stirling's approximation** (see Appendix A)

$$\ln (x!) = x \ln x - x \tag{2-4}$$

valid for $x >> 1$, to obtain

$$\begin{aligned} \ln \Omega_t &= \ln \Omega_R + n \ln n - n - \sum_j n_j \ln n_j + \sum_j n_j \\ &= \ln \Omega_R + n \ln n - \sum_j n_j \ln n_j \end{aligned} \tag{2-5}$$

where the identity $n \equiv \sum_j n_j$ has been used.

Now maximize Equation (2-5), subject to constraints which may be imposed upon the members, to obtain (according to Postulate 2) the most probable values of the n_j's; compute the probabilities P_j from

$$P_j = \frac{n_j^*}{n} \tag{2-6}$$

where n_j^* is the most probable number of members in the jth quantum state. The probabilities given by Equation (2-6) are the probabilities required for the calculation of expected values of mechanical quantities from Equation (2-1). An application of this procedure is found in the following chapter.

Example

As a simple example of the aforementioned concepts of distribution, ensemble quantum state, and most probable distribution, consider an ensemble of four isolated members, each member having two allowed quantum states. (If each member is isolated, the need for a reservoir is obviated and the discussion is simplified.) The five possible distributions and the 16 possible ensemble quantum states are indicated in Figure 2-2, where member quantum numbers are identified by the numerals 1 and 2. According to Postulate 2, the most probable distribution is $n_1^* = n_2^* = 2$, for which distribution $\Omega_t = 6$ and $P_1 = P_2 = 1/2$. Note that Equation (2-5) was not used here; Equation (2-5) is valid only for $n >> 1$, whereas n equals, in this example, only 4. If the number of possible member quantum states were larger, a larger fraction of ensemble quantum states would have distributions near the most probable distribution and Figure 2-2 would resemble more closely Figure 2-1. (See Problem 2-3.) If constraints (in addition to $\sum_j P_j = 1$) were imposed, a distribution with unequal P_j's would be realized—as will be shown in Chapter 3.

PROBLEMS

2-1 In an application of the combinatorial formula, consider four hands of cards, each hand containing 13 cards (the order within a hand being immaterial), with the 52 cards forming a conventional deck. How many different deals are possible? Simplify your result using Stirling's approximation; write the final answer in exponential form.

2-2 In order to obtain a quantitative guide to the error made using Stirling's approximation, compute the error made when replacing $\ln x!$ by $x \ln x - x$ for the case in which (*a*) $x = 10$, (*b*) $x = 100$. (NOTE: $\log_{10} 10! = 6.560$; $\log_{10} 100! = 157.97$.)

2-3 Enumerate the possible distributions and compute the associated number of possible ensemble quantum states for the simple case of an ensemble of four isolated members, each member having four allowed quantum states. What is the ratio of the number of possible ensemble quantum states for the most probable distribution to the average number of possible ensemble quantum states per distribution? Compare with the ratio for the case of an ensemble of four members, each member having two allowed quantum states. What is the effect of increasing the number of allowed member quantum states on the relative importance of the most probable distribution?

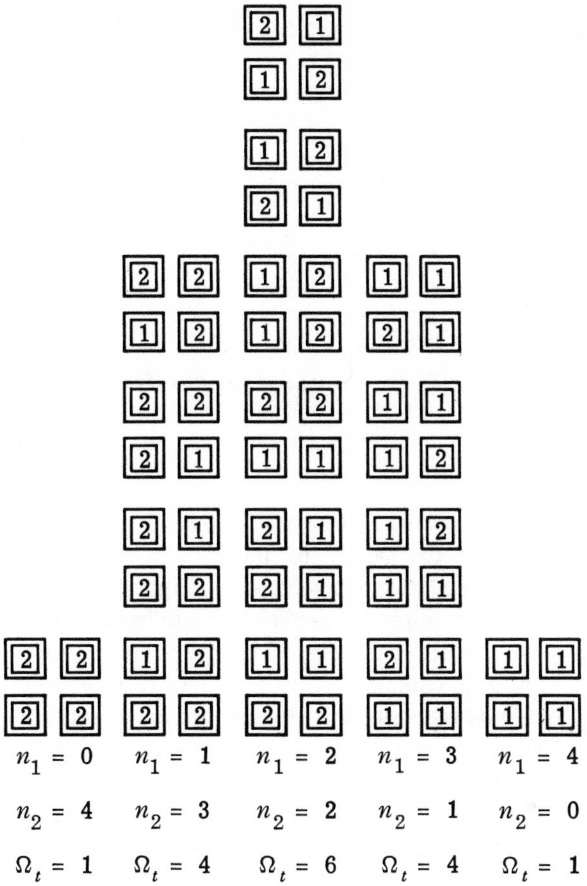

Figure 2-2 *Distributions and ensemble quantum states for a simple example.*

chapter **3**

grand partition function

If I have had any success in mathematical physics, it is,
I think, because I have been able to dodge
mathematical difficulties.
J. W. Gibbs †

Systems treated by the methods of statistical thermodynamics may be classified according to the natures of the surfaces bounding the systems and the roles of the generalized displacements. Eight of the many possible different ensembles which might be encountered are indicated in Table 3-1. Here N_i is the number of particles of type i in the system, S is entropy, $H\,(\equiv E + pV)$ is **enthalpy**, $A\,(\equiv E - TS)$ is **Helmholtz function**, $G\,(\equiv H - TS)$ is **Gibbs function**, k is Boltzmann's constant, and T is temperature. Appearance of the partition functions Q_z and the parameters β, π, and γ_i in this table anticipates their introduction either later in the present chapter (Q_z, β, and γ_i) or in Problem 5-8 (π). The fundamental equation and the analog of $\ln Q_z$ for an ensemble with independent parameters β, V, γ_i are derived in Chapter 5. After mastering the contents of the first five chapters, the reader will be able to derive the fundamental equations and the analogs of $\ln Q_z$ for the other ensembles. (The derivations for ensembles with independent parameters β, π, N_i and E, π, γ_i are suggested as exercises in Problems 5-8 and 5-9.) Note that if effects of generalized forces other than pressure are taken into account, the number of possible different ensembles is increased greatly.

The following three groups of systems have been found to be most useful: (1) systems surrounded by surfaces which do not permit passage of energy or mass, (2) systems surrounded by surfaces which permit passage of energy but not mass, and (3) systems surrounded by surfaces which permit passage of both energy and mass; values of the generalized displacements are specified. The ensembles are called, respectively, **microcanonical en-**

† Quoted by L. P. Wheeler in "Josiah Willard Gibbs," p. 53, Yale University Press, New Haven, Conn., 1952.

sembles (E, N_i, X_c given), **canonical ensembles** (β, N_i, X_c given), and **grand canonical ensembles** (β, γ_i, X_c given). (See Figure 3-1 and items 1, 2, and 4 of Table 3-1.) These three ensembles were introduced, and discussed extensively, by Gibbs in 1901. Since the independent parameters (E, N_i, X_c) of a microcanonical ensemble are typical parameters of mechanics but include no intensive parameters, a microcanonical ensemble can be related easily to mechanics but not so easily to thermodynamics. The independent parameters (β, γ_i, X_c) of a grand canonical ensemble, on the other hand, include parameters (β, γ_i) which will be shown to be analogous to intensive properties of thermodynamics. Hence a grand canonical ensemble can be related more easily to thermodynamics and less easily to mechanics. In this

Table 3-1 Several ensembles of statistical thermodynamics (All generalized forces except pressure equal zero)

System boundary conditions†	*Independent parameters*	*Fundamental equation (Q_z = relevant partition function)*	*Analog of* $\ln Q_z$
1. Impervious to energy and matter	E, V, N_i	$d \ln Q_1 = \langle\beta\rangle\, dE + \langle\pi\rangle\, dV + \sum_i \langle\gamma_i\rangle\, dN_i$	$\frac{S}{k}$
2. Impervious to matter but not energy	β, V, N_i	$d \ln Q_2 = -\langle E\rangle\, d\beta + \langle\pi\rangle\, dV + \sum_i \langle\gamma_i\rangle\, dN_i$	$-\frac{A}{kT}$
3. Impervious to energy but not matter	E, V, γ_i	$d \ln Q_3 = \langle\beta\rangle\, dE + \langle\pi\rangle\, dV - \sum_i \langle N_i\rangle\, d\gamma_i$	$\frac{H}{kT}$
4. Impervious to neither energy nor matter	β, V, γ_i	$d \ln Q_4 = -\langle E\rangle\, d\beta + \langle\pi\rangle\, dV - \sum_i \langle N_i\rangle\, d\gamma_i$	$\frac{pV}{kT}$
5. Impervious to energy and matter	E, π, N_i	$d \ln Q_5 = \langle\beta\rangle\, dE - \langle V\rangle\, d\pi + \sum_i \langle\gamma_i\rangle\, dN_i$	$-\frac{pV}{kT} + \frac{S}{k}$
6. Impervious to matter but not energy	β, π, N_i	$d \ln Q_6 = -\langle E\rangle\, d\beta - \langle V\rangle\, d\pi + \sum_i \langle\gamma_i\rangle\, dN_i$	$-\frac{G}{kT}$
7. Impervious to energy but not matter	E, π, γ_i	$d \ln Q_7 = \langle\beta\rangle\, dE - \langle V\rangle\, d\pi - \sum_i \langle N_i\rangle\, d\gamma_i$	$\frac{E}{kT}$
8. Impervious to neither energy nor matter	β, π, γ_i (except one)	$0 = -\langle E\rangle\, d\beta - \langle V\rangle\, d\pi - \sum_i \langle N_i\rangle\, d\gamma_i$	0

† Items 1 to 4 are for volume fixed, items 5 to 8 for volume that may fluctuate.

respect, a canonical ensemble occupies a position intermediate to a microcanonical ensemble and a grand canonical ensemble.

Analysis of a grand canonical ensemble involves fewer mathematical difficulties than do analyses of the other two ensembles. (A sum with no limit on N_i is more convenient than is a sum restrained by a constant value of N_i, as will become apparent in Chapter 6.) Also, the grand canonical ensemble is more general and more powerful than the other two (it permits

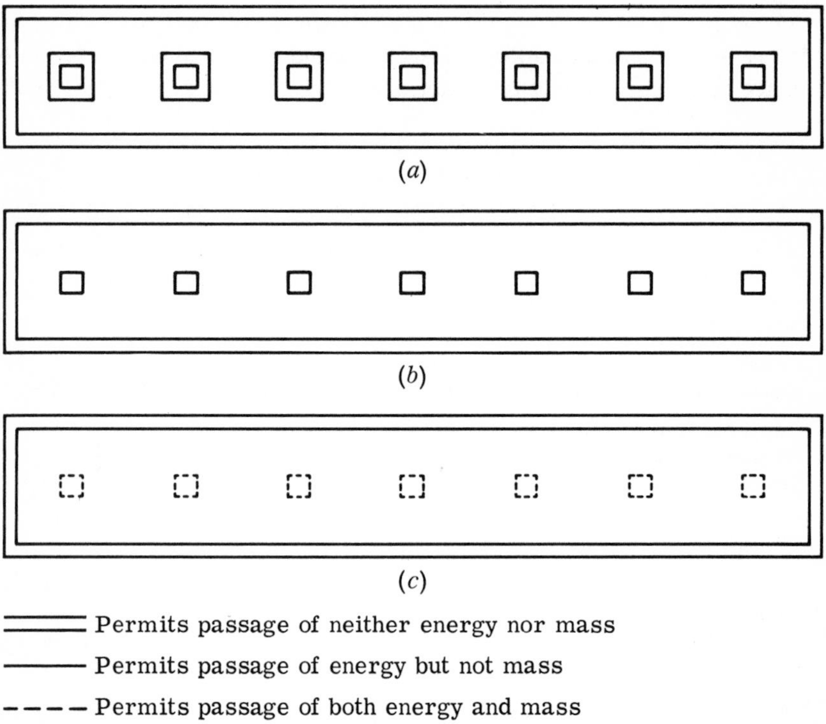

Figure 3-1 *The three most convenient ensembles, classified according to boundaries between members and reservoirs. (a) Microcanonical ensemble (E, X_e, N_i given). (b) Canonical ensemble (β, X_e, N_i given). (c) Grand canonical ensemble (β, X_e, γ_i given). (The appearance of β and γ_i anticipates their introduction later in the present chapter.)*

fluctuations of both energy and mass). Furthermore, most results of interest to thermodynamicists are independent of the nature of the ensemble which is used. [Exceptions include (1) thermodynamic properties of systems with either small numbers of particles or small energies or small volumes and (2) variances of fluctuations.] Hence most of the discussions which follow will be of grand canonical ensembles.

Consider a grand canonical ensemble of members, each member having the same generalized displacements X_c. Let the ensemble (and hence each member and the reservoir) contain particles of several types (i.e., several chemical species such as nitrogen, oxygen, and argon). The allowed quantum-mechanical states of the members are fixed by the generalized displacements X_c (including the volume V). If these members are finite and in stationary states, quantum mechanics predicts that only discrete energy levels and discrete particle numbers are allowed; that is,

$$E_j = E(j; X_1, X_2, \ldots) \tag{3-1}$$

$$N_{ij} = N_i(j) \tag{3-2}$$

may have only discrete values. Here j is an index of the member quantum state, E_j is the level of energy of the member if it is in its jth quantum state, N_{ij} is the number of particles of type i if the member is in its jth quantum state, and X_c is the value of the cth generalized displacement.[1] (Note that although the number of members n must be large, no such condition exists on the number of particles N_{ij}.) For convenience in analyses to follow, the member quantum states are ordered such that $E_{j+1} \geqq E_j$. In accordance with the definition of a grand canonical ensemble given earlier in this chapter, both energy and mass may pass through the boundary between a member and the reservoir, but not through the envelope that isolates the members and reservoir from the rest of the universe. The distribution of the members among the several member quantum states (that is, the set n_j) is **constrained** (limited) by

$$\sum_j n_j = n \tag{3-3}$$

$$E_R + \sum_j n_j E_j = E_t \tag{3-4}$$

$$N_{iR} + \sum_j n_j N_{ij} = N_{it} \qquad i = 1, 2, \ldots, K \tag{3-5}$$

where E_R, E_t, N_{iR}, N_{it} and K are, respectively, the energy of the reservoir, the total energy of the ensemble and reservoir, the number of particles of type i in the reservoir, the total number of particles of type i in the ensemble and reservoir, and the number of different types of particles. Equation (3-3) states that each member must be in one of the allowed member quantum states, whereas Equations (3-4) and (3-5) state that, regardless of how the energy and particles are distributed among the several members and the reservoir, the total energy and number of particles of type i must be conserved. (Conservation of the number of particles of type i implies that chemical reactions are neglected in this analysis. If chemical reactions

[1] The reader may find it convenient, particularly in the first reading, to consider the case in which only one type of particle is present and the only significant generalized force is pressure. For this case the subscript i may be deleted and the generalized displacements X_c may be replaced by the volume V.

occur, the results of this analysis, although still applicable, must be supplemented by the necessary and sufficient conditions for chemical equilibrium.) As outlined in Chapter 2, the most probable values of the n_j's are determined now by maximizing

$$\ln \Omega_t = \ln \Omega_R + n \ln n - \sum_j n_j \ln n_j \tag{2-5}$$

subject to constraints (3-3), (3-4), and (3-5).

To determine the values of the n_j's which maximize $\ln \Omega_t$, use Lagrange's method of undetermined multipliers. (For the reader who is unfamiliar with this method, sufficient details are provided here to explain the method.) If $\ln \Omega_t$ is to be a maximum, then the variation of $\ln \Omega_t$ must vanish for small variations of the n_j's. Hence, since (for fixed X_c)

$$\Omega_R = \Omega_R\,(E_R, N_{iR}) \tag{3-6}$$

one may write

$$-d \ln \Omega_t = -\left(\frac{\partial \ln \Omega_R}{\partial E_R}\right)_{X_{cR},\,N_{iR}} dE_R - \sum_i \left(\frac{\partial \ln \Omega_R}{\partial N_{iR}}\right)_{X_{cR},\,E_R,\,N_{i'R}} dN_{iR} + \sum_j (1 + \ln n_j)\, dn_j = 0 \tag{3-7}$$

where the subscript $N_{i'R}$ indicates that numbers of particles except N_{iR} are held constant. [Note that Equation (3-6) is a quantum-mechanical statement related closely to Equations (3-1) and (3-2); it is not equivalent to the **state principle** of classical thermodynamics, which principle may be written: "The thermodynamic state of a system in stable equilibrium is fixed by a specification of its generalized displacements and its energy." The statistical-thermodynamical analog to the state principle requires, in addition to Equation (3-6), a procedure for obtaining the expected state from the set of possible quantum states.] If the differentials appearing on the right-hand side of Equation (3-7) were all independent, i.e., if the constraints imposed by equations (3-3) to (3-5) did not exist, all the coefficients of the differentials would have to equal zero. [If one or more of these differentials were not equal to zero, one could choose values of the differentials which would lead to a violation of Equation (3-7).] But the constraints imposed by Equations (3-3) to (3-5) do exist and must be considered. Lagrange's method is a convenient procedure for handling, as follows, these constraints. Since the right-hand sides of Equations (3-3) to (3-5) are constants, the variations of these $K + 2$ quantities also must vanish for small variations of the n_j's, that is,

$$\sum_j dn_j = 0 \tag{3-8}$$

$$dE_R + \sum_j E_j\, dn_j = 0 \tag{3-9}$$

$$dN_{iR} + \sum_j N_{ij}\, dn_j = 0 \qquad i = 1,\ 2,\ \ldots,\ K \tag{3-10}$$

Note that the allowed values $E_j = E(j, X_c)$ and $N_{ij} = N_i(j)$ are not affected by these variations. Multiply Equations (3-8) to (3-10), respectively, by $\alpha - 1$, β, and γ_i, with $i = 1, 2, \cdots, K$. (The form of the multiplier $\alpha - 1$ is chosen judiciously for convenience in calculations to follow.) Add the resulting equations to Equation (3-7) to obtain

$$\left[\beta - \left(\frac{\partial \ln \Omega_R}{\partial E_R}\right)_{X_{cR}, N_{iR}}\right] dE_R + \sum_i \left[\gamma_i - \left(\frac{\partial \ln \Omega_R}{\partial N_{iR}}\right)_{X_{cR}, E_R, N_{i'R}}\right] dN_{iR}$$
$$+ \sum_j \left(\ln n_j + \alpha + \beta E_j + \sum_i \gamma_i N_{ij}\right) dn_j = 0 \quad \text{(3-11)}$$

Since the constraints, i.e., Equations (3-3) to (3-5), number $K + 2$ (where K is the number of different types of particles), only $J - 1$ (where J is the number of possible member quantum states) of the $J + K + 1$ differentials appearing in Equation (3-11) are independent. Select $J - 1$ of the n_j's as independent parameters. Then the remaining n_j is fixed by Equation (3-3), whereas E_R and the N_{iR}'s are fixed by Equations (3-4) and (3-5). Now set the coefficients of the dependent differentials equal to zero by selecting appropriate values of the multipliers α, β, and γ_i; that is, set

$$\beta = \left(\frac{\partial \ln \Omega_R}{\partial E_R}\right)_{X_{cR}, N_{iR}}$$

$$\gamma_i = \left(\frac{\partial \ln \Omega_R}{\partial N_{iR}}\right)_{X_{cR}, E_R, N_{i'R}}$$

$$\alpha = -\ln n_j - \beta E_j - \sum_i \gamma_i N_{ij}$$

[Lagrange's method of undetermined multipliers may be considered to be a method for eliminating the dependent differentials in Equation (3-7).] But each of the coefficients of the $J - 1$ remaining dn_j's also must equal zero since these dn_j's are independent. [If one or more of these coefficients of the independent dn_j's were not equal to zero, one could choose values of the dn_j's which would lead to a violation of Equation (3-11).] Hence, one way or the other, all the coefficients of the $J\,dn_j$'s are zero; that is, the required values of the n_j's are given by

$$\ln n_j^* + \alpha + \beta E_j + \sum_i \gamma_i N_{ij} = 0$$

or, solving explicitly for n_j^*,

$$n_j^* = \exp\left(-\alpha - \beta E_j - \sum_i \gamma_i N_{ij}\right) \quad \text{(3-12)}$$

The undetermined multiplier α may be eliminated by applying Equation (3-3) to the set n_j^* and substituting for n_j^* from Equation (3-12) to obtain

$$e^\alpha = \frac{\sum_j \exp\left(-\beta E_j - \sum_i \gamma_i N_{ij}\right)}{n} \quad \text{(3-13)}$$

so that Equation (3-12) may be written

$$\frac{n_j^*}{n} = \frac{\exp\left(-\beta E_j - \sum_i \gamma_i N_{ij}\right)}{\sum_j \exp\left(-\beta E_j - \sum_i \gamma_i N_{ij}\right)} \tag{3-14}$$

According to Postulate 2, Equation (3-14) provides the desired expression for the most probable value of the number of members in their jth quantum state in a grand canonical ensemble of n members.

An expression for the probabilities P_j may be obtained now by substituting into Equation (2-6) with the result

$$P_j = \frac{\exp\left(-\beta E_j - \sum_i \gamma_i N_{ij}\right)}{\sum_j \exp\left(-\beta E_j - \sum_i \gamma_i N_{ij}\right)} \tag{3-15}$$

Values of P_j computed using Equation (3-15) are used in Equation (2-1) in order to compute expected values of mechanical quantities.

The energy level E_j and the number of particles N_{ij} are inherently positive quantities. Although the undetermined multipliers β and γ_i are known to be parameters of the reservoir as a consequence of the relations

$$\beta = \left(\frac{\partial \ln \Omega_R}{\partial E_R}\right)_{X_{cR},\, N_{iR}}$$

$$\gamma_i = \left(\frac{\partial \ln \Omega_R}{\partial N_{iR}}\right)_{X_{cR},\, E_R,\, N_{i'R}}$$

their signs are not known at this time. (Note that although β and γ_i may be considered to be parameters of the ensemble, they are not parameters of the individual ensemble members.) Hence, *if* the undetermined multipliers β and γ_i are positive, the number of members per quantum state is seen to decrease exponentially as either the energy or the number of particles increases. Further discussions of the undetermined multipliers β and γ_i are postponed until Chapter 5, where they are identified with nonmechanical macroscopic properties in a comparison of results of statistical thermodynamics with results of classical thermodynamics.

The sum appearing in the denominator of the right-hand side of Equation (3-15) is called the **grand partition function** and is given the symbol Ξ (the Greek letter xi), that is,

$$\Xi(\beta, \gamma_i, X_c) \equiv \sum_j \exp\left(-\beta E_j - \sum_i \gamma_i N_{ij}\right) \tag{3-16}$$

Comparing Equations (3-13) and (3-16), it is seen that

$$\Xi = n e^{\alpha} \tag{3-17}$$

so that use of Ξ may be considered to be alternative to use of the lagrangian multiplier α. As will be shown in the following chapter, expected values of all mechanical quantities of interest to thermodynamicists may be calculated directly from Ξ. Correspondence between the lagrangian multipliers and nonmechanical-thermodynamic properties will be established in Chapter 5.

PROBLEMS

3-1 In an application of Lagrange's method of undetermined multipliers, consider points A and B in two different media. Show that the time required for light to propagate from A to B is minimized if

$$\frac{v}{v'} = \frac{\sin \phi}{\sin \phi'}$$

where v is the speed of light on the left-hand side and v' is the speed of light on the right-hand side.

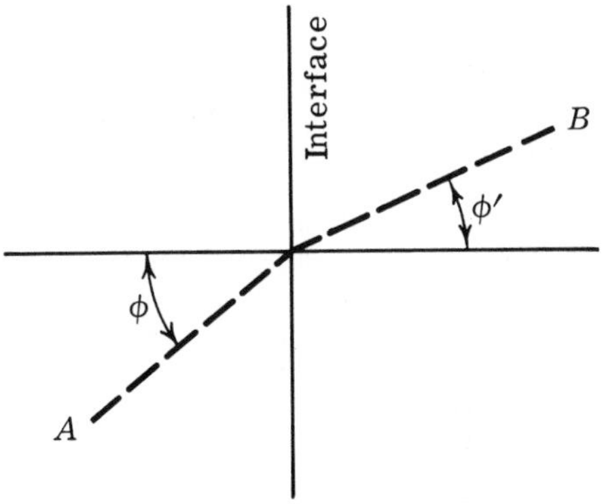

Figure P3-1

3-2 Using Lagrange's method of undetermined multipliers, show that the probability that a member of a canonical ensemble (i.e., a closed member) is in its jth quantum state is

$$P_j(\beta, N_i, X_c) = \frac{e^{-\beta E_j}}{\sum_j e^{-\beta E_j}}$$

The sum $Q = \sum_j e^{-\beta E_j}$ is the **partition function** for a canonical ensemble.

3-3 Consider two grand canonical ensembles (identified by superscripts A and B) in contact with each other. (The phrase "in contact with each other" means that each member of ensemble A is in contact with one member of ensemble B but that the two reservoirs are not in direct contact with each other.) The number of possible quantum states of the ensembles and reservoirs is given by

$$\Omega_t = \Omega_R{}^A \, \Omega_R{}^B \frac{n!}{\prod_j n_j{}^A!} \frac{n!}{\prod_k n_k{}^B!}$$

whereas the distributions of the members among the several allowed member quantum states are constrained by

$$\sum_j n_j{}^A = n \qquad \sum_k n_k{}^B = n$$

$$E_R{}^A + E_R{}^B + \sum_j n_j{}^A E_j{}^A + \sum_k n_k{}^B E_k{}^B = E_t$$

$$N_{iR}{}^A + N_{iR}{}^B + \sum_j n_j{}^A N_{ij}{}^A + \sum_k n_k{}^B N_{ik}{}^B = N_{it}$$

Deduce that if two ensembles of open members are in contact with each other and in equilibrium, then $\beta^A = \beta^B = \beta$ and $\gamma_i{}^A = \gamma_i{}^B = \gamma_i$.

3-4 The **zeroth law** of classical thermodynamics may be written: "If systems A and B are each in equilibrium with system C when in contact with system C, they are in equilibrium with each other when brought, in the same manner, into contact with each other." Compose a statistical-thermodynamical analog to this law.

3-5 Use the results of Problem 3-3 (if two ensembles of open members are in contact with each other and in equilibrium, then $\beta^A = \beta^B = \beta$ and $\gamma_i{}^A = \gamma_i{}^B = \gamma_i$) to show that

$$\ln \Xi^{AB} = \ln \Xi^A + \ln \Xi^B$$

where Ξ^{AB}, Ξ^A and Ξ^B are the partition functions for the combined ensemble, for ensemble A, and for ensemble B, respectively. Note that for a grand partition function this relation is limited to ensembles for which (1) the energy of the combined ensemble equals the sum of the energies of the separate ensembles *and* (2) the particle numbers of the combined ensemble are equal to the sums of the particle numbers of the separate ensembles. Hence for a grand partition function this relation cannot be applied to ensembles corresponding to different degrees of freedom of the same system. However, as will be seen in Chapters 8 to 14, this restriction introduces no problems.

3-6 Represent an isolated thermodynamic system by a microcanonical ensemble of isolated members. (Note that since each member is isolated, no reservoir is required.) Using Postulate 2, derive an expression relating the probability P_j with the number of possible quantum states $\Omega(E, V, N_i)$ for each member. Now apply this result to the case in which each member of the microcanonical ensemble is an ensemble (including members and reservoir) in order to show that Postulate 2 is equivalent to the postulate that "all possible quantum states of the ensemble and reservoir have the same probability."

chapter 4

expected values and fluctuations

Thermodynamics would hardly exist as a profitable discipline if it were not that the natural limit to the size of so many types of instrument which we now make in the laboratory falls in the region in which the measurements are still smooth.

P. W. Bridgman, 1941 †

Recall that the purpose of statistical thermodynamics is to provide physical interpretations (explanations) and numerical values of the mechanical quantities of classical thermodynamics. By definition, the domain of classical thermodynamics includes only macroscopic quantities–the instruments used do not record fluctuations (e.g., fluctuations in energy or pressure). (Incidentally, the great value of classical thermodynamics is due directly to the fact that the great majority of the instruments which engineers and scientists use are unable to detect fluctuations.) Hence the methods of statistical thermodynamics must include a procedure for predicting, from the results of mechanics [e.g., Equations (3-1) and (3-2)] and the results of statistics [e.g., Equation (3-15)], values of macroscopic mechanical quantities. As indicated in Chapter 2, this requirement is met by the following procedure: If A_j is the value of the mechanical quantity A when the member is in its jth quantum state, and if P_j is the probability assigned to the jth quantum state of the member, then the expected value of the quantity A is given by

$$\langle A \rangle = \sum_j P_j A_j \qquad (2\text{-}1)$$

where the sum is over all allowed quantum states of the member. As was stated in the preceding chapter, and as will be shown here for several typical

† P. W. Bridgman, "The Nature of Thermodynamics," p. 188, Harper & Row, Publishers, Incorporated, New York, 1961.

quantities, these expected values may be obtained from an operation upon the sum over allowed ensemble-member quantum states known as the partition function.

Consider first the energy. Substituting from Equation (3-15) into Equation (2-1), one obtains for the expected value of the energy

$$\begin{aligned}\langle E\rangle &= \sum_j P_j E_j \\ &= \frac{\sum_j E_j \exp\left(-\beta E_j - \sum_i \gamma_i N_{ij}\right)}{\sum_j \exp\left(-\beta E_j - \sum_i \gamma_i N_{ij}\right)} \\ &= -\left[\frac{\partial}{\partial\beta} \ln \sum_j \exp\left(-\beta E_j - \sum_i \gamma_i N_{ij}\right)\right]_{\gamma_i, X_c} \\ &= -\left(\frac{\partial \ln \Xi}{\partial \beta}\right)_{\gamma_i, X_c} \qquad (4\text{-}1)\end{aligned}$$

Similarly, one obtains for the expected value of the number of particles of type i

$$\begin{aligned}\langle N_i\rangle &= \sum_j P_j N_{ij} \\ &= \frac{\sum_j N_{ij} \exp\left(-\beta E_j - \sum_i \gamma_i N_{ij}\right)}{\sum_j \exp\left(-\beta E_j - \sum_i \gamma_i N_{ij}\right)} \\ &= -\left[\frac{\partial}{\partial\gamma_i} \ln \sum_j \exp\left(-\beta E_j - \sum_i \gamma_i N_{ij}\right)\right]_{\beta, X_c, \gamma_i'} \\ &= -\left(\frac{\partial \ln \Xi}{\partial \gamma_i}\right)_{\beta, X_c, \gamma_i'} \qquad (4\text{-}2)\end{aligned}$$

where the subscript γ_i' indicates that all γ's except γ_i are held constant. (Since the order of differentiation is immaterial, one may write

$$\frac{\partial \langle E\rangle}{\partial \gamma_i} = -\frac{\partial^2 \ln \Xi}{\partial \gamma_i \partial \beta} = \frac{\partial \langle N_i\rangle}{\partial \beta}$$

that is, the expected value of the energy is affected by a change in the value of the multiplier γ_i in the same manner that the expected value of the number of particles of type i is affected by a change in the value of the multiplier β; the energy and the number of particles are said to be "coupled.") Now consider the several generalized forces. If the member is in its jth quantum state, the change in system energy is related to the generalized forces F_{cj} and changes in generalized displacements X_c [see Equation (3-1) and Figure 4-1] by

$$dE_j = -\sum_c F_{cj}\, dX_c$$

Hence

$$F_{cj} = -\left(\frac{\partial E_j}{\partial X_c}\right)_{X_c'}$$

where the subscript X_c' indicates that all generalized displacements except X_c are held constant. (Holding the quantum state, that is, the subscript j, constant ensures that the process is adiabatic. Note, however, that an adiabatic process does not require an invariant quantum state, that is, a constant value of the subscript j. For example, any allowed quantum state may be reached by an adiabatic process from any other allowed quantum state with the same particle numbers.) Consequently, one obtains for

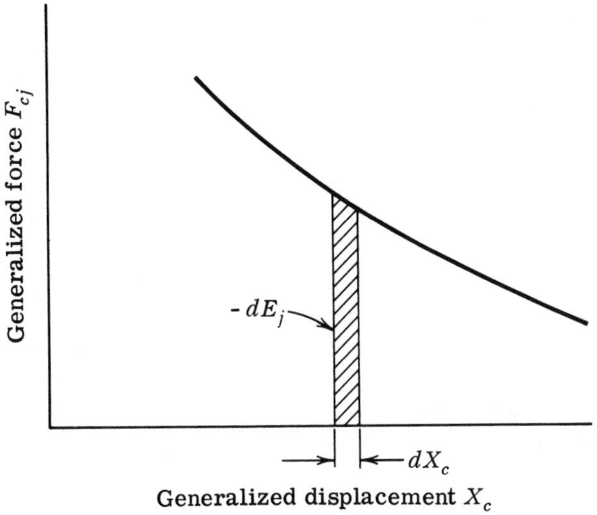

Figure 4-1 *Change in ensemble-member energy dE_j related to generalized force F_{cj} and change in generalized displacement dX_c. (Member is in its* jth *quantum state and all generalized displacements except X_c are held constant.)*

the expected value of the generalized force F_c (for example, pressure) conjugate to the generalized displacement X_c (for example, volume)

$$\langle F_c \rangle = -\sum_j P_j \left(\frac{\partial E_j}{\partial X_c}\right)_{X_c'}$$

$$= -\frac{\sum_j (\partial E_j/\partial X_c)_{X_c'} \exp\left(-\beta E_j - \sum_i \gamma_i N_{ij}\right)}{\sum_j \exp\left(-\beta E_j - \sum_i \gamma_i N_{ij}\right)}$$

$$= \frac{1}{\beta}\sum_j \left(\frac{\partial \ln \Xi}{\partial E_j}\right)_{\beta,\gamma_i}\left(\frac{\partial E_j}{\partial X_c}\right)_{X_c'} = \frac{1}{\beta}\left(\frac{\partial \ln \Xi}{\partial X_c}\right)_{\beta,\gamma_i,X_c'} \tag{4-3}$$

Using Equations (4-1) to (4-3), one is able to calculate expected values of E, N_i, and F_c by simple differentiations of the logarithm of the partition function. These expected values are essential to the establishing of a correspondence between statistical thermodynamics and classical thermodynamics, as will be shown in Chapter 5.

A measure of the magnitude of predicted fluctuations from expected values is of interest. Applications of such information include (1) interpretations (explanations) of the observation that classical thermodynamics (which does not acknowledge the existence of such fluctuations) is applicable to a large number of processes and (2) descriptions of those fluctuations which are observed, e.g., fluctuations in fluids near the critical point. As was done in the discussion of expected values, the discussion which follows is confined to mechanical quantities; that is, it is confined to properties which are well defined when the system is in a given quantum state. Hence fluctuations of quantities such as energy, number of particles, forces (including pressure), and volume are discussed, whereas fluctuations of properties such as temperature, chemical potential, and entropy are not discussed.

Contrary to the treatment of expected values, the treatment of fluctuations requires, for physical reasons, a careful choice of ensemble type, i.e., a careful choice of system boundary conditions. A choice of system boundary conditions is equivalent to a choice of which quantities may fluctuate and which quantities may not. For example, if one chooses a grand canonical ensemble, then the energy E, the number of particles N_i, and the generalized forces F_c may fluctuate, whereas the generalized displacements X_c and the parameters β and γ_i may not.

If one is approaching the subject of fluctuations for the first time, one might examine first the expected value of the deviations; that is, for the quantity A, one might compute

$$\langle A - \langle A \rangle \rangle = \sum_j P_j (A_j - \langle A \rangle) = \langle A \rangle - \langle A \rangle = 0$$

One concludes that the quantity deviates from its expected value in both directions, and that the positive and negative directions have equal probability. Thus the expected value of the deviations does not provide the desired measure of predicted fluctuations. A useful measure is provided, however, by the expected value of the square of the deviation, i.e. (for the quantity A) by

$$\begin{aligned} \langle (A - \langle A \rangle)^2 \rangle &= \sum_j P_j (A_j - \langle A \rangle)^2 \\ &= \sum_j P_j (A_j^2 - 2\langle A \rangle A_j + \langle A \rangle^2) \\ &= \sum_j P_j A_j^2 - \langle A \rangle^2 \qquad (4\text{-}4) \end{aligned}$$

This measure, inherently positive, is frequently called the **variance** and is represented by the symbol $\sigma^2(A)$. If the fluctuations are small, that is, if $\sigma(A)$ is small in comparison with $\langle A \rangle$, the curve P_j versus $A_j - \langle A \rangle$ is gaussian and is characterized completely by the variance (see Appendix B).

Depending on the boundary conditions appropriate for the system under consideration, a large number of different fluctuations might be considered.

(An indication of the number of different fluctuations which might be considered is provided by the list of different ensembles given in Table 3-1.) For a system in a grand canonical ensemble, the energy E, the number of particles N_i, and the generalized forces F_c may fluctuate. For the energy

$$\sigma^2(E) = \sum_j P_j E_j^2 - \langle E\rangle^2$$

$$= \frac{\sum_j E_j^2 \exp(-\beta E_j - \sum_i \gamma_i N_{ij})}{\sum_j \exp(-\beta E_j - \sum_i \gamma_i N_{ij})} - \left[\frac{\sum_j E_j \exp(-\beta E_j - \sum_i \gamma_i N_{ij})}{\sum_j \exp(-\beta E_j - \sum_i \gamma_i N_{ij})}\right]^2$$

$$= -\left[\frac{\partial}{\partial\beta}\frac{\sum_j E_j \exp(-\beta E_j - \sum_i \gamma_i N_{ij})}{\sum_j \exp(-\beta E_j - \sum_i \gamma_i N_{ij})}\right]_{\gamma_i, X_c} = \left(\frac{\partial^2 \ln \Xi}{\partial\beta^2}\right)_{\gamma_i, X_c} \tag{4-5}$$

Similarly, for the number of particles of type i,

$$\sigma^2(N_i) = \left(\frac{\partial^2 \ln \Xi}{\partial \gamma_i^2}\right)_{\beta, X_c, \gamma_i'} \tag{4-6}$$

and for the generalized force F_c,

$$\sigma^2(F_c) = \frac{1}{\beta^2}\left(\frac{\partial^2 \ln \Xi}{\partial X_c^2}\right)_{\beta, \gamma_i, X_c'} + \frac{1}{\beta}\left\langle\left(\frac{\partial^2 E}{\partial X_c^2}\right)_{X_c'}\right\rangle \tag{4-7}$$

(Derivations of the latter two equations are left as an exercise for the reader; see problems at end of chapter.) Hence one is able to calculate variances of mechanical quantities by differentiations of (1) the logarithm of the partition function and (2), in the case of the generalized force, the expression relating the allowed energy levels with generalized displacements. Typical values of these variances are indicated in later chapters.

Using Equations (4-1) and (4-2), one may write Equations (4-5) and (4-6) in the alternative forms

$$\sigma^2(E) = -\left(\frac{\partial \langle E\rangle}{\partial\beta}\right)_{\gamma_i, X_c} \tag{4-8}$$

$$\sigma^2(N_i) = -\left(\frac{\partial \langle N_i\rangle}{\partial\gamma_i}\right)_{\beta, X_c, \gamma_i'} \tag{4-9}$$

Hence the variances of E and N_i are simply the negatives of the variations of $\langle E\rangle$ and $\langle N_i\rangle$ due to variations in β and γ_i. In order to facilitate discussions of relative magnitudes of fluctuations and expected values, divide by squares of the expected values to obtain the dimensionless relations

$$\frac{\sigma^2(E)}{\langle E\rangle^2} = -\frac{1}{\langle E\rangle^2}\left(\frac{\partial \langle E\rangle}{\partial\beta}\right)_{\gamma_i, X_c} \tag{4-10}$$

$$\frac{\sigma^2(N_i)}{\langle N_i\rangle^2} = -\frac{1}{\langle N_i\rangle^2}\left(\frac{\partial \langle N_i\rangle}{\partial\gamma_i}\right)_{\beta, X_c, \gamma_i'} \tag{4-11}$$

Further discussions must be deferred, however, until the classical-thermodynamical analogs of β and γ_i are established (see Chapter 5). Relations similar to Equations (4-10) and (4-11) may be written for variances of other fluctuating extensive quantities (occurring perhaps in other ensembles).

Using the relation $F_{cj} = -(\partial E_j/\partial X_c)_{X_c'}$ and Equation (4-3), one may write Equation (4-7) in the alternative form

$$\sigma^2(F_c) = \frac{1}{\beta}\left(\frac{\partial \langle F_c \rangle}{\partial X_c}\right)_{\beta,\gamma_i,X_c'} - \frac{1}{\beta}\left\langle\left(\frac{\partial F_c}{\partial X_c}\right)_{X_c'}\right\rangle \tag{4-12}$$

The derivative appearing in the first term on the right-hand side is simply the variation of the expected value of the generalized force due to a variation in the conjugate generalized displacement. The derivative appearing in the second term on the right-hand side has, however, no simple thermodynamic meaning; its evaluation requires a specific model of matter. (Evaluations for specific models of matter are included in Chapters 8 and 10.) This requirement exists for variances of all intensive quantities; hence no general conclusions concerning the relative magnitudes of fluctuations and expected values of intensive quantities can be drawn without a specific model of matter.

Note that only one of two conjugate quantities exhibits fluctuations; the other quantity is an independent (nonfluctuating) parameter with value fixed by the problem statement. For example, in the case of a grand canonical ensemble, only the first quantity of each of the conjugate pairs $E - \beta$, $F_c - X_c$, and $N_i - \gamma_i$ exhibits fluctuations.

The reader may be wondering how a quantum-state probability distribution of the form developed in Chapter 3 can lead to the distributions of energy, numbers of particles, and generalized forces (with maxima at $\langle E \rangle$, $\langle N_i \rangle$, and $\langle F_c \rangle$) discussed in the present chapter. A discussion of this question also is postponed until the sign of the multiplier β has been established (Chapter 5).

PROBLEMS

4-1 For a grand canonical ensemble, derive the expression relating the variance $\sigma^2(N_i)$ for the number of particles of type i to the logarithm of the grand partition function Ξ; that is, derive Equation (4-6).

4-2 For a grand canonical ensemble, derive the expression relating the variance $\sigma^2(F_c)$ for the generalized force F_c to the logarithm of the grand partition function Ξ; that is, derive Equation (4-7).

4-3 Using the results of Problem 3-2, show that, for a canonical ensemble (i.e., for an ensemble of closed members),

$$\langle E \rangle = -\left(\frac{\partial \ln Q}{\partial \beta}\right)_{N_i,X_r}$$

$$\langle F_c \rangle = \frac{1}{\beta}\left(\frac{\partial \ln Q}{\partial X_c}\right)_{\beta,N_i,X_c'}$$

where Q (the partition function for a canonical ensemble) is defined in Problem 3-2.

4-4 Using the results of Problem 3-2, show that for a canonical ensemble (i.e., for an ensemble of closed members),

$$\sigma^2(E) = \left(\frac{\partial^2 \ln Q}{\partial \beta^2}\right)_{N_i, X_c}$$

$$\sigma^2(F_c) = \frac{1}{\beta^2}\left(\frac{\partial^2 \ln Q}{\partial X_c^{\,2}}\right)_{\beta, N_i, X_{c'}} + \frac{1}{\beta}\left\langle\left(\frac{\partial^2 E}{\partial X_c^{\,2}}\right)_{X_{c'}}\right\rangle$$

where Q is defined in Problem 3-2.

chapter **5**

correspondence between classical and statistical thermodynamics

The laws of thermodynamics, as empirically determined, . . . express the laws of mechanics for such systems as they appear to beings who have not the fineness of perception to enable them to appreciate quantities of the order of magnitude of those which relate to single particles, and who cannot repeat their experiments often enough to obtain any but the most probable results.
J. W. Gibbs, 1901 †

As indicated in Chapter 1, classical thermodynamics and statistical thermodynamics are considered here to be equally fundamental and equally valid; in all cases in which these two disciplines describe the same phenomena, they must be in correspondence. The correspondences of the mechanical properties

$$E \sim \langle E \rangle \tag{5-1a}$$

$$N_i \sim \langle N_i \rangle \tag{5-1b}$$

$$F_c \sim \langle F_c \rangle \tag{5-1c}$$

follow immediately from Postulate 1 of Chapter 2. (The symbol $\sim$ means "corresponds to"; it will be used whenever one side of an equation is written in the nomenclature of classical thermodynamics and the other side is written in the nomenclature of statistical thermodynamics.) Identifications of the lagrangian multipliers of statistical thermodynamics with the corresponding properties of classical thermodynamics, and of the entropy of

† H. A. Bumstead and R. G. Van Name (eds.), "The Collected Works of J. Willard Gibbs," vol. II, p. viii, Yale University Press, New Haven, Conn., 1948.

classical thermodynamics with the corresponding quantity of statistical thermodynamics, are provided in the present chapter.

In principle, the $K + 2$ parameters Ξ, β, and γ_i (with K equal to number of different types of particles) may be obtained as functions of $\langle E\rangle$ and $\langle N_i\rangle$ by substitution of Equation (3-15)

$$P_j = \frac{\exp\left(-\beta E_j - \sum_i \gamma_i N_{ij}\right)}{\Xi} \tag{3-15}$$

into the $K + 2$ equations

$$\sum_j P_j = 1 \qquad \sum_j P_j E_j = \langle E\rangle \qquad \sum_j P_j N_{ij} = \langle N_i\rangle$$

For an open system, however, the appropriate independent thermodynamic properties are X_c, T, and μ_i, where T is absolute temperature and μ_i is chemical potential per particle of type i. Since the dependence of $\langle E\rangle$ and $\langle N_i\rangle$ on X_c, T, and μ_i has not been established, this procedure is not followed here. Instead, two alternative forms of the appropriate fundamental equation of statistical thermodynamics are developed which are analogous to two alternative forms of the appropriate fundamental equation of classical thermodynamics; term-by-term comparisons of the equations of statistical thermodynamics with the equations of classical thermodynamics provide the desired identifications.

For an open system with specified generalized displacements (independent variables T, μ_i, and X_c) the appropriate fundamental equation of classical thermodynamics may be written (see Appendix C)

$$d\sum_c F_c X_c = S\,dT + \sum_c F_c\,dX_c + \sum_i N_i\,d\mu_i \tag{5-2}$$

where S is entropy. (Recall that the **entropy change** may be calculated from

$$dS = \frac{đQ_r}{T}$$

where $đQ_r$ is the heat which must be added reversibly in order to effect the state change associated with the entropy change dS and which may be determined quantitatively, for a closed system and a process involving no work effects, from

$$đQ_r = dE$$

The **chemical potential** is defined as the coefficient of dN_i in the fundamental equation

$$dE = T\,dS - \sum_c F_c\,dX_c + \sum_i \mu_i\,dN_i \tag{5-3}$$

that is, by

$$\mu_i = \left(\frac{\partial E}{\partial N_i}\right)_{S,\,X_c,\,N_i{}'}$$

where the subscript N_i' means that all particle numbers are held constant except N_i.) The alternative form of Equation (5-2) which will be used is its dimensionless form. Divide by $k'T$, in Equation (5-2), all parameters which have the units of energy, where k' is a constant with units of energy per unit temperature but with value undetermined at this point, and rearrange to obtain

$$d\left(\frac{\sum_c F_c X_c}{k'T}\right) = \left(\sum_c F_c X_c - TS - \sum_i \mu_i N_i\right) d\left(\frac{1}{k'T}\right) + \frac{1}{k'T}\sum_c F_c\, dX_c + \sum_i N_i\, d\left(\frac{\mu_i}{k'T}\right)$$

Integrate Equation (5-3) holding the intensive properties, but not the extensive properties, constant

$$E = TS - \sum_c F_c X_c + \sum_i \mu_i N_i$$

Eliminate entropy from the latter two equations to obtain the desired dimensionless fundamental equation

$$d\left(\frac{\sum_c F_c X_c}{k'T}\right) = -E\, d\left(\frac{1}{k'T}\right) + \frac{1}{k'T}\sum_c F_c\, dX_c + \sum_i N_i\, d\left(\frac{\mu_i}{k'T}\right) \qquad (5\text{-}4)$$

Equations (5-2) and (5-4) are to be compared to the analogous equations of statistical thermodynamics.

The statistical-thermodynamical analog of Equation (5-2) is derived by differentiating $\beta^{-1} \ln \Xi$, keeping in mind that $\ln \Xi$ is a function of only the parameters β, γ_i, and X_c [see Equations (3-1), (3-2), and (3-16)]. One obtains

$$d\left(\frac{\ln \Xi}{\beta}\right) = \ln \Xi\, d\left(\frac{1}{\beta}\right) + \frac{1}{\beta}\left[\left(\frac{\partial \ln \Xi}{\partial \beta}\right)_{\gamma_i, X_c} d\beta + \sum_c \left(\frac{\partial \ln \Xi}{\partial X_c}\right)_{\beta, \gamma_i, X_c'} dX_c + \sum_i \left(\frac{\partial \ln \Xi}{\partial \gamma_i}\right)_{\beta, X_c, \gamma_i'} d\gamma_i\right]$$

Substitute for the several partial derivatives from Equations (4-1) to (4-3), and rearrange. Then

$$\begin{aligned} d\left(\frac{\ln \Xi}{\beta}\right) &= \ln \Xi\, d\left(\frac{1}{\beta}\right) + \frac{1}{\beta}\left(-\langle E\rangle\, d\beta + \beta \sum_c \langle F_c\rangle\, dX_c - \sum_i \langle N_i\rangle\, d\gamma_i\right) \\ &= \left(\ln \Xi + \beta\langle E\rangle + \sum_i \gamma_i \langle N_i\rangle\right) d\left(\frac{1}{\beta}\right) + \sum_c \langle F_c\rangle\, dX_c - \sum_i \langle N_i\rangle\, d\left(\frac{\gamma_i}{\beta}\right) \end{aligned} \qquad (5\text{-}5)$$

The analog of Equation (5-4) is derived by differentiating $\ln \Xi$ and following the same steps used in deriving Equation (5-5). One obtains

$$d \ln \Xi = -\langle E\rangle\, d\beta + \beta \sum_c \langle F_c\rangle\, dX_c - \sum_i \langle N_i\rangle\, d\gamma_i \qquad (5\text{-}6)$$

(Note that this equation is an extension of the equation given in the fourth line of Table 3-1 to the case involving several generalized forces.) Correspondence of Equation (5-2) to Equation (5-5) is obtained if

$$\sum_c F_c X_c \sim \frac{\ln \Xi}{\beta} \tag{5-7a}$$

$$S\,dT \sim \left(\ln \Xi + \beta \langle E \rangle + \sum_i \gamma_i \langle N_i \rangle\right) d\left(\frac{1}{\beta}\right) \tag{5-7b}$$

$$\mu_i \sim -\frac{\gamma_i}{\beta} \tag{5-7c}$$

whereas correspondence of Equation (5-4) to Equation (5-6) is obtained if, in addition to Equations (5-7*a*) and (5-7*c*),

$$\frac{1}{k'T} \sim \beta \tag{5-7d}$$

Eliminate β from Equations (5-7*a*) to (5-7*c*) using Equation (5-7*d*) to obtain finally

$$\frac{\sum_c F_c X_c}{k'T} \sim \ln \Xi \tag{5-8a}$$

$$\frac{S}{k'} \sim \ln \Xi + \beta \langle E \rangle + \sum_i \gamma_i \langle N_i \rangle \tag{5-8b}$$

$$\frac{\mu_i}{k'T} \sim -\gamma_i \tag{5-8c}$$

Note that if independent parameters are β, γ_i/β and X_c, then

$$\frac{S}{k'} \sim -\beta^2 \left(\frac{\partial}{\partial \beta} \frac{\ln \Xi}{\beta}\right)_{X_c, \gamma_i/\beta}$$

Hence one may now calculate values of entropy (up to a multiplicative constant) also by simple differentiation of the logarithm of the partition function.

An alternative form of Equation (5-8*b*) may be written if one notes that, substituting from Equation (3-15) for P_j,

$$\begin{aligned} -\sum_j P_j \ln P_j &= \sum_j P_j \left(\ln \Xi + \beta E_j + \sum_i \gamma_i N_{ij}\right) \\ &= \ln \Xi + \beta \langle E \rangle + \sum_i \gamma_i \langle N_i \rangle \end{aligned} \tag{5-9}$$

so that

$$\frac{S}{k'} \sim -\sum_j P_j \ln P_j \tag{5-10}$$

This form, which occurs irrespective of the type of ensemble being considered, emphasizes the correspondence of entropy to disorder, randomness, or lack of information. Note that the value of the right-hand side (1) is a maximum whenever all the P_j's are equal, and (2) either remains the same or becomes smaller if a constraint (restriction) is placed on the P_j's.

Equation (5-10) explains the paradox which is said to exist when a reversible mechanical system has nonzero entropy—a paradox that cannot be explained by classical (nonstatistical) thermodynamics. It indicates that if a mechanical system undergoes reversible processes, but the state of the system is not known with precision sufficient to set all P_j's for the ensemble corresponding to the system equal to either 0 or 1, then the entropy is nonzero in spite of the fact that the processes are reversible. For additional discussions of the statistical-thermodynamical interpretation of entropy and its role in the second and third laws of thermodynamics, see Appendix E.

For the convenience of the reader, the several correspondences which have been established are summarized in Table 5-1. Using these correspondences, statistical-thermodynamical analogs of other classical-thermodynamical properties (e.g., enthalpy, Helmholtz function, and Gibbs function) may be deduced.

Table 5-1 Correspondence between classical and statistical thermodynamics

Classical thermodynamics (open system)	*Statistical thermodynamics (grand-canonical ensemble)*
E	$\langle E \rangle$
N_i	$\langle N_i \rangle$
F_c	$\langle F_c \rangle$
$\dfrac{\sum_c F_c X_c}{k'T}$	$\ln \Xi$
$-\dfrac{\mu_i}{k'T}$	γ_i
$\dfrac{1}{k'T}$	β
$\dfrac{S}{k'}$	$-\sum_j P_j \ln P_j$

As was found for a grand canonical ensemble (Table 5-1), most properties of a classical-thermodynamical system are (for other ensembles also) in correspondence with either independent parameters of the corresponding ensemble or expected values of mechanical quantities of the ensemble members. These "independent parameters of the corresponding ensemble" may be either extensive ensemble-member parameters (for example, E, V, and N_i) or intensive reservoir parameters (for example, β, π, and γ_i); the "mechanical quantities of the ensemble members" are quantities which have well-defined values (for example, E_j, N_{ij}, p_j, and V_j) when a member is in a given quantum state. Classical-thermodynamical properties which do not fall in the aforementioned categories include temperature, for the case in which energy is an independent parameter; chemical potential, for the case in which the number of particles is an independent parameter; entropy; and the analog of the logarithm of the partition function. If E and N_i are independent parameters, then $1/kT$ and $-\mu_i/kT$ are analogous to the derivative of the logarithm of the partition function with respect to E and N_i, respectively, holding all other independent parameters constant; e.g., for a microcanonical ensemble, the symbols $\langle\beta\rangle$ and $\langle\gamma_i\rangle$ appearing in line 1 of Table 3-1 are defined by

$$\langle\beta\rangle \equiv \left(\frac{\partial \ln Q_1}{\partial E}\right)_{V, N_i}$$

$$\langle\gamma_i\rangle \equiv \left(\frac{\partial \ln Q_1}{\partial N_i}\right)_{E, V, N_i'}$$

The analogs of $1/kT$ and $-\mu_i/kT$ are not expected values of ensemble-member quantities since β_j and γ_{ij} are devoid of meaning. Procedures for evaluating the logarithm of the partition function and the analog of entropy have been established earlier. Note that the only properties of a classical-thermodynamical system which are in correspondence with quantities of *individual* ensemble members are properties which are both independent and extensive—parameters which are (by definition) the same for all members.

Although the value of the constant k' has not been established by the preceding discussions, it can be shown at this point that k' is universal and is positive. The fact that it is universal follows from the correspondence $\beta \sim (k'T)^{-1}$, the statistical-thermodynamical result that β is uniform for two arbitrary systems in equilibrium with each other (Problem 3-3), and the classical-thermodynamical result that T is uniform for two arbitrary systems in equilibrium with each other. The fact that it is positive is shown in Problem 5-2. Since k' is a universal constant, its value may be established by comparing statistical-thermodynamical results with experimental results for any convenient system; a thermally perfect gas will be used for this purpose in Chapter 6.

Now that the classical-thermodynamical analog of β is established, one can discuss the question of how a quantum-state probability distribution of the form

$$P_j = \frac{\exp\left(-\beta E_j - \sum_i \gamma_i N_{ij}\right)}{\Xi} \qquad (3\text{-}15)$$

where

$$\Xi(\beta, X_c, \gamma_i) \equiv \sum_j \exp\left(-\beta E_j - \sum_i \gamma_i N_{ij}\right) \qquad (3\text{-}16)$$

can lead to the distributions of energy, numbers of particles, and generalized forces with maxima at $\langle E\rangle$, $\langle N_i\rangle$, and $\langle F_c\rangle$. For definiteness, examine the dependence of P_j on E_j for given values of the N_i's (Figure 5-1). (Keep in mind that, although assigning a value to j fixes the values of all the N_i's, assigning values to all the N_i's does not fix the value of j; many values of E_j are possible for each set of values assigned to the N_i's.) Note that for each set of values assigned to the N_i's the maximum value of P_j occurs for $E_j = 0$ and (for $\beta > 0$) P_j decreases exponentially as E_j increases. If Figure 5-1 told the entire story, one would conclude that a relatively large fraction of ensemble members have a low energy level. However, Figure 5-1 does not tell the entire story. Quantum mechanics predicts that, in general, more than one quantum state may have the same energy level and, similarly, more than one quantum state may have the same number of particles. The resulting situation is clarified perhaps by examining the probability that a system has energy E and particle numbers N_i (not quan-

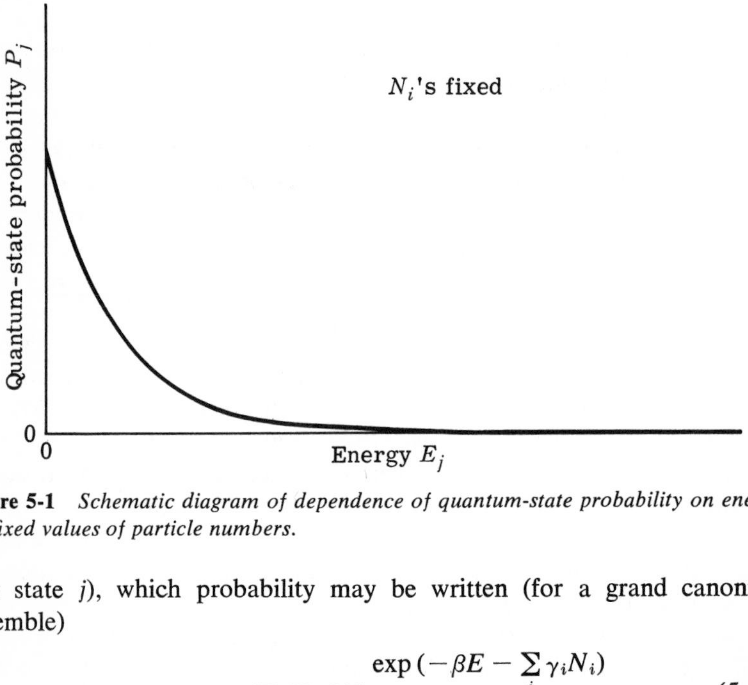

Figure 5-1 *Schematic diagram of dependence of quantum-state probability on energy for fixed values of particle numbers.*

tum state j), which probability may be written (for a grand canonical ensemble)

$$P_{E,N_i} = \Omega(E, X_c, N_i) \frac{\exp\left(-\beta E - \sum_i \gamma_i N_i\right)}{\Xi} \tag{5-11}$$

where $\Omega(E, X_c, N_i)$ is the number of possible member quantum states for a given set of values of E, X_c, and N_i, and

$$\Xi(\beta, X_c, \gamma_i) \equiv \sum_{E, N_i} \Omega(E, X_c, N_i) \exp\left(-\beta E - \sum_i \gamma_i N_i\right) \tag{5-12}$$

Note that the summation indicated here is over energy levels E and particle numbers N_i (not over quantum states j); use of Equations (3-16) and (5-12) must lead, of course, to the same value of Ξ. The factor $\Omega(E, X_c, N_i)$, known as the **degeneracy**, depends strongly on the values of E, X_c, and N_i. For definiteness, examine its dependence on E for given values of the X_c's and N_i's. Quantum mechanics predicts that $\Omega(E, X_c, N_i)$ is of order unity for $E = 0$ and that it increases rapidly as E increases (Figure 5-2). Hence the probability P_{E,N_i} is seen to be the product of a factor which decreases exponentially as E increases (Figure 5-1) and a factor which increases rapidly as E increases (Figure 5-2)—a product which has a maximum at $\langle E \rangle$ (Figure 5-3). The discontinuity in the abscissa of Figure 5-3 is included in order to emphasize that the maximum indicated in Figure 5-3 occurs (for typical systems of macroscopic size) at values of E such that the factors P_j and Ω are, respectively, exceedingly small and exceedingly large in comparison with their values at $E = 0$. Similar explanations can be

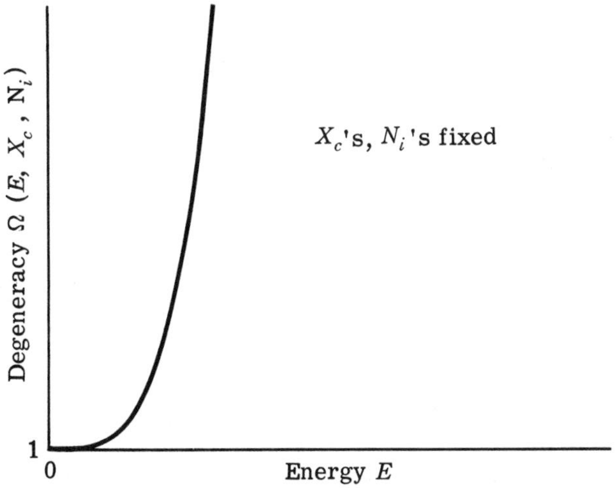

Figure 5-2 *Schematic diagram of dependence of degeneracy on energy for fixed values of generalized displacements and particle numbers.*

provided for other fluctuating variables, e.g., numbers of particles and generalized forces. (For a more quantitative discussion see Appendix E. For a discussion of probabilities and entropy as functions of availabilities see Appendix F.)

From the discussions of the preceding paragraph, it is seen that probabilities and partition functions may be approached from two alternative viewpoints: (1) one may use the probability P_j that a member is in its jth quantum state, Equation (3-15), and sum the partition function over member quantum states, Equation (3-16); or (2) one may use the probability P_{E,N_i} that a member has energy E and particle numbers N_i, Equation (5-11), and sum the partition function over energy levels and particle numbers, Equation (5-12). The approach used by a given author may be identified by looking for the degeneracy factor which is required when using the latter approach. The former approach is used more often in this book.

Now that the classical-thermodynamical analogs of β and γ_i have been established, the discussion (initiated in Chapter 4) of relative magnitudes of fluctuations and expected values is resumed. Since kT and μ_i are intensive properties, the established correspondences indicate that β and γ_i are intensive parameters. Hence (except for the special case in which the extensive quantities $\langle E \rangle$ and $\langle N_i \rangle$ can exhibit finite variations with infinitesimal variations in the intensive parameters β and γ_i, that is, except for the case of a substance in more than one phase) the right-hand sides of Equations (4-10) and (4-11) approach zero as the ensemble-member size approaches

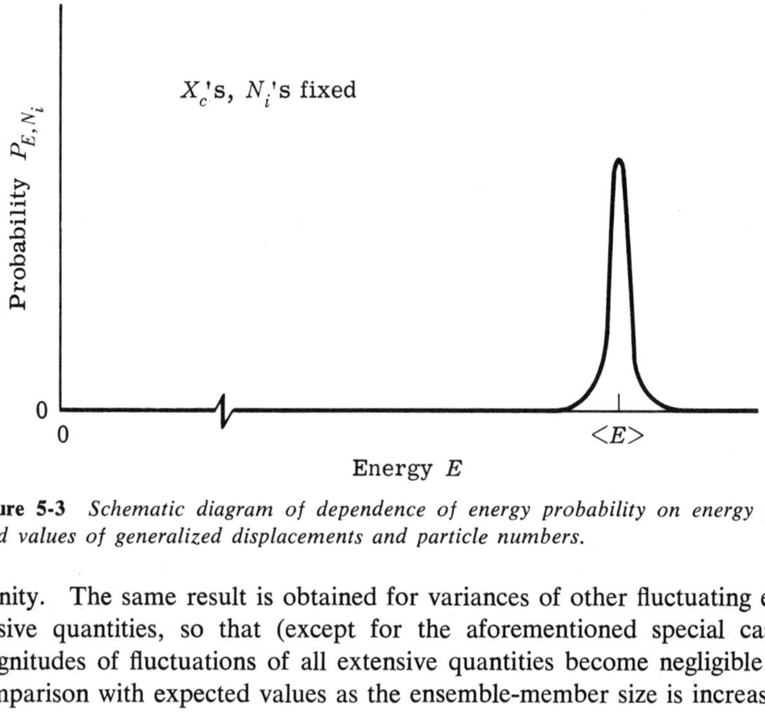

Figure 5-3 *Schematic diagram of dependence of energy probability on energy for fixed values of generalized displacements and particle numbers.*

infinity. The same result is obtained for variances of other fluctuating extensive quantities, so that (except for the aforementioned special case) magnitudes of fluctuations of all extensive quantities become negligible in comparison with expected values as the ensemble-member size is increased indefinitely.

Example

In order to place some of these comments on a more quantitative basis, consider the limitations on relative variations of γ_i and $\langle N_i \rangle$ which exist if fluctuations are sufficiently large that

$$\frac{\sigma^2(N_i)}{\langle N_i \rangle^2} >> \frac{1}{\langle N_i \rangle}$$

Then, from Equation (4-11),

$$-\frac{1}{\langle N_i\rangle^2}\left(\frac{\partial\langle N_i\rangle}{\partial\gamma_i}\right)_{\beta, X_c, \gamma_i'} >> \frac{1}{\langle N_i\rangle}$$

which may be rearranged to read

$$-\frac{1}{\langle N_i\rangle}\frac{d\langle N_i\rangle}{d\gamma_i} >> 1$$

where it is understood that β, X_c, and γ_i' are held constant. It is seen that fluctuations sufficiently large that $\sigma^2(N_i)/\langle N_i\rangle^2 >> 1/\langle N_i\rangle$ can occur only in ensemble members with states for which the fractional change in the extensive quantity $\langle N_i\rangle$ is large in comparison with the change in the dimensionless intensive parameter γ_i, that is, in ensemble members containing a substance in more than one phase.

As indicated in Chapter 4, general conclusions concerning the relative magnitudes of fluctuations and expected values of *intensive* quantities cannot be drawn without a specific model of matter.

Statistical thermodynamics provides also descriptions of processes which are in correspondence with the processes known in classical thermodynamics as "reversible performance of work by a closed system" and "reversible addition of heat to a closed system." For a closed system (a system with boundaries across which heat, but not matter, may pass), one may write, as a consequence of the first law of classical thermodynamics,

$$dE = đQ - đW \tag{5-13}$$

where $đQ$ is **heat** added to system and $đW$ is work done by system. Compare this equation with the derivative of Equation (2-1) applied to energy of a closed system:

$$d\langle E\rangle = \sum_j E_j\, dP_j + \sum_j P_j\, dE_j \tag{5-14}$$

Since E_j is a function of only the generalized displacements, Equation (5-14) may be rewritten

$$\begin{aligned} d\langle E\rangle &= \sum_j E_j\, dP_j + \sum_j P_j \sum_c \left(\frac{\partial E_j}{\partial X_c}\right)_{X_c'} dX_c \\ &= \sum_j E_j\, dP_j - \sum_j P_j \sum_c F_{cj}\, dX_c \\ &= \sum_j E_j\, dP_j - \sum_c \langle F_c\rangle\, dX_c \end{aligned} \tag{5-15}$$

where the second line follows from the discussion which precedes Equation (4-3). Since, from classical thermodynamics,

$$đW_r = \sum_c F_c\, dX_c$$

it follows from Equations (5-13) to (5-15) that

$$đW_r \sim -\sum_j P_j\, dE_j \tag{5-16}$$

$$đQ_r \sim \sum_j E_j\, dP_j \tag{5-17}$$

where $đW_r$ is work done reversibly by the closed system and $đQ_r$ is heat added reversibly to the closed system. It is seen that work done reversibly by a closed system corresponds to a decrease in the values of the allowed energy levels of the system with no change in the probability that the system is in a given quantum state, whereas heat added reversibly to a closed system corresponds to a change in the probability that the system is in a given quantum state with no change in the values of the allowed energy levels of the system. Hence a work effect is possible only if the system can assume states which *were not* allowed initially, whereas a heat effect involves only changes to states which *were* allowed initially.

Note that the discussions of the preceding paragraph are consistent with the fact that the work done and the heat added are functions of the process involved and are not unique functions of the final and initial states of the system. For example, the same change in state may be realized as a consequence of either a reversible heat addition to the system or an irreversible performance of work on the system.

Consider now the several laws of thermodynamics. The laws of statistical thermodynamics are considered here to differ from the laws of classical thermodynamics only in that the laws of statistical thermodynamics refer to ensembles and to expected values, whereas the laws of classical thermodynamics refer to systems and to exact values, that is, classical thermodynamics does not acknowledge that fluctuations are possible. (Although it has been shown, so far, only for extensive quantities, all fluctuations in a single-phase system become negligible relative to expected values as the system size is increased indefinitely, so that one may consider the laws of classical thermodynamics to describe, in principle, the limit as the system size is increased indefinitely.) Since the domain of classical thermodynamics includes only macroscopic properties, correspondence of these laws is required only for macroscopic systems and for macroscopic measurements made on these systems. For such systems and measurements, however, the indicated difference between the two statements of the laws exist only in principle and not in practice; one does not observe (for such systems and measurements) the fluctuations from the expected values which are predicted by statistical thermodynamics. Hence correspondence of the several laws of thermodynamics is realized also. (For statistical-mechanical interpretations of the second and third laws of thermodynamics see Appendix E.)

PROBLEMS

5-1 Use Lagrange's method of undetermined multipliers to verify that $-\sum_j P_j \ln P_j$, constrained only by $\sum_j P_j = 1$, is a maximum whenever all the P_j's are equal.

5-2 Using the results of Problem 3-2, show that, if $\beta \sim 1/k'T$, then, for a canonical ensemble (i.e., for an ensemble of closed members),

$$\sigma^2 (E) = \left(\frac{1}{\beta}\right)^2 \frac{\langle C_V \rangle}{k'}$$

where (in the language of statistical thermodynamics)

$$\frac{\langle C_V \rangle}{k'} \equiv \left(\frac{\partial \langle E \rangle}{\partial (1/\beta)}\right)_{N_i, X_c}$$

or (in the language of classical thermodynamics)

$$C_V \equiv \left(\frac{\partial E}{\partial T}\right)_{N_i, X_c}$$

Hence, since $\sigma^2 (E)$ and $\langle C_V \rangle$ are always positive, it is seen that the value of the constant k' must be positive.

5-3 Using the relation established in the preceding problem and information concerning the behavior of C_V, discuss the behavior of $\sigma^2 (E)$ for (*a*) an ensemble of members containing a pure substance at its critical point and (*b*) an ensemble of members containing a pure substance in more than one phase and not near its critical point.

5-4 Beginning with Equations (4-1) to (4-3), and using the results of the present chapter, show that the value of the grand partition function Ξ increases as values of temperature, chemical potential, and volume increase.

5-5 In an examination of the dependence of the probabilities P_j and the entropy S on temperature, consider a canonical ensemble of members for which (see Problem 3-2)

$$P_j (\beta, X_c, N_i) = \frac{e^{-\beta E_j}}{\sum_j e^{-\beta E_j}}$$

Show that if only one quantum state ($j = 1$) is associated with the lowest possible energy level, then

$$\lim_{\beta \to \infty} P_j = \begin{cases} 1 & j = 1 \\ 0 & j > 1 \end{cases}$$

so that, from Equation (5-10),

$$\lim_{T \to 0} \frac{S}{k'} \sim - \lim_{\beta \to \infty} \sum_j P_j \ln P_j = 0$$

Note that as temperature increases (β decreases), the probabilities tend to become uniform so that, if an infinite number of quantum states are possible,

$$\lim_{T \to \infty} \frac{S}{k'} \sim - \lim_{\beta \to 0} \sum_j P_j \ln P_j = \infty$$

Sketch qualitative curves of probability P_j versus energy level E_j for three different values of temperature. Discuss the dependence of randomness or disorder on temperature. [HINT: If only one quantum state ($j = 1$) is associated with the lowest possible energy level, the form

$$P_j(\beta, X_c, N_i) = \frac{e^{-\beta(E_j - E_1)}}{1 + \sum_{j \neq 1} e^{-\beta(E_j - E_1)}}$$

where $E_j > E_1$, for $j \neq 1$, is found to be convenient.]

5-6 For a system in which all generalized forces except pressure are negligible, show that $\ln \Xi$ must be of the form $\ln \Xi = Vf(\beta, \gamma_i)$, where $f(\beta, \gamma_i)$ is a function of β and γ_i. [HINT: Examine Equations (4-3) and (5-7*a*).]

5-7 From experimental data for a certain gas in the presence of negligible external fields,

$$\frac{\mu}{kT} = \ln p - \frac{5}{2} \ln T + \text{const}$$

Using the methods of Chapters 4 and 5, write $\sigma(E)/\langle E \rangle$ and $\sigma(N)/\langle N \rangle$ as functions of $\langle N \rangle$ for an ensemble of open members containing (and surrounded by) this gas. Hence note that if appropriate macroscopic experimental data are available, variances of extensive quantities may be evaluated—even if no molecular model exists.

5-8 Consider ensemble members with independent parameters N, β, and π and with fluctuating variables γ, E, and V. (Parameters β and π are lagrangian multipliers related to E and V.) What is the partition function for an ensemble of such members? What is the appropriate dimensionless fundamental equation? How would one calculate expected values $\langle \gamma \rangle$, $\langle E \rangle$, and $\langle V \rangle$ from the partition function? This ensemble is important since both E and V fluctuate in many physical systems.

5-9 Consider ensemble members with independent parameters E, γ, and π and with fluctuating variables β, N, and V. (Parameters γ and π are lagrangian multipliers related to N and V.) What is the partition function for an ensemble of such members? What is the appropriate dimensionless fundamental equation? How would one calculate expected values $\langle \beta \rangle$, $\langle N \rangle$, and $\langle V \rangle$ from the partition function?

chapter **6**

systems with negligible effects of interparticle forces

Mathematics is *a language.*
J. W. Gibbs †

The analysis up to now has been relatively general; the most restricting postulate which has been made is that only discrete energy levels E_j and discrete particle numbers N_{ij} are allowed for a finite system in a stationary state. However, calculations of the allowed energy levels of thermodynamic systems require, in general, considerations of the interactions of either the microscopic particles or the subsystems of the system. (Examples of microscopic particles include molecules, electrons, and photons; examples of subsystems include different modes of vibration in a monatomic crystal, different degrees of freedom in a polyatomic molecule, and molecules adsorbed on different groups of adsorption sites.) Such calculations are, in general, so difficult that they require major efforts. In many systems of interest to the engineer and scientist, however (including gases at densities not too high), one may neglect, to good approximation, effects of interparticle forces and write the energy of the system as the sum of the energies of the microscopic particles (or subsystems) in the system. (The particles or degrees of freedom still interact sufficiently, nevertheless, to maintain all parts of the system in thermal equilibrium and to impose symmetry restrictions on the quantum-mechanical wave functions.) For such systems, the quantum-mechanical problem of predicting allowed quantum states (with corresponding energy levels) is reduced now from a many-body problem to essentially a single-body (or few-body) problem. The statistical-thermodynamical problem of calculating the value of the partition function also is simplified greatly, but, due to the symmetry restrictions on the quantum-mechanical wave functions, not quite to the point at which one is able to

† Quoted by M. Rukeyser in "Willard Gibbs," p. 431, Doubleday & Company, Inc., Garden City, N. Y., 1942.

write the system partition function as a simple product of single-particle partition functions. (If both the effects of interparticle forces and the symmetry restrictions on the quantum-mechanical wave functions could be ignored, the particles could be considered independent and one could write the system partition function as a simple product of single-particle partition functions.) The remainder of this book will be devoted to systems with negligible effects of interparticle forces. With only two exceptions, the particles will be considered indistinguishable.

If the particles are indistinguishable, the required computations for a system with negligible effects of interparticle forces are made by listing the allowed particle quantum states and indicating the number of particles in each particle quantum state (rather than by listing the particles and indicating the quantum state of each particle); i.e., one writes

$$E_j = \sum_i E_{ij} = \sum_i \sum_k \varepsilon_{ik} N_{ikj} \tag{6-1}$$

$$N_j = \sum_i N_{ij} = \sum_i \sum_k N_{ikj} \tag{6-2}$$

where E_j = energy of ensemble member in its jth quantum state

N_j = number of particles in ensemble member in its jth quantum state

E_{ij} = that portion of energy of ensemble member associated with particles of type i when ensemble member is in its jth quantum state

N_{ij} = number of particles of type i when ensemble member is in its jth quantum state

ε_{ik} = energy of particle of type i when in its kth quantum state

N_{ikj} = number of particles of type i in their kth quantum state when ensemble member is in its jth quantum state

Then the grand partition function Ξ [see Equation (3-16)] may be written

$$\begin{aligned} \Xi &= \sum_j \exp\left(-\beta E_j - \sum_i \gamma_i N_{ij}\right) \\ &= \sum_j \exp\left[-\sum_i \sum_k (\beta \varepsilon_{ik} + \gamma_i) N_{ikj}\right] \\ &= \sum_j \prod_i \prod_k e^{-(\beta \varepsilon_{ik} + \gamma_i) N_{ikj}} \end{aligned} \tag{6-3}$$

(The reader who wishes to strengthen his confidence in the equality of the last two lines may wish to examine Problem 6-1.) Recall that the summation over j is the summation over all possible member quantum states and that a possible member quantum state is specified completely by specifying a value for each of the N_{ikj}'s. Since the system being examined is an open system (a system surrounded by a surface which permits the passage of both energy and mass), no constraint (such as the statement "$N_{ij} = \sum_k N_{ikj}$

is independent of the system quantum state j") is placed on the possible values of the N_{ikj}'s by the surfaces surrounding the ensemble members. Hence one may replace specifications of all possible member quantum states by specifications of all possible values and combinations of the N_{ikj}'s and write

$$\Xi = \prod_i \prod_k \sum_{\eta=0}^{\max N_{ik}} e^{-(\beta\varepsilon_{ik}+\gamma_i)\eta}$$

where $\max N_{ik}$ is the maximum number of particles of type i which may occupy simultaneously the kth particle quantum state. The reader who wishes to strengthen his confidence in the statement that this equation includes all possible values and combinations of the N_{ikj}'s, and that it is equivalent to Equation (6-3), may wish to examine the following example.

Example

Consider, for simplicity, the case in which particles of only one type are present. In this case, the continued product over i and the subscript i may be neglected, and the aforementioned equations may be written

$$\Xi = \sum_j \prod_k e^{-(\beta\varepsilon_k+\gamma)N_{kj}}$$

$$= \prod_k \sum_{\eta=0}^{\max N_k} e^{-(\beta\varepsilon_k+\gamma)\eta}$$

Limit further the consideration to the special case in which only three particle quantum states exist, and in which no more than one particle may occupy a given particle quantum state at one time. Then the following eight member quantum states are possible:

j	N_{1j}	N_{2j}	N_{3j}
1	0	0	0
2	0	0	1
3	0	1	0
4	1	0	0
5	1	1	0
6	1	0	1
7	0	1	1
8	1	1	1

One obtains, using the first equation,

$$\Xi = 1 + e^{-(\beta\varepsilon_3+\gamma)} + e^{-(\beta\varepsilon_2+\gamma)} + e^{-(\beta\varepsilon_1+\gamma)}$$
$$+ e^{-(\beta\varepsilon_1+\gamma)-(\beta\varepsilon_2+\gamma)} + e^{-(\beta\varepsilon_1+\gamma)-(\beta\varepsilon_3+\gamma)}$$
$$+ e^{-(\beta\varepsilon_2+\gamma)-(\beta\varepsilon_3+\gamma)} + e^{-(\beta\varepsilon_1+\gamma)-(\beta\varepsilon_2+\gamma)-(\beta\varepsilon_3+\gamma)}$$

whereas, using the second equation (with $\max N_k = 1$),

$$\Xi = (1 + e^{-(\beta\varepsilon_1+\gamma)})(1 + e^{-(\beta\varepsilon_2+\gamma)})(1 + e^{-(\beta\varepsilon_3+\gamma)})$$

Carrying out the indicated multiplications, one sees that the two equations yield the same result.

The advantage of the latter form of the expression for Ξ is that the sum

$$\sum_{\eta=0}^{\max N_{ik}} e^{-(\beta\varepsilon_{ik}+\gamma_i)\eta}$$

is for a single quantum state of a single type of particle. (Keep in mind that, since this sum is not over allowed quantum states of a distinguishable particle, it is not a single-particle partition function.) As will be shown in the following paragraphs, this sum may be expressed, depending on the symmetry restrictions imposed on the quantum-mechanical wave functions, in one of two closed forms even without detailed knowledge of the allowed energy levels of the particles. Note that this factoring of a sum of products into a product of sums is not possible for systems containing fixed numbers of indistinguishable particles; a treatment of either an isolated or a closed system would have been more difficult at this point.

Up to the present point, the only result of quantum mechanics which has been used is that only discrete energy levels and discrete particle numbers are allowed for a finite system in a stationary state. Now, the symmetry restrictions on the quantum-mechanical wave functions, referred to several times previously, are to be added. First, however, a few comments concerning these wave functions are in order (particularly for the benefit of the reader who has not encountered previously the concept of a wave function). In quantum mechanics all observable phenomena may be described quantitatively by associating with every bit of matter a field having a wavelike character. The function which describes this field is called a **wave function**. Like electric, magnetic, and gravity fields, the field described by this wave function cannot be observed directly. However, expected values of mechanical quantities may be calculated from this wave function and compared with observations. It is found that if the coordinates of two indistinguishable particles in a system are interchanged, the wave function representing the state of the system either remains unchanged or changes sign. If the wave function remains unchanged, it is symmetrical; if the wave function changes sign, it is antisymmetrical. Particles with half-integral spin (for example, neutrons, protons, and electrons), and larger particles containing an odd number of subparticles with half-integral spin (for example, D and He^3) have antisymmetrical wave functions; particles with integral spin (for example, photons) and larger particles containing an even number of subparticles with half-integral spin (for example, H, D_2, and He^4) have symmetrical wave functions. (The terms **half-integral spin** and **integral spin** used here refer to the coefficient of $\hbar$ in the magnitude of the angular-momentum component along any prescribed axis, where $\hbar$ is Planck's constant divided by 2π.) It is found that in a system of particles with antisymmetric wave functions no more than one particle can be in a given particle quantum state at one time, that is, max $N_{ik} = 1$. (This statement is called sometimes the **Pauli exclusion principle**, encountered perhaps by the reader in studies of the behavior of electrons in atoms and, consequently, the organization of the periodic table.) On the other hand, in a system of particles with symmetric wave functions, any number of particles can be in a given particle quantum state at one time, that is, max $N_{ik} = \infty$. Systems of particles with antisymmetric wave functions are called **Fermi-Dirac systems**; systems of particles with symmetric wave functions are called **Bose-Einstein systems**.

The application of these statements is clarified perhaps by Tables 6-1 and 6-2. Table 6-1 illustrates (for several of the lightest atoms) how the spins of an odd number of subparticles with half-integral spin combine to produce a half-integral spin of the larger particle composed of these subparticles, whereas the spins of an even number of subparticles with half-integral spin combine to produce an integral spin of the larger particle composed of these subparticles. In Table 6-2, the Pauli exclusion principle is applied to systems containing more than one atom of a given type in order to relate (for the atoms examined in Table 6-1) the value of max N_{ik} and the type of system to the number of subparticles (each with half-integral spin) in the atom. Note that the conclusions (the last two columns) of Table 6-2 depend only on whether the spin of the atom is integral or half-integral, not upon the magnitude of the spin. Hence, since failure to apply the Pauli exclusion principle to the appropriate subparticles does not change the conclusion concerning the integral or half-integral nature of the atomic spin, the conclusions of Table 6-2 can be reached even if one has no information concerning the restrictions on the subparticle spins imposed by the Pauli exclusion principle.

Table 6-1 Atomic spins

Atom	*Neutron spins*	*Proton spins*	*Electron spins*	*Atomic spin*	*Angular momentum*
H	None	$\uparrow$ or $\downarrow$	$\uparrow$ or $\downarrow$	$\begin{smallmatrix}\uparrow\\\uparrow\end{smallmatrix}$ or 0 or $\begin{smallmatrix}\downarrow\\\downarrow\end{smallmatrix}$	$0, \pm\hbar$
D	$\uparrow$ or $\downarrow$	$\uparrow$ or $\downarrow$	$\uparrow$ or $\downarrow$	$\begin{smallmatrix}\uparrow\\\uparrow\\\uparrow\end{smallmatrix}$ or $\uparrow$ or $\downarrow$ or $\begin{smallmatrix}\downarrow\\\downarrow\\\downarrow\end{smallmatrix}$	$\pm\frac{1}{2}\hbar, \pm\frac{3}{2}\hbar$
He^3	$\uparrow$ or $\downarrow$	$\uparrow + \downarrow$	$\uparrow + \downarrow$	$\uparrow$ or $\downarrow$	$\pm\frac{1}{2}\hbar$
He^4	$\uparrow + \downarrow$	$\uparrow + \downarrow$	$\uparrow + \downarrow$	0	0

NOTES: (1) Neutrons, protons, and electrons have spins with magnitude of angular-momentum component along any prescribed axis equal to $\hbar/2$; (2) The entry "$\uparrow$ or $\downarrow$" means that one subparticle is found and that its spin direction may be either parallel or antiparallel to an arbitrary direction; (3) The entry "$\uparrow + \downarrow$" means that two subparticles are found and that (due to the Pauli exclusion principle) their spin directions are antiparallel.

Table 6-2 The Pauli exclusion principle applied to systems of atoms

Atom	*No. of neutrons*	*No. of protons*	*No. of electrons*	*Value of max N_{ik}*	*Type of system*
H	0	1	1	∞	BE†
D	1	1	1	1	FD‡
He^3	1	2	2	1	FD‡
He^4	2	2	2	∞	BE†

†An even number of subparticles with half-integral spin leads to an atom with symmetrical wave function, max $N_{ik} = \infty$, and a Bose-Einstein system of atoms.

‡An odd number of subparticles with half-integral spin leads to an atom with antisymmetrical wave function, max $N_{ik} = 1$, and a Fermi-Dirac system of atoms.

In some systems, irrespective of the symmetry restrictions on the quantum-mechanical wave functions, one finds that the distribution of particles among the several particle quantum states is such that the probability of finding more than one particle in a given quantum state is negligible. In principle, these systems must be divided into the two aforementioned groups. In practice, however, these systems are placed in a third group called **Maxwell-Boltzmann systems**. The conditions under which the Fermi-Dirac and Bose-Einstein systems may be approximated by Maxwell-Boltzmann systems are discussed at greater length in later paragraphs.

Consider first the Fermi-Dirac systems. The Pauli exclusion principle, which states that no more than one particle may be in a given particle quantum state at any given time, applies to these systems. Hence max $N_{ik} = 1$, so that

$$\sum_{\eta=0}^{\max N_{ik}} e^{-(\beta\varepsilon_{ik}+\gamma_i)\eta} = 1 + e^{-\beta\varepsilon_{ik}-\gamma_i}$$

and

$$\Xi_{\mathrm{FD}} = \prod_i \prod_k (1 + e^{-\beta\varepsilon_{ik}-\gamma_i}) \tag{6-4}$$

Systems described by Equation (6-4) include systems of neutrons, protons, electrons, monatomic deuterium, and helium-3.

Consider next the Bose-Einstein systems. Any number of particles may be in any given particle quantum state at any given time. Hence max $N_{ik} = \infty$, so that

$$\sum_{\eta=0}^{\max N_{ik}} e^{-(\beta\varepsilon_{ik}+\gamma_i)\eta} = \sum_{\eta=0}^{\infty} x^\eta$$

with $x = \exp(-\beta\varepsilon_{ik} - \gamma_i)$. This series converges only if $|x| < 1$. Hence, for Bose-Einstein systems, values of the multiplier γ_i are restricted by the inequality $-\gamma_i < \beta\varepsilon_{ik}$ which must be satisfied for all values of k; if the lowest energy level is zero and β is finite, then γ_i must be positive. (No such restriction on the values of γ_i exists for Fermi-Dirac systems.) The convergent series may be written in the convenient closed form

$$\sum_{\eta=0}^{\infty} x^\eta = \frac{1}{1-x}$$

as may be verified by carrying out the division indicated in the right-hand side of the equality. Hence

$$\Xi_{\text{BE}} = \prod_i \prod_k (1 - e^{-\beta\varepsilon_{ik}-\gamma_i})^{-1} \tag{6-5}$$

Systems described by Equation (6-5) include systems of photons, hydrogen atoms, diatomic deuterium molecules, and helium-4. Equations (6-4) and (6-5) are written sometimes in the compact form

$$\Xi_{\text{FD, BE}} = \prod_i \prod_k (1 \pm e^{-\beta\varepsilon_{ik}-\gamma_i})^{\pm 1} \tag{6-6}$$

with the upper signs corresponding to the Fermi-Dirac system and the lower signs corresponding to the Bose-Einstein system.

Consider finally the Maxwell-Boltzmann systems. A system may be classed as a Maxwell-Boltzmann system if the probability of finding more than one particle in a given quantum state is negligible irrespective of whether one uses the calculation procedures of Fermi-Dirac or Bose-Einstein systems. In order to see the implications of this requirement, examine the expression for the expected values of the number of particles for Fermi-Dirac and Bose-Einstein systems, i.e., examine

$$\langle N_i \rangle = -\left(\frac{\partial \ln \Xi}{\partial \gamma_i}\right)_{\beta, X_c, \gamma_{i'}} \tag{4-2}$$

From Equation (6-6),

$$\begin{aligned} \ln \Xi_{\text{FD, BE}} &= \ln \prod_i \prod_k (1 \pm e^{-\beta\varepsilon_{ik}-\gamma_i})^{\pm 1} \\ &= \sum_i \sum_k \ln (1 \pm e^{-\beta\varepsilon_{ik}-\gamma_i})^{\pm 1} \end{aligned} \tag{6-7}$$

Hence

$$\langle N_i \rangle_{\text{FD, BE}} = \sum_k \frac{1}{e^{\beta\varepsilon_{ik}+\gamma_i} \pm 1}$$

Since $\langle N_i \rangle = \sum_k \langle N_{ik} \rangle$, where $\langle N_{ik} \rangle$ is the expected value of the number of particles in their kth quantum state for particles of type i, it follows that

$$\langle N_{ik} \rangle_{\text{FD, BE}} = \frac{1}{e^{\beta\varepsilon_{ik}+\gamma_i} \pm 1}$$

This expected value is small in comparison with unity for both the Fermi-Dirac and the Bose-Einstein cases provided that

$$e^{\beta\varepsilon_{ik}+\gamma_i} >> 1$$

or, in the language of classical thermodynamics, provided that

$$\exp\left(\frac{\varepsilon_{ik} - \mu_i}{k'T}\right) >> 1$$

(For some systems, this inequality is realized for all values of ε_{ik}, that is, γ_i has large positive values. For other systems, this inequality is realized only for sufficiently large ε_{ik}, that is, γ_i has either small or negative values.)

Then

$$\langle N_{ik}\rangle_{\text{MB}} = \frac{1}{e^{\beta\varepsilon_{ik}+\gamma_i}}$$

and
$$\langle N_i\rangle_{\text{MB}} = \sum_k \frac{1}{e^{\beta\varepsilon_{ik}+\gamma_i}} \tag{6-8}$$

Also, since [for $\exp(\beta\varepsilon_{ik} + \gamma_i) >> 1$] the exponential $\exp(-\beta\varepsilon_{ik} - \gamma_i)$ is small in comparison with unity, one may expand the logarithm appearing in Equation (6-7) in an infinite series and retain only the terms up to and including first-order terms in $\exp(-\beta\varepsilon_{ik} - \gamma_i)$ to obtain

$$\ln \Xi_{\text{MB}} = \sum_i \sum_k e^{-\beta\varepsilon_{ik}-\gamma_i} \tag{6-9}$$

In practice, any atomic or molecular gas with temperature sufficiently high and pressure sufficiently low so that effects of interparticle forces may be neglected is described adequately by Equation (6-9).

Using the results of the preceding paragraph the value of the constant k' (unknown up to the present point) may be established. Summing Equation (6-8) over i,

$$\langle N\rangle_{\text{MB}} = \sum_i \sum_k e^{-\beta\varepsilon_{ik}-\gamma_i}$$

Comparing with Equation (6-9), one obtains

$$\langle N\rangle_{\text{MB}} = \ln \Xi_{\text{MB}}$$

From Equation (5-8*a*), for a system with negligible effects of external fields,

$$\frac{pV}{k'T} \sim \ln \Xi$$

Hence, for a Maxwell-Boltzmann system with negligible effects of external fields,

$$\frac{pV}{k'T} \sim \langle N\rangle_{\text{MB}}$$

But conditions sufficient for application of a Maxwell-Boltzmann system with negligible effects of external fields are sufficient also for application of the classical-thermodynamical equation of state for a **thermally perfect gas**, i.e., for application of

$$\frac{pV}{kT} = N$$

where k is **Boltzmann's constant.** Hence

$$k' = k$$

establishing, once and for all time, the identity and value of k'; the prime on k' will be omitted in the remainder of this book. The **gas constant** R, used frequently in classical thermodynamics, is related to Boltzmann's constant by $R = N_A k$, where N_A is Avogadro's constant. Numerical values are given in Appendix K.

The thermal equations of state for Fermi-Dirac and Bose-Einstein systems with negligible effects of external fields may be written now using Equations (6-7) and (5-8*a*), and setting $k' = k$, in the form

$$\left(\frac{pV}{kT}\right)_{\text{FD, BE}} \sim \sum_i \sum_k \ln\left(1 \pm e^{-\beta\varepsilon_{ik}-\gamma_i}\right)^{\pm 1}$$

These equations of state are not as convenient, however, as is the comparable equation of state for the Maxwell-Boltzmann system.

The essential differences between the three types of systems are brought out in a comparison of the expected values of the number of particles in the kth particle quantum state. For convenience, consider systems containing only one type of particle. Then the subscript i may be deleted so that one may write

$$\langle N_k \rangle = \frac{1}{e^{\beta\varepsilon_k+\gamma} + 1} \qquad \text{Fermi-Dirac} \qquad (6\text{-}10)$$

$$\langle N_k \rangle = \frac{1}{e^{\beta\varepsilon_k+\gamma}} \qquad \text{Maxwell-Boltzmann} \qquad (6\text{-}11)$$

$$\langle N_k \rangle = \frac{1}{e^{\beta\varepsilon_k+\gamma} - 1} \qquad \text{Bose-Einstein} \qquad (6\text{-}12)$$

These three distributions are compared graphically in Figure 6-1, where the expected value of the number of particles in the kth quantum state is plotted as a function of the dimensionless energy of the kth particle quantum state. In agreement with statements made earlier, it is seen that, in a Fermi-Dirac system, $\langle N_k \rangle$ can never exceed unity; in a Bose-Einstein system, $\langle N_k \rangle$ can exceed unity (for small values of $\beta\varepsilon_k + \gamma$); in the event that $\beta\varepsilon_k + \gamma >> 1$, the Maxwell-Boltzmann approximation predicts values of $\langle N_k \rangle$ intermediate to and approximately equal to the values obtained for the other two systems. For a given value of γ, the larger number of particles in a Bose-Einstein system (relative to a Maxwell-Boltzmann system) corresponds to an effective attraction between the particles; the smaller number of particles in a Fermi-Dirac system (relative to a Maxwell-Boltzmann system) corresponds to an effective repulsion between the particles.

The effects of temperature and chemical potential on the distribution of particles among the particle quantum states in a Fermi-Dirac system is clarified perhaps by reference to Figure 6-2, where the expected value of the number of particles in the kth particle quantum state is plotted as a function of the energy of the kth particle quantum state for several temperatures, and by reference to Table 6-3, where the expected value of the number of particles in the kth particle quantum state is given for several limiting values of chemical potential and temperature. Note that for constant T, if $\mu \to -\infty$, then the number density (number per unit volume) of particles in the system approaches zero; whereas if $\mu \to +\infty$, then (for an infinite number of particle quantum states) the number density of particles in the system approaches infinity. Also, for constant μ, if $T = 0$, the

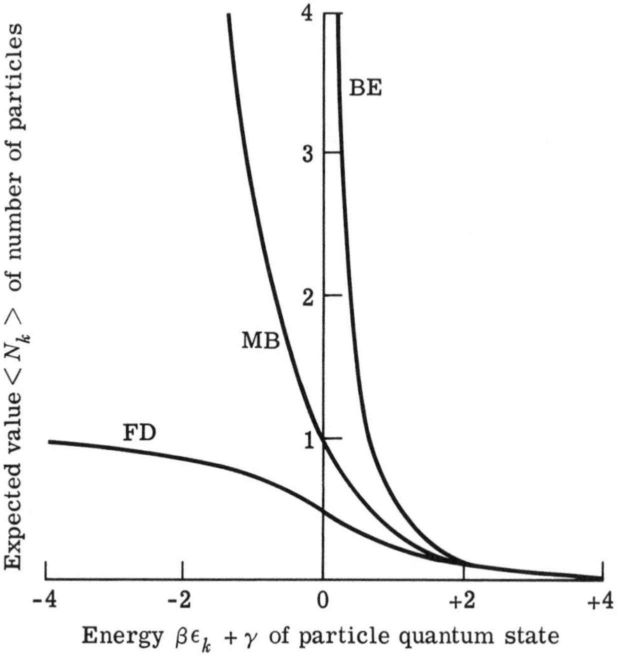

Figure 6-1 *Expected value of the number of particles in their* kth *quantum state as a function of dimensionless energy of the* kth *quantum state for the Fermi-Dirac, Maxwell-Boltzmann, and Bose-Einstein systems.*

particles occupy completely (one particle per particle quantum state) all particle quantum states with $\varepsilon_k < \mu$ and leave unoccupied all particle quantum states with $\varepsilon_k > \mu$; that is, the energy of a Fermi-Dirac system is large even at $T = 0$.

Table 6-3 Expected value of number of particles in *k*th particle quantum state for several limiting cases of Fermi-Dirac system

Particle energy ε_k	*Chemical potential* μ	*Temperature T*	*Number of particles* $\langle N_k \rangle$
Finite	$\to -\infty$	Constant	$\to 0$
Finite	$\to +\infty$	Constant	$\to 1$
Finite, $\varepsilon_k > \mu$	Constant	$\to 0$	$\to 0$
Finite, $\varepsilon_k < \mu$	Constant	$\to 0$	$\to 1$
Finite	Constant	$\to \infty$	$\to 0.5$

The effects of temperature and chemical potential on the distribution of particles among the particle quantum states in a Bose-Einstein system is clarified perhaps by reference to Figure 6-3, where the expected value of the number of particles in the kth particle quantum state is plotted as a function of the energy of the kth particle quantum state for several temperatures,

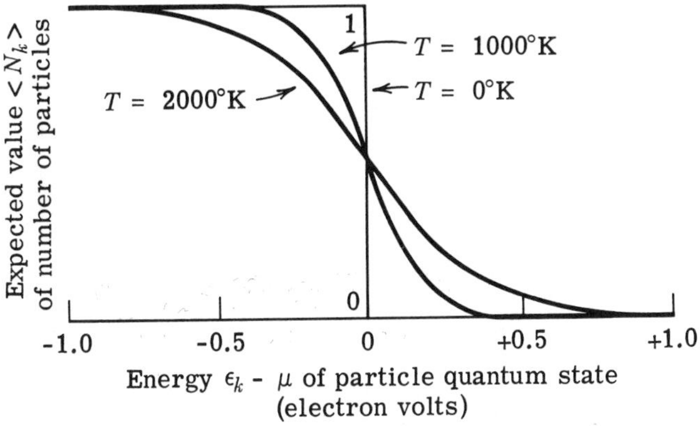

Figure 6-2 *Expected value of the number of particles in their* kth *quantum state as a function of energy of the* kth *quantum state for the Fermi-Dirac system and several values of temperature.*

and by reference to Table 6-4, where the expected value of the number of particles in the kth particle quantum state is given for several limiting values of chemical potential and temperature. Note that if T is constant and $\mu \to -\infty$, the number density of particles in the system approaches zero; whereas if μ is constant and $T \to \infty$, then the number density of particles in the system approaches infinity. Also, if $\langle N \rangle$ is nonzero and $T \to 0$, then μ must equal the particle **ground-state energy level**, i.e., the lowest allowed particle energy level. (If, for $T \to 0$, μ did not equal the particle ground-state energy level, then $\langle N_k \rangle$ would equal zero for *all* particle quantum states and the system would contain no particles.) Hence, if $\langle N \rangle$ is nonzero and $T \to 0$, all particle quantum states with $\varepsilon_k > \varepsilon_1$ are unoccupied and each particle is in its ground state. This behavior as $T \to 0$ differs radically from the behavior of a Fermi-Dirac system as $T \to 0$.

Table 6-4 Expected value of number of particles in kth particle quantum state for several limiting cases of Bose-Einstein system

Particle energy ε_k	*Chemical potential* μ	*Temperature T*	*Number of particles* $\langle N_k \rangle$
Finite	$\to -\infty$	Constant	$\to 0$
Finite, $\varepsilon_k > \mu$	Constant	$\to 0$	$\to 0$
Ground state, ε_1	ε_1	$\to 0$	$\to \langle N \rangle$
Finite	Constant	$\to \infty$	$\to \infty$

Note that the discussion in the preceding paragraph used the expected value of the number of particles in the kth particle quantum state and did not use probabilities. Since the particles are indistinguishable, the application of probabilities to given particles is inappropriate. One could, however, define probabilities by

$$P_k \equiv \frac{\langle N_k \rangle}{\langle N \rangle}$$

and interpret P_k, for a system containing a large number of particles, as the

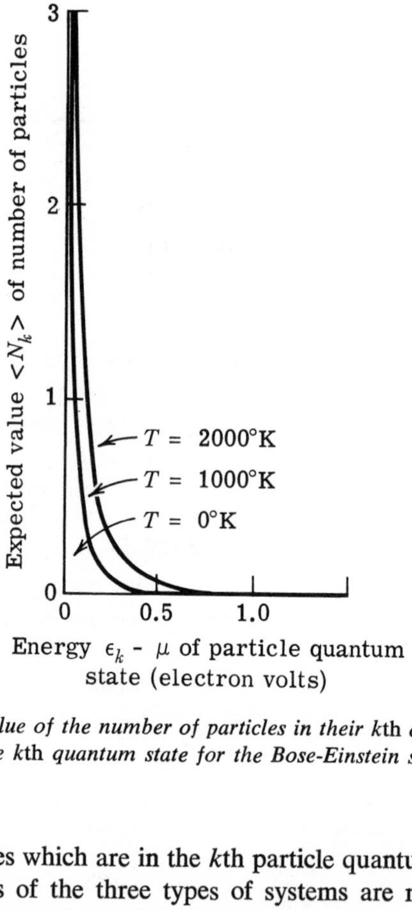

Figure 6-3 *Expected value of the number of particles in their* k*th quantum state as a function of energy of the* k*th quantum state for the Bose-Einstein system and several values of temperature.*

fraction of the particles which are in the kth particle quantum state. However, the comparisons of the three types of systems are made clearer by the use of $\langle N_k \rangle$ (in Figures 6-1 to 6-3, for example) rather than P_k.

An advantage of using (when appropriate) the Maxwell-Boltzmann system is brought out in an examination of the expressions for $\langle N \rangle$, obtained by summing Equations (6-10) to (6-12) over all allowed particle quantum states:

$$\langle N\rangle = \sum_k \frac{1}{e^{\beta\varepsilon_k+\gamma}+1} \qquad \text{Fermi-Dirac} \qquad (6\text{-}13)$$

$$\langle N\rangle = \frac{1}{e^{\gamma}}\sum_k \frac{1}{e^{\beta\varepsilon_k}} \qquad \text{Maxwell-Boltzmann} \qquad (6\text{-}14)$$

$$\langle N\rangle = \sum_k \frac{1}{e^{\beta\varepsilon_k+\gamma}-1} \qquad \text{Bose-Einstein} \qquad (6\text{-}15)$$

and the expressions for ln Ξ, obtained by rewriting Equations (6-7) and (6-9) for systems containing only one type of particle:

$$\ln\Xi = \sum_k \ln(1+e^{-\beta\varepsilon_k-\gamma}) \qquad \text{Fermi-Dirac}$$

$$\ln\Xi = \frac{1}{e^{\gamma}}\sum_k \frac{1}{e^{\beta\varepsilon_k}} \qquad \text{Maxwell-Boltzmann}$$

$$\ln\Xi = \sum_k \ln(1-e^{-\beta\varepsilon_k-\gamma})^{-1} \qquad \text{Bose-Einstein}$$

This examination reveals that, in general (and in agreement with earlier statements), β, γ, and X_c appear as convenient independent variables and $\langle N\rangle$ and Ξ as dependent variables. For a Maxwell-Boltzmann system, however, two simplifications are realized: (1) $\langle N\rangle_{MB} = \ln\Xi_{MB}$ and (2) if one wishes, one may consider β, $\langle N\rangle$, and X_c as independent variables and γ as a dependent variable without introducing any computational inconveniences; explicitly,

$$\gamma = \ln\frac{\sum_k e^{-\beta\varepsilon_k}}{\langle N\rangle} \qquad \text{Maxwell-Boltzmann} \qquad (6\text{-}16)$$

(If one wishes to consider β, $\langle N\rangle$, and X_c as independent variables in either a Fermi-Dirac or a Bose-Einstein system, one must treat the corresponding equation containing $\langle N\rangle$ as an expression which relates *implicitly* γ with β, $\langle N\rangle$, and X_c.) The advantages of being able to use β, $\langle N\rangle$, and X_c as independent variables, if one wishes, are extended if one recalls, from Equation (5-8*a*), that, for the case in which effects of external fields are negligible,

$$\frac{pV}{kT} \sim \ln\Xi \qquad (6\text{-}17)$$

so that

$$\frac{pV}{kT} \sim \sum_k \ln(1+e^{-\beta\varepsilon_k-\gamma}) \qquad \text{Fermi-Dirac} \qquad (6\text{-}18)$$

$$\frac{pV}{kT} \sim \frac{1}{e^{\gamma}}\sum_k \frac{1}{e^{\beta\varepsilon_k}} \qquad \text{Maxwell-Boltzmann} \qquad (6\text{-}19)$$

$$\frac{pV}{kT} \sim \sum_k \ln(1-e^{-\beta\varepsilon_k-\gamma})^{-1} \qquad \text{Bose-Einstein} \qquad (6\text{-}20)$$

Hence, analogous to Equation (6-16), one may write

$$\gamma \sim \ln\left(\frac{kT}{pV}\sum_k e^{-\beta\varepsilon_k}\right) \qquad \text{Maxwell-Boltzmann} \qquad (6\text{-}21)$$

so that, for a Maxwell-Boltzmann system with negligible effects of external fields, one may consider alternatively (using classical-thermodynamical language) T, p, and V as independent variables. Fortunately (for ease in computations) the behavior of a great majority of substances may be described, for a great majority of temperatures and pressures of interest to engineers and scientists, to good approximation by Maxwell-Boltzmann systems. Exceptions include liquid helium, thermal radiation, and electrons in metals.

The concepts of Fermi-Dirac, Bose-Einstein, and Maxwell-Boltzmann systems of indistinguishable particles with negligible effects of interparticle forces introduced in this chapter will be supplemented in Chapters 9, 12, and 14 by the concept of a system of independent distinguishable subsystems. Since this latter concept is used only in special applications (e.g., in discussions of crystals), it will be developed at the time of application.

PROBLEMS

6-1 Carry out the indicated summations and multiplications to show that

$$\exp\left[-\sum_{i=1}^{2}\sum_{k=1}^{3}(\beta\varepsilon_{ik}+\gamma_i)N_{ikj}\right] = \prod_{i=1}^{2}\prod_{k=1}^{3} e^{-(\beta\varepsilon_{ik}+\gamma_i)N_{ikj}}$$

that is, verify, for a particular case, the equality of the last two lines of Equation (6-3).

6-2 Show that, for a system of indistinguishable particles with negligible interparticle forces,

$$S \sim -k\sum_k [\langle N_k\rangle \ln\langle N_k\rangle \pm (1 \mp \langle N_k\rangle)\ln(1 \mp \langle N_k\rangle)]$$

where the upper sign corresponds to a Fermi-Dirac system and the lower sign to a Bose-Einstein system. How may this expression be written for a Maxwell-Boltzmann system? [HINT: Begin with Equation (5-8*b*).]

6-3 Prove, for a system of indistinguishable particles with negligible effects of interparticle forces, that

$$\ln \Xi_{\text{FD}} < \ln \Xi_{\text{MB}} < \ln \Xi_{\text{BE}}$$

These inequalities are valid also for systems in which effects of interparticle forces are not negligible.

6-4 If effects of interparticle forces are negligible, does the average internal energy per particle depend on number density for a Fermi-Dirac system? For a Maxwell-Boltzmann system? For a Bose-Einstein system? Under the same conditions, does the chemical potential per particle depend on number density? (HINT: The student may find it helpful to answer the last question first.)

chapter 7

quantum mechanics

...any one who would make his attitude concerning the hypothesis of quanta depend on whether the significance of the quantum of action for the elementary physical processes is made clear in every respect or may be demonstrated by some simple dynamical model, misunderstands, I believe, the character and the meaning of the hypothesis of quanta. It is impossible to express a really new principle in terms of a model following old laws.

M. Planck, 1912 †

The quantum-mechanical results used in the first six chapters have been quite modest. In Chapter 3 the result was introduced that if a system is finite and in a stationary state then only discrete energy levels and discrete particle numbers are allowed; in Chapter 6, the result was added that if a system contains particles with antisymmetric wave functions then no more than one of these particles can be in a given particle quantum state at one time. Based on these results, the procedure was developed for calculating values of macroscopic quantities for systems of indistinguishable particles with negligible effects of interparticle forces. In order to apply this procedure to particular systems, information concerning the energy levels of the allowed particle quantum states must be available. Although the results of classical mechanics are adequate in some cases, this information is obtained, in general, either from experiments or from quantum-mechanical calculations. (The numerous phenomena which are described inadequately by classical mechanics include thermal radiation at intermediate wavelengths, emission from atoms and molecules in a discontinuous spectrum, diffraction of particles of matter, ejection of electrons from matter by incident photons, variation of heat capacities with temperature, the

† M. Planck, "The Theory of Heat Radiation," p. ix, Dover Publications, Inc., New York, 1959.

contribution of the electron gas to the heat capacity of a metal, and the behavior of liquid helium.)

The discussion of quantum mechanics included here is extremely brief and very elementary; it might be thought of as a "recipe" for obtaining (for relatively simple systems) some results of interest to statistical thermodynamics. Experimental bases are not given; alternative procedures are not discussed; and extensive (and more advanced) additions are required in most applications. The present chapter provides, however, a minimum background for the quantum mechanics used in the following chapters; the agreement of the results of those chapters with results of experiments provides some support for use of the "recipe" given here.

Two alternative formulations of quantum mechanics have evolved—the wave-function formulation of Schrödinger and the matrix-algebra formulation of Heisenberg. The wave-function formulation emphasizes, from the beginning, the experimental fact that both matter and thermal radiation exhibit both particlelike and wavelike properties, i.e., it emphasizes the wave-particle duality. (As examples of this wave-particle duality, electrons exhibit wavelike properties as well as particlelike properties, whereas photons exhibit particlelike properties as well as wavelike properties.) The matrix-algebra formulation is more concise and is independent of special coordinate systems. Because of its more extensive use of physical models, the wave-function formulation is used here.

In this formulation, all mechanical phenomena may be described quantitatively by associating with every bit of matter a field having a wavelike character. The function which describes this field is represented by the symbol Ψ and is called a wave function. As in the case of electric, magnetic, and gravity fields, the field described by Ψ cannot be observed directly. However, as will be indicated in the following paragraph, if Ψ is known, one is able to calculate immediately either the probability that the value of a mechanical quantity is in a given range of values or, alternatively, the expected value of any mechanical quantity. (Typical examples of these mechanical quantities include momentum and position of a moving particle.) These predictions are to be compared respectively with the distribution and with the average value of the results of a series of independent measurements. The probabilities (as well as the implied uncertainties) used here are inherent in physical measurements; they can be approximated by certainties only in those limiting cases in which quantum mechanics may be approximated by classical mechanics.

In the discussion of the basic postulates of quantum mechanics which will be given in subsequent paragraphs, the terms "dynamical variables" and "operators" are used frequently. **Dynamical variables** are defined to be mechanical quantities whose expected values may be calculated using the methods of quantum mechanics. **Operators** are defined to be prescriptions for mathematical operations on a function of the independent variables of the system. (In the present chapter, the "independent variables of the system" are independent variables of a mechanical system with ϕ degrees of freedom, namely, ϕ spatial coordinates and time. They are almost always much more numerous than are the independent variables of a thermodynamical system used in previous chapters.) In quantum mechanics, each dynamical variable is represented by an operator. Examples of dynamical variables and operators are given in the following paragraph.

The following five basic postulates may be used as a "recipe" for obtaining, for relatively simple nonrelativistic systems, some results (e.g., allowed quantum states and associated energy levels) of interest to statistical thermodynamics:

Postulate 1: To each system with ϕ degrees of freedom, one may assign a wave function $\Psi(q_1, q_2, \ldots, q_\phi, t)$ where $q_1, q_2, \ldots, q_\phi$ are generalized coordinates and t is time. (See Appendix G for a brief review of generalized coordinates, conjugate momenta, and scale factors.)

Postulate 2: If the system is conservative (i.e., if the potential energy of the system is a function of the generalized coordinates only), then the Schrödinger wave equation may be constructed from the classical expression for the total energy of the system

$$\frac{1}{2}\sum_{x=1}^{\phi}\frac{(p_x/h_x)^2}{m_x} + U(q_1, q_2, \ldots, q_\phi) = \varepsilon$$

where $p_x (\equiv m_x h_x^2\, dq_x/dt)$ is the momentum conjugate to the generalized coordinate q_x, h_x is a **scale factor** selected so that $h_x\, dq_x$ represents actual displacement in direction q_x, m_x is mass, U is potential energy, and ε is total energy.[1] Substitute the following operators for the dynamical variables:

Dynamical variable		*Operator*
q_x	$\rightarrow$	q_x
p_x	$\rightarrow$	$\dfrac{\hbar}{i}\dfrac{\partial}{\partial q_x}$
ε	$\rightarrow$	$-\dfrac{\hbar}{i}\dfrac{\partial}{\partial t}$

where $\hbar$ is Planck's constant divided by 2π and i is $\sqrt{-1}$. Operate upon the wave function $\Psi(q_1, q_2, \ldots, q_\phi, t)$ with the resulting operator to obtain the **Schrödinger wave equation**; if the generalized coordinates are all rectangular coordinates, then $h_x = 1$ and one obtains, for a single-particle system,

$$-\frac{\hbar^2}{2m}\left(\frac{\partial^2\Psi}{\partial x^2}+\frac{\partial^2\Psi}{\partial y^2}+\frac{\partial^2\Psi}{\partial z^2}\right)+U(x,y,z)\,\Psi=-\frac{\hbar}{i}\frac{\partial\Psi}{\partial t} \tag{7-1}$$

Postulate 3: The wave function Ψ and its spatial derivatives $\partial\Psi/\partial q_x$ must be finite, continuous, and single-valued for all values of $q_1, q_2, \ldots, q_\phi$.

Postulate 4: The integral of the square of the absolute value of the wave function Ψ is finite, i.e., one may normalize Ψ (multiply Ψ by the appropriate factor) such that

$$\int_{q_1}\int_{q_2}\cdots\int_{q_\phi}\Psi^*\Psi h_1\,dq_1\,h_2\,dq_2\cdots h_\phi\,dq_\phi = 1 \tag{7-2}$$

where Ψ^*, the complex conjugate of Ψ, is formed by replacing each i in Ψ by $-i$. (Recall that $|\Psi|^2 \equiv \Psi^*\Psi$.)

Postulate 5: The **expected value** of any dynamical variable, for example, A, may be calculated from the wave function Ψ by the formula

$$\langle A\rangle = \int_{q_1}\int_{q_2}\cdots\int_{q_\phi}\Psi^* A_{\text{oper}}\Psi h_1\,dq_1\,h_2\,dq_2\cdots h_\phi\,dq_\phi \tag{7-3}$$

where A_{oper} is the operator representing A.

[1]The reader may find it convenient, particularly in the first reading, to consider a single particle with mass m in a rectangular coordinate system so that the generalized coordinates $q_1, q_2, \ldots, q_\phi$ reduce to x, y, z, the masses m_x equal m, and the scale factors h_x equal unity.

These five postulates contain the heart of quantum mechanics; they indicate the procedures for establishing the wave function Ψ and for calculating from Ψ the expected values of dynamical variables. Although they would have to be generalized slightly in some applications (e.g., in applications to systems with significant electromagnetic fields), the principles would be essentially as indicated here. As written, these five postulates are adequate for the prediction of those quantum states and associated energy levels required in the remainder of this book.

Brief comments on each of the five basic postulates are contained in the following five paragraphs. Further clarification of their meanings will be found in the applications contained at the end of the present chapter and in succeeding chapters.

The wave function Ψ introduced in Postulate 1 may be considered to be the communication link which connects the macroscopic world with the microscopic world. To the extent that the use of Ψ leads to predictions which agree with measurements, the field described by Ψ may be considered to be just as real as an electromagnetic or gravity field.

In the prescription given in Postulate 2 for the construction of the wave equation, some ambiguity exists since the order in which operators are applied is significant in some cases. For example, $q_x(\partial/\partial q_x)\Psi \neq (\partial/\partial q_x)q_x\Psi$. If h_x is a function of the dynamical variables, then the order in which the operators of p_x and $1/h_x$ are to be applied is ambiguous. This ambiguity is reduced by constructing first the wave equation in rectangular coordinates ($h_x = 1$) and then transforming (if necessary) to other coordinates. For example, by transforming the wave equation given in Postulate 2 from rectangular coordinates to spherical polar coordinates one obtains, for a single-particle system,

$$-\frac{\hbar^2}{2mr^2}\left(\frac{\partial}{\partial r}r^2\frac{\partial\Psi}{dr} + \frac{1}{\sin\theta}\frac{\partial}{\partial\theta}\sin\theta\frac{\partial\Psi}{\partial\theta} + \frac{1}{\sin^2\theta}\frac{\partial^2\Psi}{\partial\phi^2}\right) + U(r,\theta,\phi)\Psi = -\frac{\hbar}{i}\frac{\partial\Psi}{\partial t} \tag{7-4}$$

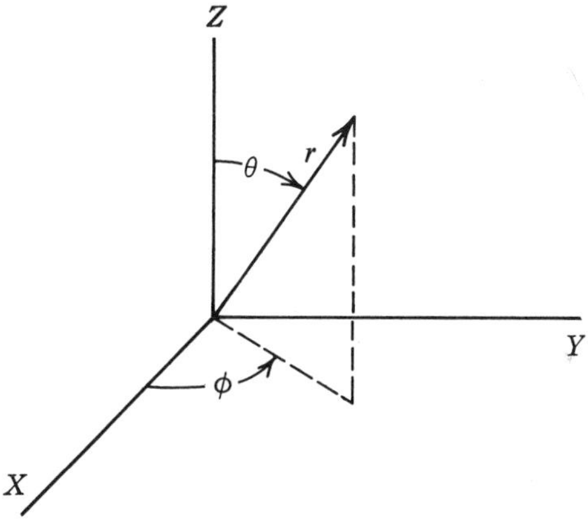

Figure 7-1 *Spherical polar coordinates.*

where r, θ, and ϕ are spherical polar coordinates as defined in Figure 7-1. Regarding the motivation for the given prescription, the best that can be said is perhaps that it has evolved, as a consequence of inspiration, by extremely capable investigators and that it has been found to lead to useful results.

Postulate 3 states merely that Ψ must be a well-behaved function—a reasonable requirement if it is to describe real systems. This postulate may be relaxed to permit discontinuities in the spatial derivatives $\partial\Psi/\partial q_x$ for cases in which the potential energy $U(q_1, q_2, \ldots, q_\phi)$ is approximated by a discontinuous function.

The integrand $\Psi^*\Psi h_1\,dq_1\,h_2\,dq_2 \cdots h_\phi\,dq_\phi$ appearing in Postulate 4 may be interpreted as the probability that the ϕ degrees of freedom are respectively within displacements $h_1\,dq_1, h_2\,dq_2, \ldots, h_\phi\,dq_\phi$. Equating the integral to unity is equivalent to stating that the probability of each generalized coordinate having some value is unity. The combined effect of Postulates 3 and 4 is to select from the many functions which would satisfy the Schrödinger wave equation only certain functions; that is, the combined effect leads to quantization. The fact that only certain wave functions (eigenfunctions) are allowed is no more unusual than the fact that only certain modes of vibration of a resonating string are allowed.

Postulate 5 rewards the labors involved in the application of the first four postulates; it translates information concerning the invisible matter field into expected values of dynamical variables. [Information concerning probable deviations from the expected value of an observable quantity is provided by the variance (see Appendix B).] All quantum-mechanical predictions of dynamical variables require the application of Postulate 5 or its equivalent. Note that the expected values predicted by Postulate 5 are averages for a specified quantum state (neither requiring nor providing any information concerning the relative probabilities of the possible quantum states), whereas the expected values predicted by Equation (2-1) are averages over all possible quantum states (requiring information, provided by statistical thermodynamics, concerning the relative probabilities of the possible quantum states).

The Schrödinger wave equation written, for example, in Postulate 2 may be separated into a time-independent equation and a coordinate-independent equation. Substitute

$$\Psi(x, y, z, t) = \psi(x, y, z)\,\phi(t) \tag{7-5}$$

into

$$-\frac{\hbar^2}{2m}\left(\frac{\partial^2\Psi}{\partial x^2} + \frac{\partial^2\Psi}{\partial y^2} + \frac{\partial^2\Psi}{\partial z^2}\right) + U(x, y, z)\,\Psi = -\frac{\hbar}{i}\frac{\partial\Psi}{\partial t} \tag{7-1}$$

and divide by $\psi(x, y, z)\,\phi(t)$ to obtain

$$\frac{1}{\psi}\left[-\frac{\hbar^2}{2m}\left(\frac{\partial^2\psi}{\partial x^2} + \frac{\partial^2\psi}{\partial y^2} + \frac{\partial^2\psi}{\partial z^2}\right) + U\psi\right] = -\frac{\hbar}{i}\frac{1}{\phi}\frac{d\phi}{dt} \tag{7-6}$$

Since the left-hand side is not a function of time and the right-hand side is not a function of the coordinates, Equation (7-6) can hold only if each side is a function of some constant. If one designates the constant by c, then

$$-\frac{\hbar^2}{2m}\left(\frac{\partial^2\psi}{\partial x^2} + \frac{\partial^2\psi}{\partial y^2} + \frac{\partial^2\psi}{\partial z^2}\right) + U\psi = c\psi \tag{7-7}$$

and

$$-\frac{\hbar}{i}\frac{d\phi}{dt} = c\phi \tag{7-8}$$

The latter equation may be integrated after separating variables; absorbing the integration constant by modifying the value of the integration constant appearing in ψ yields

$$\phi(t) = \exp\left(-i\frac{c}{\hbar}t\right) \tag{7-9}$$

so that now

$$\Psi(x, y, z, t) = \psi(x, y, z) \exp\left(-i\frac{c}{\hbar}t\right) \tag{7-10}$$

where $\psi(x, y, z)$ is the amplitude of $\Psi(x, y, z, t)$. It will be found that Postulates 3 and 4 will allow only certain wave functions and that these certain wave functions are realized for only particular values of the constant c. Designate these certain wave functions and particular values of the constant by the subscript k. Then Equation (7-10) is written

$$\Psi_k(x, y, z, t) = \psi_k(x, y, z) \exp\left(-i\frac{c_k}{\hbar}t\right) \tag{7-11}$$

A large portion of quantum mechanics is concerned with the problem of determining the allowed ψ_k's and c_k's.

As an example of the application of Postulate 5, and in order to give added meaning to the constants c_k, consider the expected value of the energy of the system. From Equation (7-3), if the generalized coordinates are all rectangular coordinates ($h_x = 1$), then, for a single-particle system,

$$\begin{aligned} \langle\varepsilon\rangle &= \iiint \Psi^*\left(-\frac{\hbar}{i}\frac{\partial}{\partial t}\right)\Psi\, dx\, dy\, dz \\ &= \iiint \psi_k^* \exp\left(i\frac{c_k}{\hbar}t\right)\psi_k \exp\left(-i\frac{c_k}{\hbar}t\right) c_k\, dx\, dy\, dz \\ &= c_k \iiint \Psi^*\Psi\, dx\, dy\, dz \\ &= c_k \end{aligned} \tag{7-12}$$

where Postulate 4 has been used in going from the third line to the fourth line. It is seen that the constants c_k are the allowed (discrete) energy levels of the system. Hence the constant c_k will be replaced, in discussions which follow, by the allowed energy levels ε_k. For example, the time-independent wave equation and Equation (7-11) will be written

$$-\left(\frac{\partial^2\psi_k}{\partial x^2} + \frac{\partial^2\psi_k}{\partial y^2} + \frac{\partial^2\psi_k}{\partial z^2}\right) = \frac{2m}{\hbar^2}(\varepsilon_k - U)\psi_k \tag{7-13} ◀$$

and

$$\Psi_k(x, y, z, t) = \psi_k(x, y, z) \exp\left(-i\frac{\varepsilon_k}{\hbar}t\right) \tag{7-14} ◀$$

Keep in mind that specification of the kth quantum state of a system requires specification of one quantum number for each degree of freedom of the system.

As indicated already in Chapter 5, more than one quantum state may have the same energy level and the same numbers of particles; quantum states with the same energy level and the same number of particles are known as **degenerate quantum states**. Each member of a set of degenerate quantum states is described by a different wave function. However, any linear combination of wave functions associated with a set of degenerate quantum states is also a solution of the Schrödinger wave equation. Hence the membership of a set of degenerate quantum states is not unique. (It is limited, however, since only a limited number, equal to the degeneracy, of possible members of this set are independent.) This situation leads, in principle, to ambiguities when listing degenerate quantum states. These ambiguities have no effect, however, on the calculations of statistical thermodynamics; if one lists energy levels and particle numbers, and uses a degeneracy factor, the ambiguities are avoided; if one lists quantum states and chooses the membership of a set of degenerate quantum states arbitrarily, one finds that all statistical-thermodynamical calculation results which can be compared with experimental measurements are independent of the choice which was made. The author finds frequently that listing quantum states is more convenient than listing energy levels and particle numbers and using degeneracy factors.

As indicated at the beginning of this chapter, the discussion of quantum mechanics included here is extremely brief and very elementary. This discussion provides, however, a minimum background for the quantum mechanics used in the following chapters. Analyses of more complex systems would require slight generalizations of the postulates given here (and, in many cases, more formidable mathematics); the principles, however, would be essentially as indicated here.

Example

As a simple example of some of the concepts introduced in this chapter, consider a single particle with nonzero rest mass and with negligible internal degrees of freedom moving in a one-dimensional box with impenetrable walls. Neglect effects of external fields and select the zero of potential energy such that the potential energy of the particle within the box is zero (see Figure 7-2). The appropriate time-independent wave equation is

$$-\frac{d^2\psi_k}{dx^2} = \frac{2m}{\hbar^2}\varepsilon_k\psi_k$$

where m is the mass of the particle. Since the walls are impenetrable, the probability of finding the particle at either $x = 0$ or $x = l$, where l is the length of the box, is zero. Hence, from Postulate 4, ψ_k must be zero for either $x = 0$ or $x = l$, and from the continuity requirement of Postulate 3, ψ_k must approach 0 as either wall is approached from inside the box. Well-behaved wave functions which satisfy both the given wave equation and this boundary condition are found only for

$$\varepsilon_k = \frac{\hbar^2}{2m}\left(\frac{k\pi}{l}\right)^2$$

where $k = 1, 2, \cdots$ (see Figure 7-2). The associated normalized wave functions are

$$\psi_k = \left(\frac{2}{l}\right)^{1/2} \sin k\pi \frac{x}{l}$$

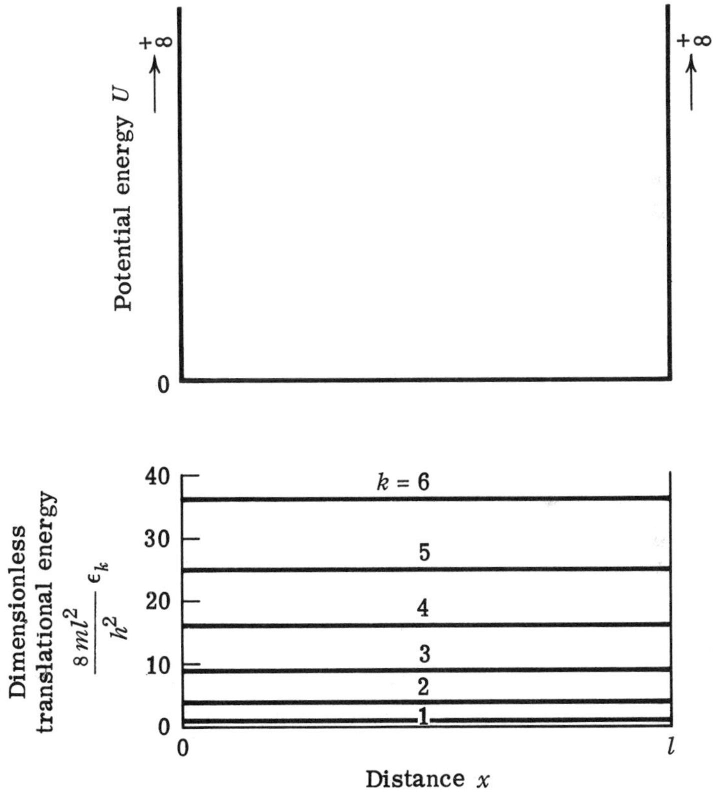

Figure 7-2 *Potential energy and several possible dimensionless translational energies for a single particle in a one-dimensional box.*

(see Figure 7-3) as may be verified by substituting ε_k and ψ_k into the given wave equation and ψ_k into

$$\int_0^l \psi_k^2\, dx = 1$$

The probability that a particle in quantum state k will be found, in a given measurement, between x and $x + dx$ is given by

$$|\psi_k|^2\, dx = \psi_k^*\, \psi_k\, dx$$

(see Figure 7-3), whereas the expected values of the x position and the x momentum are given, respectively, by

$$\langle x \rangle = \int_0^l \psi_k^2 \, x \, dx = \frac{l}{2}$$

$$\langle p_x \rangle = \int_0^l \psi_k \frac{\hbar}{i} \frac{d\psi_k}{dx} \, dx = 0$$

where p_x is momentum (not pressure). (Positive and negative values of momentum are equally probable.) These results are extended to the case of a three-dimensional box in Problem 7-1.

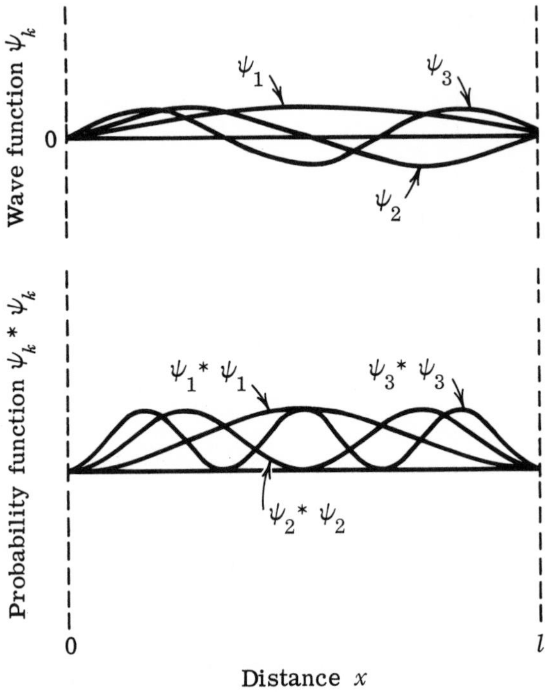

Figure 7-3 *Several possible wave functions and probability functions for a single particle in a one-dimensional box. ($\psi_k^* \psi_k \, dx$ is the probability that the particle is between x and $x + dx$.)*

PROBLEMS

7-1 Consider a particle with nonzero rest mass and with negligible internal degrees of freedom moving in a rectangular box with impenetrable walls. For the case in which effects of external potentials are negligible, show that the time-independent wave function

$$\psi_k = \left(\frac{8}{V}\right)^{1/2} \sin\left(k_1 \pi \frac{x}{l_1}\right) \sin\left(k_2 \pi \frac{y}{l_2}\right) \sin\left(k_3 \pi \frac{z}{l_3}\right)$$

satisfies the time-independent wave equation provided that

$$\varepsilon_k = \frac{\hbar^2}{2m}\left[\left(\frac{k_1\pi}{l_1}\right)^2 + \left(\frac{k_2\pi}{l_2}\right)^2 + \left(\frac{k_3\pi}{l_3}\right)^2\right]$$

where k_1, k_2, and k_3 are quantum numbers with allowed values of 1, 2, . . . ; l_1, l_2, and l_3 are lengths of edges of the box; and V is volume of the box. Let the origin of the coordinate system coincide with one corner of the box. Check normalization of ψ_k and continuity of ψ_k at walls. Compute expected values of the x position and the x momentum.

7-2 Consider a harmonic oscillator with potential energy

$$U(x) = \frac{1}{2}ax^2$$

Solutions of the time-independent wave equation for this system (with ψ finite at $x = \pm\infty$) are given by

$$\psi_l = \left(-\frac{1}{\alpha}\right)^l \left(\frac{\alpha}{\pi^{1/2}\, 2^l l!}\right)^{1/2} e^{1/2(\alpha x)^2} \frac{d^l e^{-(\alpha x)^2}}{dx^l}$$

for

$$\varepsilon_l = h\nu\left(l + \frac{1}{2}\right)$$

with $l = 0, 1, 2, \cdots$, $\nu = (a/m)^{1/2}/2\pi$, and $\alpha = 2\pi(\nu m/h)^{1/2}$. For the special case in which $l = 0$, verify that the given expression for ψ_0 satisfies the time-independent wave equation for a harmonic oscillator. (Take the zeroth derivative of a function to be the function.)

7-3 From Problem 7-1, the translational-energy level of a particle with nonzero rest mass in its kth quantum state is proportional to the negative two-thirds power of the volume of the box, that is,

$$\varepsilon_k = \frac{a_k}{V^{2/3}}$$

where a_k is a proportionality constant. Using the relation (see Chapter 4)

$$p_k = -\frac{d\varepsilon_k}{dV}$$

where p_k is pressure exerted by the particle in its kth quantum state, show that, for a system with an equilibrium distribution of $\langle N\rangle$ particles with negligible interparticle forces,

$$\langle p\rangle V = \frac{2}{3}\langle E\rangle$$

where

$$\langle p\rangle = \sum_k \langle N_k\rangle p_k \qquad \text{and} \qquad \langle E\rangle = \sum_k \langle N_k\rangle \varepsilon_k$$

Note that this result requires only that the particles have nonzero rest mass and negligible effects of interparticle forces; it is valid equally for Fermi-Dirac, Maxwell-Boltzmann, and Bose-Einstein systems.

7-4 Calculate, for a particle with nonzero rest mass and with negligible internal degrees of freedom moving in a rectangular box (see Problem 7-1), the expected value of $(p_x^2 + p_y^2 + p_z^2)/2m$ where p_x, p_y, and p_z are components of momentum. (A squared operator is the operator applied twice.) Compare your result with the expression for ε_k given in Problem 7-1. Of the several expected values calculated in Problem 7-1 and here, which values are sharp (i.e., certain) values?

7-5 Evaluate, for a harmonic oscillator (see Problem 7-2) in its ground state ($l = 0$),

$$\langle \text{Kinetic energy} \rangle \equiv \frac{\langle p_x^2 \rangle}{2m}$$

$$\langle \text{Potential energy} \rangle \equiv \frac{1}{2} a \langle x^2 \rangle$$

where p_x is momentum. Compare the expected values of these two energies.

chapter 8

perfect monatomic gas

The most interesting facts are those which can be used several times, those which have a chance of recurring. . . . Which, then, are the facts that have a chance of recurring? In the first place, simple facts.
H. Poincaré, 1908 †

In the remaining chapters of this book, the fundamentals outlined in the preceding chapters are applied to a series of relatively simple specific examples; it is believed that these examples will simultaneously clarify the fundamentals and illustrate the capability of statistical thermodynamics to provide physical interpretations and numerical values of thermodynamic properties. (Recall that classical thermodynamics provides neither physical interpretations nor numerical values.) Calculations for more complicated models differ from the calculations presented here chiefly in that they are more tedious.

Consider first a **perfect monatomic gas** (i.e., a monatomic gas with negligible effects of interparticle forces) composed of only one type of atom, subjected to negligible effects of external fields, and limited to the temperature range in which effects of electron excitations are negligible. As stated previously, any atomic or molecular gas with temperature sufficiently high and pressure sufficiently low so that effects of interparticle forces may be neglected (i.e., any thermally perfect atomic or molecular gas) is described adequately by a Maxwell-Boltzmann system. (A quantitative sufficient condition for use of a Maxwell-Boltzmann system for a monatomic gas is given later in this chapter.) Hence the appropriate grand partition function may be obtained from Equation (6-9), deleting the subscript i, with the result

$$\ln \Xi_{\text{MB}} = e^{-\gamma} \sum_k e^{-\beta \varepsilon_k} \tag{8-1}$$

(For convenience, the subscript MB is omitted in the remainder of this

† H. Poincaré, "Science and Method," p. 17, Dover Publications, Inc., New York, 1952.

chapter.) Since effects of electron excitations are considered to be negligible in this example, the allowed atomic energy levels result from considerations of translational motions only. From Problem 7-1, the allowed energies of translational motions for a particle, with negligible energies of internal degrees of freedom, moving in a rectangular box with edge lengths l_1, l_2, and l_3 are

$$\varepsilon_k = \frac{h^2}{8m}\left[\left(\frac{k_1}{l_1}\right)^2 + \left(\frac{k_2}{l_2}\right)^2 + \left(\frac{k_3}{l_3}\right)^2\right] \tag{8-2}$$

where h is Planck's constant, m is mass of particle, and k_1, k_2, and k_3 are translational quantum numbers (one for each of three translational degrees of freedom) with allowed values $1, 2, \cdots$. For convenience, the energy level associated with the internal configuration of an atom with no electron excitations is set arbitrarily equal to zero. However, as a consequence of magnetic moments which are interpreted as nuclear spins, net electron spins, and orbital angular momentum, an atom with no electron excitation may have more than one allowed internal quantum state. Designate the number of allowed internal quantum states of an atom with no electron excitations by g_e, called sometimes the **ground-state degeneracy**. (The **ground state** is defined as the lowest energy state.) Since spins of elementary particles within atoms tend to cancel pairwise, the degeneracy g_e is of order unity. Select the zero of potential energy such that the potential energy of an atom within the box is zero (see Figure 8-1). Then, substituting from Equation (8-2) into Equation (8-1) and performing the summation over allowed internal quantum states, one obtains

$$\ln \Xi = e^{-\gamma} \sum_{k_1, k_2, k_3} g_e \exp\left\{-\frac{\beta h^2}{8m}\left[\left(\frac{k_1}{l_1}\right)^2 + \left(\frac{k_2}{l_2}\right)^2 + \left(\frac{k_3}{l_3}\right)^2\right]\right\} \tag{8-3}$$

where the appearance of the ground-state degeneracy g_e is the direct consequence of summing over allowed internal quantum states. Since the value of the translational quantum number for a given degree of freedom may be chosen independently of the values chosen for the other two degrees of freedom, and since the exponential appearing in Equation (8-3) is factorable, one may factor the series appearing in Equation (8-3) into a product of three series,

$$\ln \Xi = e^{-\gamma} g_e \sum_{k_1=1}^{\infty} \exp\left[-\frac{\beta h^2}{8m}\left(\frac{k_1}{l_1}\right)^2\right] \sum_{k_2=1}^{\infty} \exp\left[-\frac{\beta h^2}{8m}\left(\frac{k_2}{l_2}\right)^2\right] \times \sum_{k_3=1}^{\infty} \exp\left[-\frac{\beta h^2}{8m}\left(\frac{k_3}{l_3}\right)^2\right] \tag{8-4}$$

Each series may be represented graphically by a series of columns of unit width and decreasing height (Figure 8-2). If the difference in the heights of successive columns is small in comparison with unity, the combined areas of the columns may be represented, to good approximation, by the area under a continuous curve. This condition is met, for the series appearing in Equation (8-4), if $\beta h^2/8ml_1^2$, $\beta h^2/8ml_2^2$, and $\beta h^2/8ml_3^2$ are small in comparison with unity. Largely because of the small numerical value of Planck's constant h, these dimensionless groups have small values for all temperatures of interest (including temperatures of a small fraction of 1°K), for all atomic masses, and for typical macroscopic system dimensions; e.g., for hydrogen atoms at 1°K in a cubic box with edges of 1 cm, $\beta h^2/8ml^2$

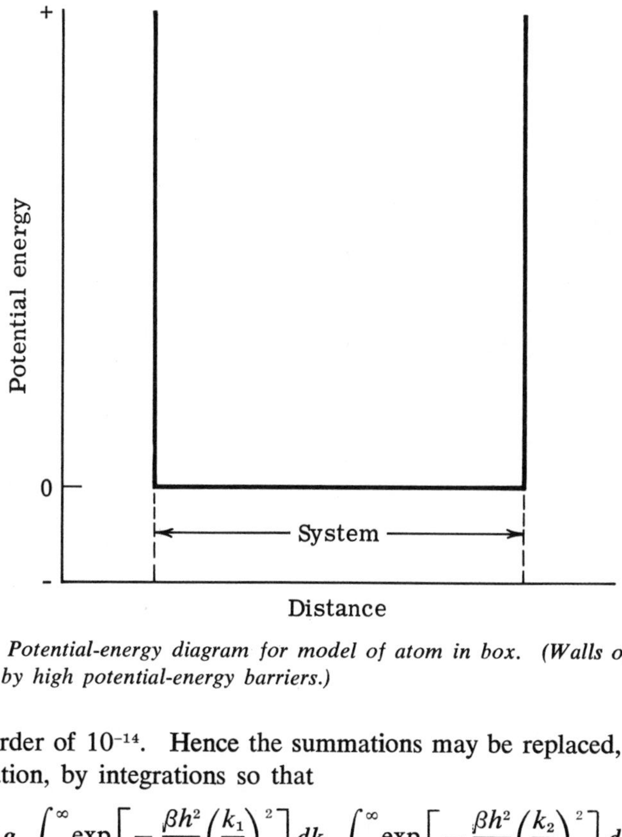

Figure 8-1 *Potential-energy diagram for model of atom in box. (Walls of box are represented by high potential-energy barriers.)*

is of the order of 10^{-14}. Hence the summations may be replaced, to good approximation, by integrations so that

$$\ln \Xi = e^{-\gamma} g_e \int_0^\infty \exp\left[-\frac{\beta h^2}{8m}\left(\frac{k_1}{l_1}\right)^2\right] dk_1 \int_0^\infty \exp\left[-\frac{\beta h^2}{8m}\left(\frac{k_2}{l_2}\right)^2\right] dk_2 \times \int_0^\infty \exp\left[-\frac{\beta h^2}{8m}\left(\frac{k_3}{l_3}\right)^2\right] dk_3$$

$$= e^{-\gamma} g_e \left(\frac{2m}{\beta h^2}\right)^{3/2} V \left(2\int_0^\infty e^{-x^2}\,dx\right)^3$$

where x represents, as the case may be, either $(\beta h^2/8m)^{1/2}(k_1/l_1)$, $(\beta h^2/8m)^{1/2}(k_2/l_2)$, or $(\beta h^2/8m)^{1/2}(k_3/l_3)$. The definite integral appearing here occurs so frequently in analysis that it has been given a name (gamma function of 1/2 and is tabulated in handbooks. One finds that

$$2\int_0^\infty \exp(-x^2)\,dx$$

has the value $\sqrt{\pi}$, so that

$$\ln \Xi = e^{-\gamma} g_e \left(\frac{2\pi m}{\beta h^2}\right)^{3/2} V \tag{8-5}$$

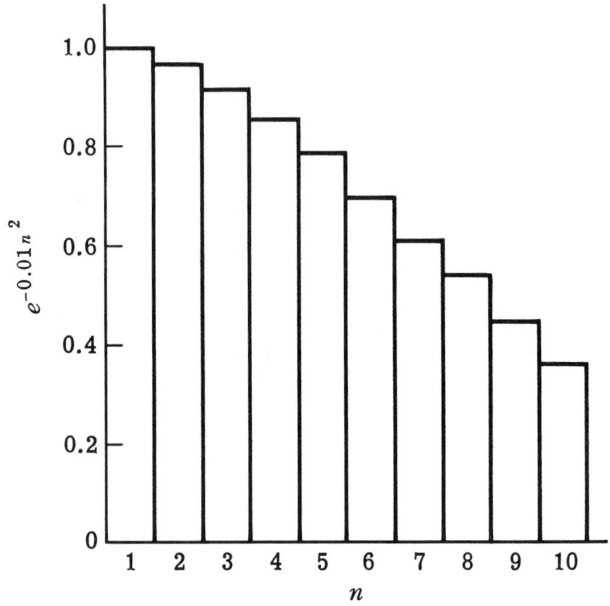

Figure 8-2 *Graphical representation of the first 10 terms of the series*

$$\sum_{n=1}^{\infty} \exp(-0.01\,n^2)$$

The value of the series equals the combined areas of the columns.

Equation (8-5) relates explicitly the logarithm of the grand partition function Ξ with the independent variables β, γ, and V.

Expected values and variances of the mechanical quantities of thermodynamics may be calculated now for a perfect monatomic gas using the methods of Chapter 4. One obtains

$$\langle E\rangle = -\left(\frac{\partial \ln \Xi}{\partial \beta}\right)_{\gamma, V} = \frac{3}{2}\frac{\ln \Xi}{\beta} \tag{8-6}$$

$$\langle N\rangle = -\left(\frac{\partial \ln \Xi}{\partial \gamma}\right)_{\beta, V} = \ln \Xi \tag{8-7}$$

$$\langle p \rangle = \frac{1}{\beta}\left(\frac{\partial \ln \Xi}{\partial V}\right)_{\beta,\gamma} = \frac{\ln \Xi}{\beta V} \tag{8-8}$$

$$\sigma^2(E) = \left(\frac{\partial^2 \ln \Xi}{\partial \beta^2}\right)_{\gamma,V} = \frac{15}{4}\frac{\ln \Xi}{\beta^2} \tag{8-9}$$

$$\sigma^2(N) = \left(\frac{\partial^2 \ln \Xi}{\partial \gamma^2}\right)_{\beta,V} = \ln \Xi \tag{8-10}$$

$$\sigma^2(p) = \frac{1}{\beta^2}\left(\frac{\partial^2 \ln \Xi}{\partial V^2}\right)_{\beta,\gamma} + \left\langle \frac{1}{\beta}\frac{d^2 E}{dV^2}\right\rangle$$

Equation (8-2) implies that the allowed translational energy levels vary as $V^{-2/3}$. Hence

$$\left\langle \frac{d^2 E}{dV^2}\right\rangle = \left\langle \frac{2}{3}\frac{5}{3}\frac{E}{V^2}\right\rangle = \frac{10}{9}\frac{\langle E \rangle}{V^2}$$

so that

$$\sigma^2(p) = 0 + \frac{5}{3}\frac{\ln \Xi}{(\beta V)^2} \tag{8-11}$$

Since $\ln \Xi$ is given explicitly as a function of β, γ, and V by Equation (8-5), one may consider, alternatively, β, γ, and V to be the independent variables in Equations (8-6) to (8-11).

Relative deviations from expected values are indicated more clearly if one computes the ratio of the **standard deviation** $\sigma(A)$ to the expected value $\langle A \rangle$ and substitutes for $\ln \Xi$ from Equation (8-7). In this method of presentation,

$$\frac{\sigma(E)}{\langle E \rangle} = \sqrt{\frac{5}{3}\frac{1}{\langle N \rangle}}$$

$$\frac{\sigma(N)}{\langle N \rangle} = \sqrt{\frac{1}{\langle N \rangle}}$$

$$\frac{\sigma(p)}{\langle p \rangle} = \sqrt{\frac{5}{3}\frac{1}{\langle N \rangle}}$$

Since a typical macroscopic system contains a very large number of particles (of the order of 10^{23}), it is apparent from these ratios that relative deviations from expected values of these properties are negligible, in practice, for most physical systems.

Finally, using the correspondences established in Chapter 5, one obtains for the entropy

$$\frac{S}{k} \sim \ln \Xi + \beta \langle E \rangle + \gamma \langle N \rangle = \left(\frac{5}{2} + \gamma\right) \ln \Xi \tag{8-12}$$

where $\langle E \rangle$ and $\langle N \rangle$ were eliminated, in favor of Ξ, using Equations (8-6) and (8-7).

The equations of classical thermodynamics corresponding to Equations (8-5) to (8-7) and (8-12) would be (see Table 5-1)

$$pV = g_e\, e^{\mu/kT}\left(\frac{2\pi mkT}{h^2}\right)^{3/2} VkT \tag{8-5$'$}$$

$$E = \frac{3}{2}pV \tag{8-6$'$}$$

$$N = \frac{pV}{kT} \tag{8-7$'$}$$

$$\frac{S}{k} = \left(\frac{5}{2} - \frac{\mu}{kT}\right)\frac{pV}{kT} \tag{8-12$'$}$$

(The elimination of the equation corresponding to Equation (8-8) is consistent with the elimination of $\ln \Xi$ without the introduction of a new variable. Recall that Equation (8-6′) was derived already in Problem 7-3 for a much more general model.) Although these equations are written with independent variables T, μ, and V in mind, other choices of independent variables are equally (or more) convenient in some cases. For example, these equations may be rearranged to obtain, for the case in which the independent variables are T, N, and V,

$$A = -NkT\ln\left[g_e\left(\frac{2\pi mkT}{h^2}\right)^{3/2}\frac{V}{N}e\right] \tag{8-13}$$

$$E = \frac{3}{2}NkT \tag{8-14}$$

$$p = \frac{NkT}{V} \tag{8-15}$$

$$\frac{S}{k} = -\frac{A}{kT} + \frac{3}{2}N \tag{8-16}$$

$$\frac{\mu}{kT} = \frac{A}{NkT} + 1 \tag{8-17}$$

and for the case in which the independent variables are T, N, and p,

$$G = -NkT\ln\left[g_e\left(\frac{2\pi mkT}{h^2}\right)^{3/2}\frac{kT}{p}\right] \tag{8-18}$$

$$E = \frac{3}{2}NkT \tag{8-19}$$

$$V = \frac{NkT}{p} \tag{8-20}$$

$$\frac{S}{k} = -\frac{G}{kT} + \frac{5}{2}N \tag{8-21}$$

$$\frac{\mu}{kT} = \frac{G}{NkT} \tag{8-22}$$

where $A\,(\equiv E - TS)$ is the Helmholtz function and $G\,(\equiv E + pV - TS)$ is the Gibbs function. (Recall from Chapter 6 that γ or, alternatively, μ is a convenient dependent variable only for those systems which may be treated as Maxwell-Boltzmann systems.) Equations (8-5′), (8-13), and (8-18) are fundamental equations; Equations (8-6′), (8-14), and (8-19) are caloric equations of state; Equations (8-7′), (8-15), and (8-20) are thermal equations of state; Equations (8-12′), (8-16), and (8-21) are entropy equations; and Equations (8-17) and (8-22) are chemical-potential equations for a perfect monatomic gas.

Example

In an application of the aforementioned results, consider the change in chemical potential associated with an isothermal change in pressure for a perfect monatomic gas. Rearranging Equation (8-5′), one may write

$$\mu = -kT \ln \left[g_e \left(\frac{2\pi mkT}{h^2} \right)^{3/2} \frac{kT}{p} \right]$$

Hence, for an isothermal change from state 1 to state 2,

$$\mu\,(p_2, T) - \mu\,(p_1, T) = kT \ln \frac{p_2}{p_1}$$

This (specialized) form of the equation is applicable to perfect polyatomic gases as well as to a perfect monatomic gas. Hence the chemical potential of a perfect gas increases logarithmically as the pressure (alternatively, the density) increases isothermally.

Recall that Equations (8-6) to (8-8) and (8-12) are obtained by appropriate differentiations of Equation (8-5). Similarly, Equations (8-6′), (8-7′), (8-12′), (8-14) to (8-17), and (8-19) to (8-22) may be obtained by appropriate differentiations of Equations (8-5′), (8-13), and (8-18). One finds

$$E = -\left(\frac{\partial\,(pV/kT)}{\partial\,(1/kT)} \right)_{V,\,\mu/kT} \tag{8-6″}$$

$$N = \left(\frac{\partial pV}{\partial \mu} \right)_{T,\,V} \tag{8-7″}$$

$$S = \left(\frac{\partial pV}{\partial T} \right)_{V,\,\mu} \tag{8-12″}$$

$$E = \left(\frac{\partial\,(A/kT)}{\partial\,(1/kT)} \right)_{V,\,N} \tag{8-14′}$$

$$p = -\left(\frac{\partial A}{\partial V} \right)_{T,\,N} \tag{8-15′}$$

$$S = -\left(\frac{\partial A}{\partial T}\right)_{V,N} \tag{8-16'}$$

$$\mu = \left(\frac{\partial A}{\partial N}\right)_{T,V} \tag{8-17'}$$

$$E = \left(\frac{\partial (G/kT)}{\partial (1/kT)}\right)_{p/kT,N} \tag{8-19'}$$

$$V = \left(\frac{\partial G}{\partial p}\right)_{T,N} \tag{8-20'}$$

$$S = -\left(\frac{\partial G}{\partial T}\right)_{p,N} \tag{8-21'}$$

$$\mu = \left(\frac{\partial G}{\partial N}\right)_{T,p} \tag{8-22'}$$

Application of the title "fundamental equation" to Equations (8-5′), (8-13), and (8-18) is seen now to be justified.

The sufficient condition

$$e^{\beta\varepsilon_k+\gamma} >> 1$$

given in Chapter 6 for applicability of the Maxwell-Boltzmann approximation, may be written now, for a perfect monatomic gas, in a more meaningful form. Combining Equations (8-5) and (8-7), and solving for e^γ, one obtains, for a perfect monatomic gas,

$$e^\gamma = g_e\left(\frac{2\pi m}{\beta h^2}\right)^{3/2}\frac{V}{\langle N\rangle}$$

Since $\beta\varepsilon_k$ is either zero or positive and g_e is either equal to or larger than unity, the given inequality is satisfied certainly if

$$\left(\frac{2\pi m}{\beta h^2}\right)^{3/2}\frac{V}{\langle N\rangle} >> 1$$

or, using the nomenclature of classical thermodynamics, if

$$\left(\frac{2\pi mkT}{h^2}\right)^{3/2}\frac{V}{N} >> 1 \tag{8-23}$$

Minimum values of the left-hand side are realized at the critical point (see Problem 8-11); values for several gases with relatively low values of critical temperatures and critical volumes are given in Table 8-1. It is seen that the sufficient condition (8-23) is satisfied by most gases, even at the critical point. This result supports the statement that the Maxwell-Boltzmann approximation is applicable to all atomic and molecular gases with temperatures sufficiently high and pressures sufficiently low so that effects of interparticle forces may be neglected, that is, so that the gases may be treated as thermally perfect gases.

Table 8-1 Values of $(2\pi mkT/h^2)^{3/2}\,(V/N)$ at critical point for several gases with relatively low critical temperatures

Gas	T_c, °K	$\left(\frac{2\pi mkT}{h^2}\right)^{3/2}\frac{V}{N}$
He	5.3	5.86
H_2	33.3	3.66×10
D_2	38.4	1.14×10^2
Ne	44.5	1.14×10^3
N_2	126.2	2.03×10^4

Although the sufficient condition (8-23) for applicability of the Maxwell-Boltzmann approximation has been formulated explicitly for the case of a monatomic gas, it is applicable to the case of a polyatomic gas also. Recall from Chapter 6 that a system may be classed as a Maxwell-Boltzmann system if the probability of finding more than one particle in a given quantum state is negligible. For given N, V, and T, a polyatomic gas has many more allowed quantum states than does a monatomic gas. Hence if the probability of finding more than one particle in a given quantum state is negligible considering only translational degrees of freedom, then it is certainly negligible considering both translational *and* internal degrees of freedom.

A convenient quantum-mechanical interpretation of the sufficient condition (8-23) is provided by considerations of the quantum-mechanical wavelengths associated with the individual atoms. This wavelength is given by the **de Broglie equation**

$$\lambda = \frac{h}{mv} \tag{8-24}$$

where λ is wavelength and v is particle speed. Typical speeds of particles in an equilibrium gas are of the order of $(2\pi kT/m)^{1/2}$. Hence the parameter

$$\Lambda = \left(\frac{h^2}{2\pi mkT}\right)^{1/2} \tag{8-25}$$

is a typical quantum-mechanical wavelength associated with particles in an equilibrium gas; it is called the **thermal de Broglie wavelength**. In terms of this wavelength, the sufficient condition (8-23) may be written

$$\frac{1}{\Lambda^3}\frac{V}{N} >> 1 \tag{8-26}$$

But $(V/N)^{1/3}$ is a distance of the order of magnitude of the average distance between nearest-neighbor particles. Hence the Maxwell-Boltzmann approximation is applicable (i.e., quantum effects are negligible) whenever the average distance between nearest-neighbor particles is large in comparison with the thermal de Broglie wavelength.

In a slight extension of the analysis of the present chapter, one might examine the flux of particles crossing, in one direction, an arbitrary plane in a thermally perfect gas. (This flux provides an upper bound to the rate of evaporation from a condensed phase.) For a discussion of this extension, see Appendix I.

PROBLEMS

8-1 Calculate the value of the temperature at which $(2\pi mkT/h^2)^{3/2}(V/N) = 10^3$ for helium gas at atmospheric pressure. (Relate V/N to temperature and pressure using the equation of state for a thermally perfect gas.)

8-2 According to the usual definition of the **constant-volume heat capacity,**

$$C_V = \left(\frac{\partial E}{\partial T}\right)_{N,V}$$

Would the definition

$$C_V \stackrel{?}{=} \left(\frac{\partial E}{\partial T}\right)_{\mu/kT,\,V}$$

yield the same result? [HINT: Compare results obtained for a perfect monatomic gas using Equations (8-5′), (8-6′), and (8-14).] Provide a physical explanation for your answer.

8-3 Calculate the value of $\sigma(E)/\langle E\rangle$ for a system in a canonical ensemble containing a perfect monatomic gas. Compare the result of this calculation with the result of a similar calculation for a grand canonical ensemble. Provide a physical explanation for the result of this comparison.

8-4 Combine Equations (6-9) and (8-5) to show that for a system containing several types of atoms with negligible interparticle forces

$$\ln \Xi = \sum_i g_{ei}\, e^{-\gamma_i}\left(\frac{2\pi m_i}{\beta h^2}\right)^{3/2} V$$

so that, for independent variables T, V, and μ_i,

$$pV = \sum_i g_{ei}\, e^{\mu_i/kT}\left(\frac{2\pi m_i kT}{h^2}\right)^{3/2} VkT$$

$$E = \frac{3}{2}\sum_i g_{ei}\, e^{\mu_i/kT}\left(\frac{2\pi m_i kT}{h^2}\right)^{3/2} VkT$$

$$N_i = g_{ei}\, e^{\mu_i/kT}\left(\frac{2\pi m_i kT}{h^2}\right)^{3/2} V$$

$$\frac{S}{k} = \sum_i \left(\frac{5}{2} - \frac{\mu_i}{kT}\right) g_{ei}\, e^{\mu_i/kT}\left(\frac{2\pi m_i kT}{h^2}\right)^{3/2} V$$

and, for independent variables T, V, and N_i,

$$A = -\sum_i N_i kT \ln\left[g_{ei}\left(\frac{2\pi m_i kT}{h^2}\right)^{3/2}\frac{V}{N_i}\,e\right]$$

$$E = \frac{3}{2}\sum_i N_i kT \qquad p = \frac{\sum N_i kT}{V}$$

$$\frac{S}{k} = \sum_i N_i \ln\left[g_{ei}\left(\frac{2\pi m_i kT}{h^2}\right)^{3/2}\frac{V}{N_i}\,e^{5/2}\right]$$

$$\frac{\mu_i}{kT} = -\ln\left[g_{ei}\left(\frac{2\pi m_i kT}{h^2}\right)^{3/2}\frac{V}{N_i}\right]$$

whereas for independent variables T, p, and N_i,

$$G = -\sum_i N_i kT \ln\left[g_{ei}\left(\frac{2\pi m_i kT}{h^2}\right)^{3/2} \frac{kT}{p}\frac{\sum_i N_i}{N_i}\right]$$

$$E = \frac{3}{2}\sum_i N_i kT \qquad V = \frac{\sum_i N_i kT}{p}$$

$$\frac{S}{k} = \sum_i N_i \ln\left[g_{ei}\left(\frac{2\pi m_i kT}{h^2}\right)^{3/2} \frac{kT}{p}\frac{\sum_i N_i}{N_i} e^{5/2}\right]$$

$$\frac{\mu_i}{kT} = -\ln\left[g_{ei}\left(\frac{2\pi m_i kT}{h^2}\right)^{3/2} \frac{kT}{p}\frac{\sum_i N_i}{N_i}\right]$$

8-5 Use the results of Problem 8-4 to derive an equation for the entropy change when several different perfect monatomic gases, initially separated and each at the same temperature and pressure, are mixed with no change in either temperature or pressure. What would the entropy change be if the atoms of the quantities to be mixed were alike? Describe your results qualitatively using the concept of randomness or disorder. The fact that this entropy change approaches zero discontinuously as the several types of atoms become alike is known as **Gibbs' paradox.**

8-6 Using the results of the present chapter, show that the entropy change for a perfect monatomic gas may be written (for fixed N) in the two alternative forms

$$S(V_2, T_2) - S(V_1, T_1) = Nk \ln\left(\frac{T_2}{T_1}\right)^{3/2} \frac{V_2}{V_1}$$

and

$$S(p_2, T_2) - S(p_1, T_1) = Nk \ln\left(\frac{T_2}{T_1}\right)^{5/2} \frac{p_1}{p_2}$$

Compare these expressions with the two alternative forms

$$S(V_2, T_2) - S(V_1, T_1) = C_V \ln\frac{T_2}{T_1} + Nk \ln\frac{V_2}{V_1}$$

and

$$S(p_2, T_2) - S(p_1, T_1) = C_p \ln\frac{T_2}{T_1} - Nk \ln\frac{p_2}{p_1}$$

which are used frequently in classical thermodynamics for a perfect gas in a closed system.

8-7 In classical thermodynamics it is frequently convenient to separate the chemical potential for a thermally perfect gas into

$$\frac{\mu}{kT} = \frac{\mu^o(T)}{kT} + \ln\frac{p}{p^o}$$

where p^o is an arbitrary constant with units of pressure. Using the results of the present chapter, derive an expression for $\mu^o(T)$ for a perfect monatomic gas.

8-8 In an alternative derivation of Equation (8-5) (a derivation which emphasizes the role of the degeneracy of a particle energy level), consider a perfect monatomic gas in a cubic box with edge length l. Then Equation (8-3) may be written

$$\ln \Xi = e^{-\gamma} \sum_k G_k \exp\left(-\frac{\beta h^2 k^2}{8ml^2}\right)$$

$$= e^{-\gamma} \int_0^\infty G(k) \exp\left(-\frac{\beta h^2 k^2}{8ml^2}\right) dk$$

where G_k is the number of quantum states with energy

$$\varepsilon_k = \frac{h^2k^2}{8ml^2}$$

and $G(k)\,dk$ is the number of quantum states with energy between ε_k and $\varepsilon_k + d\varepsilon_k$. Using a three-dimensional quantum-number space (see Figure 10-3), show that

$$G(k)\,dk = g_e \frac{4\pi k^2}{8}\,dk$$

(Keep in mind that quantum numbers are positive inherently, so that quantum-number space occupies only one octant of all space.) Carry out the indicated integration to obtain Equation (8-5). Compare the role of the degeneracy $G(k)\,dk$ used in this derivation with the role of the degeneracy $\Omega(E, X_c, N_i)$ discussed in Chapter 5.

8-9 Consider a balloon filled with a perfect monatomic gas. If the gas is heated, at constant pressure, from temperature T_1 to temperature T_2, what is the change in energy density (energy per unit volume) of the gas?

8-10 How is the temperature ratio related to the volume ratio in a reversible adiabatic expansion of a fixed quantity of a perfect monatomic gas?

8-11 For a gas at a given pressure, the minimum value of the parameter $(2\pi mkT/h^2)^{3/2}\,V/N$, appearing in Equation (8-23), is realized at the saturation temperature. Values for saturated steam are given in the accompanying table, where the last entry is for the critical point. Using these tabulated values, establish the point along the saturated-vapor curve at which the minimum value of $(2\pi mkT/h^2)^{3/2}\,V/N$ is realized.

Absolute pressure, lb/in.²	*Saturation temperature, °R*	*Specific volume, ft³/lb*
0.20	513	1,526
15	672	26.29
200	841	2.288
1,000	1004	0.4456
3,206.2	1165	0.0503

SOURCE: J. H. Keenan and F. G. Keyes, "Thermodynamic Properties of Steam," Table 2, John Wiley & Sons, Inc., New York, 1936.

chapter **9**

einstein monatomic crystal

If a person masters the fundamentals of his subject and has learned to think and work independently, he will surely find his way and besides will better be able to adapt himself to progress and changes than the person whose training principally consists in the acquiring of detailed knowledge.
A. Einstein, 1936 †

As a second example of the application of the methods of statistical thermodynamics, a particularly simple model of a solid known as an Einstein monatomic crystal is considered. This model is simple, conceptually and mathematically, and leads to results which are correct qualitatively (but not quantitatively).

In this model, identical atoms are considered to vibrate with relatively small amplitudes about equilibrium positions which are arranged in some given lattice structure. This lattice structure is taken to be symmetrical about the equilibrium position of a given atom so that the potential energy of this atom (due to attractions and repulsions of other atoms) is symmetrical about its equilibrium position (see Figure 9-1). This potential energy is a minimum at the equilibrium point; if the atom is displaced, e.g., toward the right-hand side, then the potential energy increases, largely as a consequence of the attraction of the nearest neighbor on the left-hand side and the repulsion of the nearest neighbor on the right-hand side. Forces of nearest neighbors are considered to be sufficiently large, and amplitudes of vibration sufficiently small, so that migrations of atoms are negligible.

The lattice structure, including the spacing between equilibrium positions of nearest-neighbor atoms, is determined by interparticle forces, temperature, and pressure (or tension). The spacing between nearest-neighbor atoms is, in a first approximation, that spacing which minimizes the inter-

† A. Einstein, "Out of My Later Years," p. 35, Wisdom Library Paperbacks, Philosophical Library, Inc., New York, 1950.

particle potential energies. This first approximation is modified by effects of pressure (or tension) and temperature. Note that the type of lattice and the spacing between equilibrium positions of nearest neighbors determine completely the molecular volume V/N.

Since migrations of atoms are considered to be negligible, one may consider the atoms to be distinguishable. For example, one may label all equilibrium positions of the atoms and consider then that these labels belong to the respective atoms vibrating about these equilibrium positions. (This idealized model is an exception to the general quantum-mechanical result that identical particles are indistinguishable.) Furthermore, the number of particles in a system under consideration is fixed. Hence the following analysis will be of a canonical ensemble of members which contain distin-

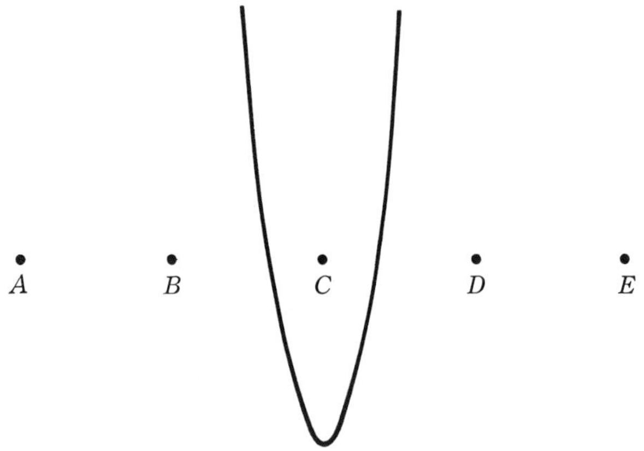

Figure 9-1 *Schematic diagram of potential energy (ordinate) of an atom in a crystal as a function of displacement (abscissa) from its equilibrium position. (Points A, B, C, D, and E indicate equilibrium positions of atoms.)*

guishable particles (rather than for the grand canonical ensemble of members which contain indistinguishable particles discussed in preceding chapters). Note that the concept of a system of distinguishable subsystems supplements the concept of a system of indistinguishable particles introduced in Chapter 6.

In spite of the important role of interparticle forces in crystals, it is found that the Einstein model of a monatomic crystal may be treated mathematically as a system of independent subsystems. As long as the vibration amplitudes are small, the allowed quantum states (and associated energy levels) of each subsystem may be computed independently without even any concern for symmetry restrictions on the wave functions.

If effects of internal (nuclear and electronic) configurations of the atoms on energy changes are negligible in comparison with effects of atom vibrations, then each atom has three (vibrational) degrees of freedom. For convenience, these degrees of freedom may be taken to coincide with the x, y, and z axes of a rectangular coordinate system located with origin at the equilibrium position and with the three coordinate axes passing through the equilibrium positions of neighboring atoms. If the force constants are the same along all three axes, then the potential energy of a displaced atom may be written

$$U(x, y, z) = U(0) + \frac{1}{2} a (x^2 + y^2 + z^2) \tag{9-1}$$

where $U(0)$ is potential energy at the equilibrium position and a is the **force constant**

$$a = \left.\frac{\partial^2 U}{\partial x^2}\right|_0 = \left.\frac{\partial^2 U}{\partial y^2}\right|_0 = \left.\frac{\partial^2 U}{\partial z^2}\right|_0 \tag{9-2}$$

Terms of odd orders in x, y, and z do not appear since the potential is taken to be a symmetrical function of x, y, and z; terms of fourth and higher orders are omitted since the vibration amplitudes are considered to be small. The reference point for energy is fixed by assigning zero energy to infinitely separated atoms at rest. The shape of the potential-energy curve is a function of the type of lattice and the spacing between equilibrium positions; that is, it is a function of the molecular volume V/N. Hence both $U(0)$ and a are functions of V/N or, alternatively, of species type, temperature, and pressure (or tension).

These functions of V/N complicate the use of grand canonical ensembles in statistical-thermodynamical studies of crystals. For constant volume, both $U(0)$ and a depend on the number of particles. Hence sums over system quantum states with different numbers of particles would be complicated. As mentioned previously, canonical ensembles will be used here.

According to Equation (9-1), the three degrees of freedom of a given atom are independent and equivalent; hence a crystal containing N atoms may be treated as $3N$ independent subsystems. For the purposes of the present analysis, each of these subsystems may be considered to be a one-dimensional oscillator; since all atoms have the same spring constant, each of these oscillators vibrates at the same frequency. The energy E_j of the system in its jth quantum state may be written

$$E_j = \frac{NU(0)}{2} + \sum_{n=1}^{3N} \varepsilon_{nj} \tag{9-3}$$

where ε_{nj} is the vibrational energy of the nth oscillator when the system is in its jth quantum state. The first term on the right-hand side is the potential energy (with negative value) of N crystal atoms at rest in their equilibrium positions relative to the potential energy of N infinitely separated atoms at rest. If the factor 1/2 were not present in this term, then each interparticle interaction would be counted twice.

In the development of expressions for canonical ensembles of crystals, a constraint involving the total number of particles in the ensemble and the reservoir would not appear; Equation (3-5) would be reduced to a duplication of Equation (3-3). Hence, the lagrangian multiplier γ would not appear, and the counterpart to the grand partition function, Equation (3-16), may be written

$$Q = \sum_j e^{-\beta E_j} \tag{9-4}$$

where Q is the partition function for a canonical ensemble. (See also Problem 3-2.) Note that the absence of the multiplier γ in the partition function for a canonical ensemble does not mean that γ (alternatively, the corresponding chemical potential of classical thermodynamics) is zero; it means simply that γ (alternatively, μ) is a dependent variable rather than an independent variable. Substituting from Equation (9-3) into Equation (9-4), one obtains

$$\begin{aligned} Q &= \exp\left[-N\frac{\beta U(0)}{2}\right]\sum_j \exp\left(-\beta \sum_{n=1}^{3N} \varepsilon_{nj}\right) \\ &= \exp\left[-N\frac{\beta U(0)}{2}\right]\sum_j \prod_{n=1}^{3N} e^{-\beta\varepsilon_{nj}} \end{aligned}$$

The sum (over ensemble-member quantum states) of products appearing here may be factored into a product of sums (over oscillator quantum states) with the result

$$Q = \exp\left[-N\frac{\beta U(0)}{2}\right]\prod_{n=1}^{3N} q_n \tag{9-5}$$

where

$$q_n \equiv \sum_l e^{-\beta\varepsilon_{nl}} \tag{9-6}$$

and ε_{nl} is the energy of the nth oscillator in its lth quantum state. (The reader who wishes to strengthen his confidence in this factoring of a sum of products may wish to examine Problem 9-1.) The advantage of this form of the partition function for the crystal is that the sum given in Equation (9-6) is the partition function for a single oscillator.

Incidentally, for a canonical ensemble, the partition function can be factored into a product of sums only for cases in which the particles may be treated as distinguishable independent particles. (In the present case, the subsystems, i.e., the oscillators, may be identified by labeling their equilibrium positions and indicating their oscillation paths.) If the particles are indistinguishable, the required computations are made by listing the allowed particle quantum states and indicating the number of particles in each quantum state, rather than by listing the particles and indicating the quantum state of each particle. Since, for a member in a canonical ensemble, the total number of particles, obtained by summing over all quantum states, must equal always the number of particles in the member (a fixed number), the partition function for a canonical ensemble of members which contain indistinguishable particles cannot be factored into a product of single-particle factors.

If the oscillation amplitudes are not large, the oscillations may be described, to good approximation, as harmonic oscillations [see Equation (9-1)]. For one-dimensional harmonic oscillations of an atom with nondegenerate electronic ground state and with potential energy

$$U'(x) = U(x) - U(0) = \frac{1}{2} ax^2 \tag{9-7}$$

the nondegenerate vibrational energy level associated with the lth quantum state is given by

$$\varepsilon_l = h\nu (l + ½) \tag{9-8}$$

where $l = 0, 1, 2, \ldots, \nu\, [\equiv (a/m)^{1/2}/2\pi]$ is frequency of oscillations, and m is mass of oscillating particle (see Problem 7-2). Substituting into Equation (9-6),

$$q_n = \sum_l e^{-\beta h\nu(l+½)} = e^{-\beta h\nu/2} \sum_l (e^{-\beta h\nu})^l$$

Since $e^{-\beta h\nu} < 1$, the series appearing here converges and may be written in the convenient closed form

$$\sum_l (e^{-\beta h\nu})^l = \frac{1}{1 - e^{-\beta h\nu}}$$

so that

$$q_n = \frac{e^{-\beta h\nu/2}}{1 - e^{-\beta h\nu}} = \frac{1}{e^{\beta h\nu/2} - e^{-\beta h\nu/2}} = \frac{1}{2 \sinh(\beta h\nu/2)} \tag{9-9}$$

and, from Equation (9-5),

$$Q = \exp\left[-N\frac{\beta U(0)}{2}\right]\left(2 \sinh \frac{\beta h\nu}{2}\right)^{-3N} \tag{9-10a}$$

or, using the nomenclature of classical thermodynamics,

$$Q \sim \exp\left[-N\frac{U(0)}{2kT}\right]\left(2 \sinh \frac{\theta_E}{2T}\right)^{-3N} \tag{9-10b}$$

where $\theta_E \equiv h\nu/k$. (Sometimes the parameters ν and θ_E are called, respectively, the **Einstein frequency** and the **Einstein temperature**.) Both ν and θ_E are fixed by the species type, the temperature, and the pressure; typical values are of the order of 6×10^{12} sec^{-1} and 300°K.

Note that, for $T << \theta_E$, the oscillators are found in their lowest energy (ground) state, with $l = 0$, so that

$$q_n \approx e^{-\theta_E/2T}$$

and $$Q \approx \exp\left[-N\left(\frac{U(0)}{2kT}+\frac{3}{2}\frac{\theta_E}{T}\right)\right] \qquad T << \theta_E \tag{9-11}$$

whereas, for $T >> \theta_E$,

$$\sinh\frac{\theta_E}{2T} \approx \frac{\theta_E}{2T}$$

and $$Q \approx \exp\left[-N\frac{U(0)}{2kT}\right]\left(\frac{T}{\theta_E}\right)^{3N} \qquad T >> \theta_E \tag{9-12}$$

The concept $T >> \theta_E$ must be limited, however, to temperatures which are not so high that higher order terms in the potential-energy expression, lattice imperfections, atom migrations, and melting must be considered.

Numerical values of thermodynamic properties of an Einstein monatomic crystal may be calculated now. The classical-thermodynamical dimensionless characteristic function for a system with specified generalized displacements and with boundaries which permit passage of energy but not matter is $-A/kT$, where A ($\equiv E - TS$) is the Helmholtz function (see Appendix C). Its statistical-thermodynamical analog is $\ln Q$, that is (see Problem 9-2),

▶ $$-\frac{A}{kT} \sim \ln Q \tag{9-13}$$

The associated dimensionless fundamental equations are (in classical thermodynamics, Appendix C)

$$d\left(-\frac{A}{kT}\right) = -E\,d\left(\frac{1}{kT}\right) + \frac{p}{kT}dV - \frac{\mu}{kT}dN \tag{9-14a}$$

and (in statistical thermodynamics, Table 3-1)

$$d\ln Q = -\langle E\rangle\,d\beta + \beta\langle p\rangle\,dV + \langle\gamma\rangle\,dN \tag{9-14b}$$

Since the fundamental equations are perfect differentials,

$$\langle E\rangle = -\left(\frac{\partial \ln Q}{\partial \beta}\right)_{V,N} = N\left(\frac{U(0)}{2}+\frac{3}{2}h\nu\coth\frac{\beta h\nu}{2}\right) \tag{9-15}$$

where derivatives of $U(0)$ and ν with respect to β do not appear since $U(0)$ and ν are functions of V/N and both V and N are held constant in the differentiation. The variance of the internal energy is given by

$$\sigma^2(E) = \left(\frac{\partial^2 \ln Q}{\partial \beta^2}\right)_{V,N} = 3N\left[\frac{h\nu/2}{\sinh(\beta h\nu/2)}\right]^2 \tag{9-16}$$

▶ so that $$\frac{\sigma(E)}{\langle E\rangle - NU(0)/2} = \frac{1}{\sqrt{3N}\cosh(\beta h\nu/2)} \tag{9-17}$$

Similar expressions for $\langle\gamma\rangle$ and $\langle p\rangle$ are not given here due to the complications introduced by the dependence of $U(0)$ and ν on either V with N held constant or N with V held constant. In principle, the expected values would be obtained from

$$\langle\gamma\rangle = \left(\frac{\partial \ln Q}{\partial N}\right)_{\beta, V} \tag{9-18}$$

$$\langle p\rangle = \frac{1}{\beta}\left(\frac{\partial \ln Q}{\partial V}\right)_{\beta, N} \tag{9-19}$$

An explicit expression may be written, however, for the entropy. From the definition of the Helmholtz function,

$$\frac{S}{k} = \frac{E - A}{kT}$$

so that, using Equations (9-10), (9-13), and (9-15),

$$\frac{S}{k} \sim 3N\left(\frac{\beta h\nu}{2}\coth\frac{\beta h\nu}{2} - \ln 2\sinh\frac{\beta h\nu}{2}\right) \tag{9-20}$$

Finally, an expression for the heat capacity at constant volume is of interest. In the nomenclature of statistical thermodynamics,

$$\frac{\langle C_V\rangle}{k} = -\beta^2\left(\frac{\partial\langle E\rangle}{\partial\beta}\right)_{V,N} = 3N\left[\frac{\beta h\nu/2}{\sinh(\beta h\nu/2)}\right]^2 \tag{9-21}$$

As indicated previously (see Problem 5-2), the relation

$$\sigma^2(E) = \frac{1}{\beta^2}\frac{\langle C_V\rangle}{k} \tag{9-22}$$

obtained by comparing Equations (9-16) and (9-21), is a general relation for canonical ensembles.

For the convenience of the reader, the most important results of the preceding paragraph are summarized here using the nomenclature of classical thermodynamics:

$$A = \frac{NU(0)}{2} + 3NkT\ln\left(2\sinh\frac{\theta_E}{2T}\right) \tag{9-23}$$ ◀

$$E = \frac{NU(0)}{2} + \frac{3}{2}Nk\theta_E\coth\frac{\theta_E}{2T} \tag{9-24}$$ ◀

$$\frac{S}{k} = 3N\left[\frac{\theta_E}{2T}\coth\frac{\theta_E}{2T} - \ln\left(2\sinh\frac{\theta_E}{2T}\right)\right] \tag{9-25}$$ ◀

$$\frac{C_V}{k} = 3N\left[\frac{\theta_E/2T}{\sinh(\theta_E/2T)}\right]^2 \tag{9-26}$$ ◀

Equation (9-23) is the appropriate fundamental equation for this system; the other three equations may be derived from Equation (9-23) by appropriate operations. Values of internal energy, entropy, and heat capacity are plotted as a function of temperature in Figure 9-2. Note that the difference between C_V and $3Nk$ is less than 1 percent for T greater than about $3\theta_E$.

Thermodynamic functions which involve both internal energy and a pV term may be evaluated, to good approximation, for many solids by neglecting the pV term in comparison with internal energy. For example,

$$H \approx E \tag{9-27}$$

$$G = N\mu \approx A \tag{9-28}$$

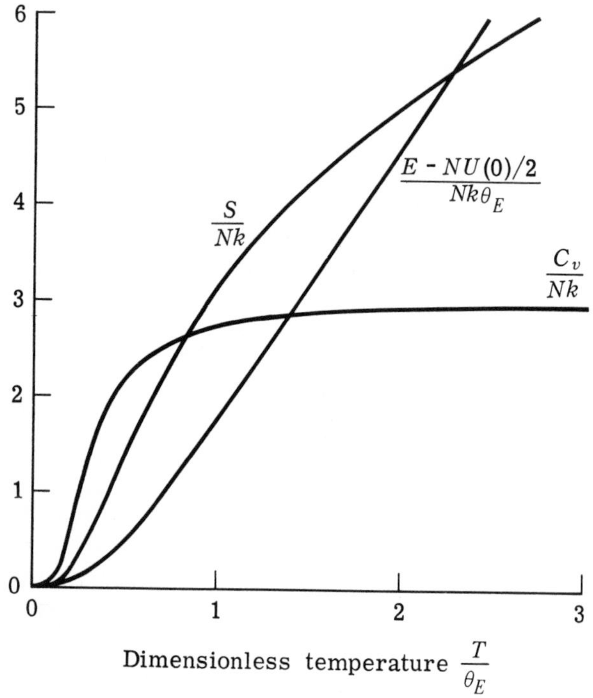

Figure 9-2 *Internal energy, entropy, and heat capacity of an Einstein monatomic crystal as a function of temperature.*

where $H (\equiv E + pV)$ is enthalpy and $G (\equiv E + pV - TS)$ is the Gibbs function. (Not only is pV small in comparison with E for many solids, but also the model used here is crude.) Note that neglecting the pV terms in Equations (9-27) and (9-28) reduces the incentive for applying Equations (9-18) and (9-19).

Consider finally the behavior of these thermodynamic functions for limiting temperatures. If $T << \theta_E$, then

$$A \rightarrow \frac{NU(0)}{2} + \frac{3Nk\theta_E}{2} \tag{9-29}$$

$$E \to \frac{NU(0)}{2} + \frac{3Nk\theta_E}{2} \tag{9-30}$$

$$\frac{S}{k} \to 0 \tag{9-31}$$

$$\frac{C_V}{k} \to 3N\left(\frac{\theta_E/T}{e^{\theta_E/2T}}\right)^2 \tag{9-32}$$

If $T >> \theta_E$, however,

$$A \to \frac{NU(0)}{2} + 3NkT \ln \frac{\theta_E}{T} \tag{9-33}$$

$$E \to \frac{NU(0)}{2} + 3NkT \tag{9-34}$$

$$\frac{S}{k} \to 3N\left(1 + \ln \frac{T}{\theta_E}\right) \tag{9-35}$$

$$\frac{C_V}{k} \to 3N \tag{9-36}$$

Since the internal energy of a monatomic gas at 0°K is zero, Equation (9-30) is the negative of the heat of sublimation of an Einstein monatomic crystal at 0°K. Equation (9-31) is consistent with the concept of no randomness in an Einstein monatomic crystal at 0°K; at that temperature every atom in the crystal is in its (nondegenerate) ground state. Equation (9-32) is correct qualitatively, but predicts heat capacities which are lower than those measured in the laboratory. (This discrepancy is due to the neglect of interactions between atoms in this model. In a more satisfactory model, e.g., in the Debye model of Chapter 14, one considers normal modes of vibration of the crystal as a whole, rather than oscillations of independent atoms.) Equation (9-36) is in reasonable agreement with experimental observations; it is known sometimes as the **law of Dulong and Petit**. In spite of the crudeness and quantitative deficiencies of the Einstein model, it is a relatively simple model which illustrates the methods and capabilities of statistical thermodynamics, leads to results which are correct qualitatively, and provides a suitable background for the discussion of adsorption in Chapter 12 and for the slightly more advanced treatment of a crystal in Chapter 14.

Example

In order to illustrate quantitatively the relative magnitudes of E and pV for a typical solid, consider 1 mole of copper (with an atomic weight of 63.57 and a specific gravity of about 8.94) at 300°K and 1 atm. At this temperature, Equation (9-34) provides (for copper) values with the correct order of magnitude:

$$\begin{aligned} 3N_AkT &= 3 \times 6.02 \times 10^{23} \times 1.38 \times 10^{-16} \times 300 \times 10^{-7} \text{ joules/mole} \\ &= 7.48 \times 10^3 \text{ joules/mole} \end{aligned}$$

At 1 atm,

$$pV = \frac{1.01 \times 10^6 \times 63.57 \times 10^{-7}}{8.94} \text{ joule/mole}$$
$$= 7.19 \times 10^{-1} \text{ joule/mole}$$

Hence, for copper at 300°K and 1 atm, E is more than four orders of magnitude greater than pV.

PROBLEMS

9-1 Carry out the indicated summations and multiplications to show that

$$\sum_j \prod_{n=1}^{2} e^{-\beta\varepsilon_{nj}} = \left(\sum_{l=1}^{2} e^{-\beta\varepsilon_{1l}}\right)\left(\sum_{l=1}^{3} e^{-\beta\varepsilon_{2l}}\right)$$

where the allowed energy levels for the first oscillator are ε_{11} and ε_{12} and the allowed energy levels for the second oscillator are ε_{21}, ε_{22}, and ε_{23}. That is, verify, for a particular case, the factoring of a sum of products used in the derivation of Equation (9-5).

9-2 Substitute for $ln\ P_j$ in

$$\frac{S}{k} \sim -\sum_j P_j \ln P_j \qquad \text{(Table 5-1)}$$

from

$$P_j(\beta, N_i, X_e) = \frac{e^{-\beta E_j}}{Q} \qquad \text{(Problem 3-2)}$$

to obtain, for a closed system,

$$\frac{S}{k} \sim \beta\langle E\rangle + \ln Q$$

Compare with the definition of the Helmholtz function A to obtain the correspondence indicated in Equation (9-13) and Table 3-1.

9-3 Consider a monatomic crystal for which the force constants for vibrations in the x, y, and z directions are different; i.e., consider a monatomic crystal for which

$$U(x, y, z) = U(0) + \frac{a}{2}x^2 + \frac{b}{2}y^2 + \frac{c}{2}z^2$$

where $a \neq b \neq c$. Derive the appropriate extension of the heat-capacity equation, Equation (9-26).

9-4 If, for a given solid substance, the constant-pressure heat capacity is known as a function of temperature (including temperatures near absolute zero), how could one evaluate the partition function as a function of temperature? Indicate all approximations made.

9-5 Graphite has a highly anisotropic structure. In an Einstein model of this solid, the force constants a and b for atom vibrations in two directions (for example, the x and y directions) are equal and so large that

$$\frac{h\nu_a}{k} = \frac{h\nu_b}{k} >> \text{room temperature}$$

whereas the force constant c for atom oscillations in the third direction (for example, the z direction) is so small that

$$\frac{h\nu_c}{k} << \text{room temperature}$$

Estimate the constant-volume heat capacity of graphite at room temperature.

9-6 Show that for a cubic lattice the isothermal compressibility is approximately related to the force constant of Equation (9-1) by

$$K \equiv -\frac{1}{V}\left(\frac{\partial V}{\partial p}\right)_T \approx \frac{6}{a}\left(\frac{V}{N}\right)^{1/3}$$

[HINT: Estimate the force per unit area required to reduce the atomic spacing from $(V/N)^{1/3}$ to $(V/N)^{1/3} - x$ (x is positive here) and the change in volume associated with this reduction in atomic spacing.]

9-7 Using the result of Problem 9-6, estimate the value of the Einstein temperature for copper. (Copper has an atomic weight of 63.57, a specific gravity of about 8.94, and at low temperatures, an isothermal compressibility of about 7.1×10^{-13} cm^2/dyne.)

chapter **10**

blackbody radiation

... I believe that (the theory thus developed) points out a possible way of accounting for the processes of radiant energy from the same point of view as for the processes of molecular motion.
M. Planck, 1907 †

In a third application of the methods of statistical thermodynamics, consider electromagnetic (or thermal) radiation in thermodynamic equilibrium—called sometimes **blackbody radiation**. It is of interest to engineers and scientists both as a limiting case of the general phenomenon of nonequilibrium electromagnetic radiation and, historically, as the earliest motivation for the invention of quantum mechanics.

Every body, as a consequence of its nonzero temperature, emits electromagnetic radiation; as its temperature increases, the rate of radiation increases and a larger fraction of the radiation occurs at shorter wavelengths (the light emitted by the body shifts from the red toward the blue). An upper limit to the quantity of electromagnetic radiation emitted in the frequency range $d\nu$ by a body at a given temperature T is found to exist; this upper limit is defined as **blackbody emission**.

As implied in the preceding paragraph, the electromagnetic radiation emitted by a real surface at a given temperature is less than the radiation emitted by the (hypothetical) **blackbody** at the same temperature. Emission from a blackbody is approached experimentally by the emission from a small hole in a cavity (see Figure 10-1). To the extent that the presence of the small hole does not disturb thermal equilibrium within the cavity, the radiation which escapes from this hole has the total intensity and the frequency distribution of radiation from a blackbody at the same temperature.

In an alternative definition, one might consider a blackbody to be a body

† M. Planck, "The Theory of Heat Radiation," p. xi, Dover Publications, Inc., New York, 1959.

which absorbs all electromagnetic radiation that falls on it. The equivalence of these two definitions follows from the fact that if a body is in equilibrium with its surroundings, then the emission and absorption rates of radiation energy in frequency range $d\nu$ must be equal. Any real surface absorbs a smaller fraction of the incident radiation than does a blackbody. Note that absorption by a blackbody is approached experimentally by the absorption by a small hole in a cavity.

Although the speed of electromagnetic radiation is very large (the speed of light), it is finite. Hence this radiation has nonzero density, e.g., the

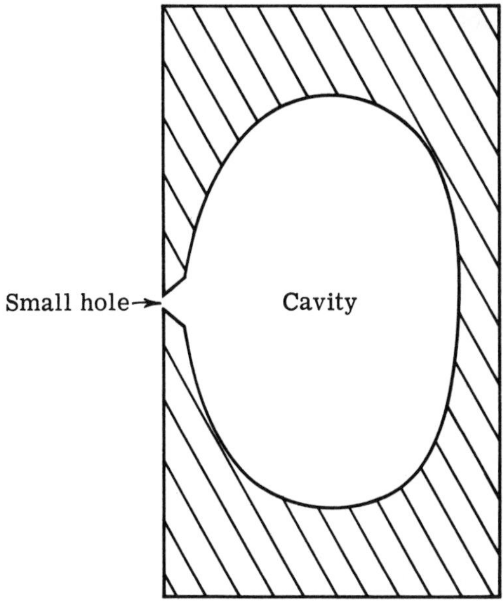

Figure 10-1 *Cross-sectional view of cavity with small hole. (With radiation in the cavity essentially in equilibrium with the cavity walls, the small hole emits and absorbs radiation essentially as a blackbody.)*

radiation energy per unit volume in frequency range $d\nu$ is nonzero. The value of this density for blackbody radiation may be computed (in principle) either from considerations of the rate of emission from a blackbody or from considerations of radiation in equilibrium with its surroundings. The latter approach, independent of the physical nature of the surroundings, is used in practice.

A convenient model for blackbody radiation is a box (see Figure 10-2), with walls of infinite electrical conductivity except for a small black area, and electromagnetic waves in thermal equilibrium with each other and in steady macroscopic state. (When emphasizing the particlelike properties of blackbody radiation, it is referred to sometimes as a **photon gas**; each

photon is a quanta of energy with magnitude $h\nu$, where ν is the wave frequency.) Infinite electrical conductivity implies that the walls reflect perfectly the electromagnetic waves (photons). The small black area serves operationally, in the absence of interactions among electromagnetic waves (photons), to establish thermal equilibrium among the several electromagnetic waves (photons) by interacting with the radiation and to facilitate interactions between the ensemble members and the reservoir. The energy and number of photons associated with an ensemble member are not constant; fluctuations may occur as a consequence of interactions with the reservoir. Note that since the reservoir is capable of converting a given number of photons (with given total energy) into a different number of photons (with the same total energy), fluctuations in the total number of photons in

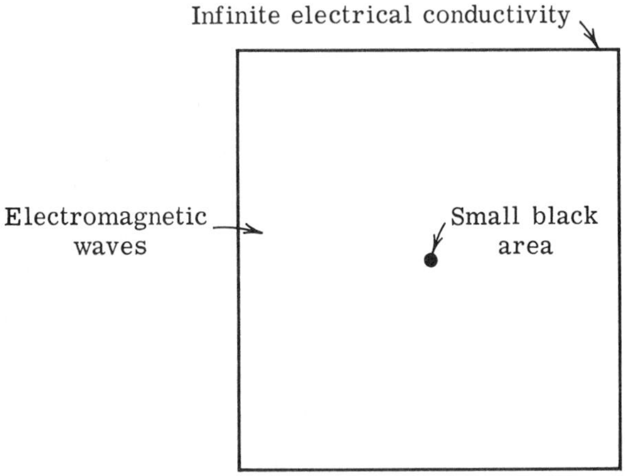

Figure 10-2 *A convenient model for blackbody radiation.*

an ensemble member would occur even if the energy associated with the ensemble member were constant.

If the photons did not possess initially an equilibrium distribution among allowed quantum states, then the number and the quantum states of the photons emitted by the small black area would differ from the number and the quantum states of the photons absorbed until equilibrium was reached. Since the number and quantum states of the photons are not changed by interactions with the areas of infinite conductivity, these interactions with the small black area are the only means by which an equilibrium distribution of allowed quantum states can be approached.

For a finite system in a stationary state, only discrete quantum states with discrete energy levels are allowed. For an electromagnetic wave (photon) with a given discrete energy level, two different quantum states are possible, i.e., a degeneracy of 2 is found. From the wave point of view, this degeneracy of 2 appears because electromagnetic waves are transverse waves and transverse waves have two degrees of freedom. (In a more precise explanation, one might state that, for an electromagnetic wave with a given discrete energy level, two independent polarizations are possible.) From the particle point of view, this degeneracy of 2 is explained by saying that photons have a spin degeneracy of 2.

If one considers the thermodynamic system to consist of only the electromagnetic waves (photons), then the appropriate ensemble is the grand canonical ensemble; both energy and particles are allowed to cross the system boundaries. In the absence of external fields, the appropriate independent variables would be V, β, and γ (V, T, and μ in the nomenclature of classical thermodynamics). However, as a consequence of the ability of the small black area to convert a given number of photons into a different number of photons, a constraint on the total number of photons in an ensemble of open members and a reservoir, such as Equation (3-5), does not exist; i.e., the lagrangian multiplier γ would not appear in the analysis. These two requirements on γ are satisfied by setting γ equal to zero for all temperatures. With $\gamma = 0$, the expected value of the number of photons in the system is determined entirely by the volume and the temperature of the system.

Photons have a spin of unity. Hence (in agreement with general comments made in Chapter 6) a system of photons may be considered to be a Bose-Einstein system. Furthermore, electromagnetic waves (photons) do not interact with each other. Consequently, the model being considered here may be studied using the methods developed for a grand canonical ensemble of Bose-Einstein members with negligible effects of interparticle forces with $\gamma = 0$, so that, from Equation (6-7),

$$\ln \Xi_{\mathrm{BE}} = \sum_k \ln \frac{1}{1 - e^{-\beta\varepsilon_k}} \tag{10-1}$$

(For convenience, the subscript BE is omitted in the remainder of this chapter.) The problem is reduced now to the problem of determining allowed quantum states (and associated energy levels ε_k) for individual photons.

Note that the Maxwell-Boltzmann approximation, which requires

$$e^{\beta\varepsilon_k + \gamma} >> 1$$

(see Chapter 6), is not applicable to a system of photons. Since $\gamma = 0$ and $\beta\varepsilon_k$ may have small values, this inequality is not satisfied in general.

Several (superficially different) procedures for determining the allowed energy levels are available. For example: (1) if one wishes to emphasize the particlelike aspects of radiation, one might adapt the result for an atom in a box, Equation (8-2), to the case of a photon in a box; (2) if one wishes to emphasize the wavelike aspects of radiation, one might examine allowed wavelengths for standing electromagnetic waves in a box; and (3) if one wishes to proceed formally from first principles, one might look for solutions of the relativistic Schrödinger wave equation (see Problem 10-1). Although none of these procedures is difficult, the first procedure is the quickest. Hence it is used here.

From Equation (8-2), for an atom in a box, the allowed energy levels are

$$\varepsilon_k = \frac{h^2}{8m}\left[\left(\frac{k_1}{l_1}\right)^2 + \left(\frac{k_2}{l_2}\right)^2 + \left(\frac{k_3}{l_3}\right)^2\right] \tag{8-2}$$

where l_1, l_2, and l_3 are lengths of edges of the rectangular box. For nonrelativistic particles, the momentum and the energy are related by $p_k^2 = 2m\varepsilon_k$. Hence, for an atom in a box, the allowed values of the square of the momentum are given by

$$p_k^2 = \frac{h^2}{4}\left[\left(\frac{k_1}{l_1}\right)^2 + \left(\frac{k_2}{l_2}\right)^2 + \left(\frac{k_3}{l_3}\right)^2\right] \tag{10-2}$$

Equation (10-2), in which the mass of the particle does not appear explicitly, holds also for a photon in a box. Now, an expression relating the momentum and the energy of a photon is required. As stated previously, the photon energy is related to the wave frequency by

$$\varepsilon_k = h\nu_k \tag{10-3}$$

Since the photon moves with the speed of light, the frequency and length of wave are related by

$$\nu_k = \frac{c}{\lambda_k} \tag{10-4}$$

where c is speed of light and λ_k is wavelength. According to the de Broglie relation, the wavelength is related to the momentum by

$$\lambda_k = \frac{h}{p_k} \tag{10-5}$$

Eliminating ν_k and λ_k from Equations (10-3) to (10-5), one obtains the required relation $\varepsilon_k = p_k c$ (see Problem 10-2). Hence, combining this relation with Equation (10-2), the allowed energy levels for a photon in a rectangular box are

$$\varepsilon_k = \frac{hc}{2}\left[\left(\frac{k_1}{l_1}\right)^2 + \left(\frac{k_2}{l_2}\right)^2 + \left(\frac{k_3}{l_3}\right)^2\right]^{1/2} \tag{10-6}$$

Note that the allowed energy levels of a photon in a box vary as the negative one-third power of the volume of the box, whereas the allowed energy levels of an atom in a box vary as the negative two-thirds power of volume of the box (see Problem 10-3).

The differences in the treatments of (1) nonrelativistic particles with nonzero rest mass and (2) photons are due to the fact that the former particles have constant mass and various speeds, whereas the latter particles have constant speed (the speed of light) and (according to the theory of relativity) various masses. Variations in momenta and energy are due, in the former case, to variations in speed and, in the latter case, to variations in mass.

In principle, one could now evaluate the partition function for a photon gas by substituting Equation (10-6) into Equation (10-1) and summing, for a Bose-Einstein system, over all allowed quantum states. However, summing over quantum states would be much more difficult in the present case than it was in the case of a perfect monatomic gas—in the present case one cannot factor the logarithm of the partition function into a product of series (one series for each degree of freedom). Hence, in practice, the sum over quantum states is replaced by a sum over wave frequencies so that

$$\ln \Xi = \sum_{\nu} G_{\nu} \ln \frac{1}{1 - e^{-\beta h\nu}} \tag{10-7}$$

where G_ν is the number of quantum states with frequency ν. This sum may be replaced, to good approximation, by an integral provided that the difference between consecutive values of $\ln(1 - e^{-\beta h\nu})^{-1}$ is small in comparison with unity. This condition is met if $\beta hc/2l$, where l is a characteristic dimension of the system, is of the order of or smaller than unity. For photons at 1°K in a box with a characteristic dimension of 1 cm, $\beta hc/2l$ is of the order of unity. Hence, for essentially all temperatures and dimensions of interest, one may write

$$\ln \Xi = \int_0^{\infty} G(\nu) \ln \frac{1}{1 - e^{-\beta h\nu}}\, d\nu \tag{10-8}$$

where $G(\nu)\, d\nu$ is the number of quantum states with frequencies between ν and $\nu + d\nu$. The evaluation of $G(\nu)\, d\nu$ is facilitated, without loss in generality, by considering a cubic box. Then, from Equations (10-3) and (10-6),

$$\nu_k = \frac{c}{2l}(k_1^2 + k_2^2 + k_3^2)^{1/2} \tag{10-9}$$

whereas $G(\nu)\, d\nu$ is twice the number of points with coordinates k_1, k_2, k_3 in one-eighth the spherical shell with radius $2l\nu/c$ and thickness $2l\, d\nu/c$ (see Figure 10-3). The factor of 2 enters because, as discussed previously, two different quantum states are possible for each energy level (i.e., for each frequency). Since a unit volume is associated with each point in quantum-number space, one obtains

$$G(\nu)\, d\nu = \frac{8\pi V \nu^2}{c^3}\, d\nu \tag{10-10}$$

where $V (\equiv l^3)$ is volume. Substituting into Equation (10-8),

$$\ln \Xi = \int_0^\infty \frac{8\pi V \nu^2}{c^3} \ln \frac{1}{1 - e^{-\beta h\nu}}\, d\nu$$

Integrating by parts

$$\ln \Xi = \frac{8\pi V \nu^3}{3c^3} \ln \frac{1}{1 - e^{-\beta h\nu}} \Big|_0^\infty + \frac{8\pi V \beta h}{3c^3} \int_0^\infty \frac{\nu^3\, d\nu}{e^{\beta h\nu} - 1}$$

The first term on the right-hand side vanishes; the remaining term may be written

$$\ln \Xi = \frac{8\pi V}{3(\beta hc)^3} \int_0^\infty \frac{x^3\, dx}{e^x - 1}$$

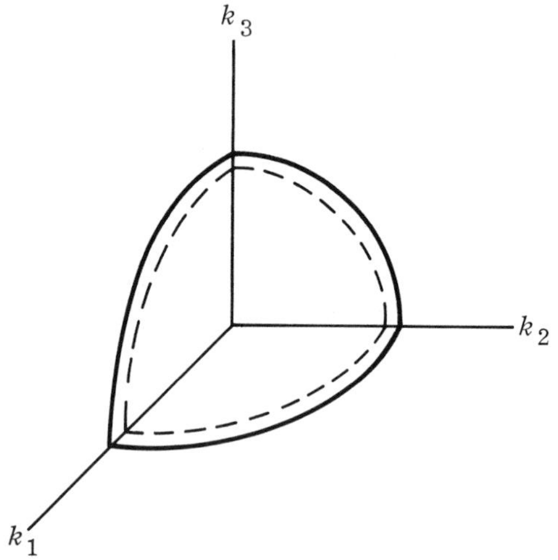

Figure 10-3 *Three-dimensional quantum-number space.*

The definite integral appearing here has value $6\zeta(4)$ where $\zeta(4) = \pi^4/90$. Hence

$$\ln \Xi = \frac{8\pi^5 V}{45(\beta hc)^3} \tag{10-11}$$

This equation explicitly relates the grand partition function with the independent variables β and V. (Keep in mind that γ is zero for all values of β.)

Expected values and variances of energy and pressure may be calculated now using the methods of Chapter 4. (Expected values and variances of the number of photons may be calculated also, but not by the standard methods of Chapter 4.) One obtains

$$\langle E \rangle = -\left(\frac{\partial \ln \Xi}{\partial \beta}\right)_V = \frac{8\pi^5}{15} \frac{V}{(hc)^3 \beta^4} \tag{10-12}$$

$$\langle p \rangle = \frac{1}{\beta}\left(\frac{\partial \ln \Xi}{\partial V}\right)_\beta = \frac{8\pi^5}{45}\frac{1}{(hc)^3\,\beta^4} \tag{10-13}$$

$$\sigma^2(E) = \left(\frac{\partial^2 \ln \Xi}{\partial \beta^2}\right)_V = \frac{32\pi^5}{15}\frac{V}{(hc)^3\,\beta^5} \tag{10-14}$$

$$\sigma^2(p) = \frac{1}{\beta^2}\left(\frac{\partial^2 \ln \Xi}{\partial V^2}\right)_\beta + \frac{1}{\beta}\left\langle\frac{d^2 E}{dV^2}\right\rangle = 0 + \frac{32\pi^5}{135}\frac{1}{V\,(hc)^3\,\beta^5} \tag{10-15}$$

In the evaluation of the last term in Equation (10-15), the allowed energy levels are taken to vary as $V^{-1/3}$, as implied by Equation (10-6). Since $\gamma = 0$ for a photon gas, expected values and variances of the number of photons cannot be calculated by differentiations of Equation (10-11) with respect to γ. The appropriate procedure is to differentiate $\ln \Xi$ with respect to γ *before* setting γ equal to zero. Differentiating

$$\ln \Xi = \sum_k \ln\,(1 - e^{-\beta\varepsilon_k - \gamma})^{-1}$$

with respect to γ, setting γ equal to zero and passing from a sum over quantum states to an integral over wave frequencies, one obtains

$$\begin{aligned}\langle N \rangle &= -\left(\frac{\partial \ln \Xi}{\partial \gamma}\right)_{\beta,V} = \sum_k \frac{1}{e^{\beta\varepsilon_k + \gamma} - 1}\\ &= \sum_k \frac{1}{e^{\beta\varepsilon_k} - 1} = \sum_\nu \frac{G_\nu}{e^{\beta h\nu} - 1}\\ &= \int_0^\infty \frac{G(\nu)}{e^{\beta h\nu} - 1}\,d\nu = \frac{8\pi V}{c^3}\int_0^\infty \frac{\nu^2}{e^{\beta h\nu} - 1}\,d\nu\\ &= \frac{8\pi V}{(\beta hc)^3}\int_0^\infty \frac{x^2}{e^x - 1}\,dx = \frac{16\pi\zeta(3)\,V}{(\beta hc)^3}\end{aligned} \tag{10-16}$$

where $\zeta(3) = 1.202$. Similarly,

$$\begin{aligned}\sigma^2(N) &= \left(\frac{\partial^2 \ln \Xi}{\partial \gamma^2}\right)_{\beta,V} = \sum_k \frac{e^{\beta\varepsilon_k + \gamma}}{(e^{\beta\varepsilon_k + \gamma} - 1)^2}\\ &= \sum_k \frac{e^{\beta\varepsilon_k}}{(e^{\beta\varepsilon_k} - 1)^2} = \sum_\nu \frac{G_\nu\, e^{\beta h\nu}}{(e^{\beta h\nu} - 1)^2}\\ &= \int_0^\infty \frac{G(\nu)\, e^{\beta h\nu}}{(e^{\beta h\nu} - 1)^2}\,d\nu = \frac{8\pi V}{c^3}\int_0^\infty \frac{e^{\beta h\nu}\,\nu^2}{(e^{\beta h\nu} - 1)^2}\,d\nu\\ &= \frac{8\pi V}{(\beta hc)^3}\int_0^\infty \frac{e^x\,x^2}{(e^x - 1)^2}\,dx = \frac{16\pi\zeta(2)\,V}{(\beta hc)^3}\end{aligned} \tag{10-17}$$

where $\zeta(2) = \pi^2/6$. Relative deviations from expected values are characterized by

$$\frac{\sigma(E)}{\langle E \rangle} = \sqrt{\frac{4}{3}\frac{\zeta(3)}{\zeta(4)}\frac{1}{\langle N \rangle}} \qquad \frac{\sigma(p)}{\langle p \rangle} = \sqrt{\frac{4}{3}\frac{\zeta(3)}{\zeta(4)}\frac{1}{\langle N \rangle}} \qquad \frac{\sigma(N)}{\langle N \rangle} = \sqrt{\frac{\zeta(2)}{\zeta(3)}\frac{1}{\langle N \rangle}}$$

For photons at 1°K in a box with a characteristic dimension of 1 cm, $\langle N \rangle$ is of the order of 10. Since $\langle N \rangle$ increases as the third power of both the temperature and the characteristic dimension, it is apparent from the given ratios that relative deviations from expected values are negligible, in practice, for most systems of photons also.

Using the correspondence established in Chapter 5, one obtains for the entropy

$$\frac{S}{k} \sim \ln \Xi + \beta \langle E \rangle + \gamma \langle N \rangle = \frac{32\pi^5}{45} \frac{V}{(\beta hc)^3} \tag{10-18}$$

where $\ln \Xi$ and $\langle E \rangle$ were eliminated, in favor of β and V, using Equations (10-11) and (10-12). Note that $\langle E \rangle$ and $\langle p \rangle$ vary as the fourth power of temperature, whereas $\langle N \rangle$ and S vary as the third power of temperature; all four functions approach zero as temperature approaches absolute zero.

The equations of classical thermodynamics corresponding to Equations (10-11), (10-12), (10-16), and (10-18) would be

$$pV = \frac{8\pi^5}{45} \frac{(kT)^4}{(hc)^3} V \tag{10-11$'$}$$

$$E = 3pV \tag{10-12$'$}$$

$$N = \frac{\zeta(3)}{\zeta(4)} \frac{pV}{kT} \tag{10-16$'$}$$

$$\frac{S}{k} = 4 \frac{pV}{kT} \tag{10-18$'$}$$

[Recall that Equation (10-12′) was derived already in Problem 10-3 for a much more general model.] Although these equations are written with independent variables T and V in mind, other choices of independent variables are possible but are usually not as convenient experimentally as are T and V. Equation (10-11′) is the fundamental equation to the extent that

$$E = -\left[\frac{\partial (pV/kT)}{\partial (1/kT)}\right]_V \tag{10-12$''$}$$

$$S = \left(\frac{\partial pV}{\partial T}\right)_V \tag{10-18$''$}$$

However, in order to derive the expression for N by differentiation of the expression for pV, one must carry out this differentiation (with respect to μ) prior to setting μ equal to zero. Equation (10-12′) is the caloric equation of state, Equation (10-16′) is the thermal equation of state, and Equation (10-18′) is the entropy equation.

Heat capacity at constant volume is given by

$$C_V = \left(\frac{\partial E}{\partial T}\right)_V = \frac{32\pi^5}{15} \left(\frac{kT}{hc}\right)^3 Vk \tag{10-19}$$

Note that the definition of C_V for photon gas differs from the usual definition of C_V (see Problem 8-2) in that the number of photons is not held constant in the constant-volume temperature change. The temperature dependence of E, S, and C_V for a photon gas will be compared in Chapter 14 with the temperature dependence of E, S, and C_V for a Debye monatomic crystal at low temperatures.

The distribution of the energy among the several frequencies (called sometimes the **spectral energy distribution**) is of interest. Differentiating one of the intermediate equalities of Equation (10-16),

$$\langle N\rangle = \frac{8\pi V}{(\beta hc)^3}\int_0^\infty \frac{(\beta h\nu)^2}{e^{\beta h\nu}-1}\,d\,(\beta h\nu)$$

with respect to $\beta h\nu$, holding β and V constant, one obtains

$$\left[\frac{d\,\langle N\rangle}{d\,(\beta h\nu)}\right]_{\beta,\,V} = \frac{8\pi V}{(\beta hc)^3}\frac{(\beta h\nu)^2}{e^{\beta h\nu}-1}$$

which, when multiplied by the dimensionless energy $[d(\beta\langle E\rangle)/d\langle N\rangle]_{\beta,\,V} = \beta h\nu$, yields

$$\left[\frac{d\,(\beta\,\langle E\rangle)}{d\,(\beta h\nu)}\right]_{\beta,\,V} = \frac{8\pi V}{(\beta hc)^3}\frac{(\beta h\nu)^3}{e^{\beta h\nu}-1} \tag{10-20}$$

or, using the nomenclature of classical thermodynamics,

$$\left[\frac{d\,(E/kT)}{d\,(h\nu/kT)}\right]_{T,\,V} = 8\pi V\left(\frac{kT}{hc}\right)^3\frac{(h\nu/kT)^3}{e^{h\nu/kT}-1} \tag{10-20'}$$

This equation is called **Planck's formula**; it is plotted in convenient dimensionless form in Figure 10-4. Note that the normalizing coefficients of the abscissa and ordinate contain, respectively, reciprocals of temperature and temperature cubed, so that radiation energy is proportional to the fourth power of temperature. The area under the curve between two frequencies equals the radiation energy in the frequency range bounded by these two frequencies; the total area under the curve equals $\pi^4/15$, in agreement with Equation (10-12).

As indicated in Figure 10-4, a maximum spectral energy density of

$$\left[\frac{d\,(E/kT)}{d\,(h\nu/kT)}\right]_{T,\,V} = 1.42 \times 8\pi V\left(\frac{kT}{hc}\right)^3 \tag{10-21}$$

is realized at a frequency of (see Problem 10-6)

$$\frac{h\nu}{kT} = 2.822 \tag{10-22}$$

It is seen that doubling the temperature increases the maximum spectral energy density by a factor of 8, the frequency at which this maximum occurs by a factor of 2, and the total energy by a factor of 16. Equation (10-22), or an equivalent statement, is known as **Wien's displacement law**.

Limiting forms of Equation (10-20′) (for relatively low and relatively high temperatures) are of interest, partly for historical reasons. If $h\nu/kT >> 1$ (that is, if the temperature is relatively low), then

$$\left[\frac{d\,(E/kT)}{d\,(h\nu/kT)}\right]_{T,V} \approx 8\pi V\left(\frac{kT}{hc}\right)^3 \frac{(h\nu/kT)^3}{e^{h\nu/kT}} \tag{10-23}$$

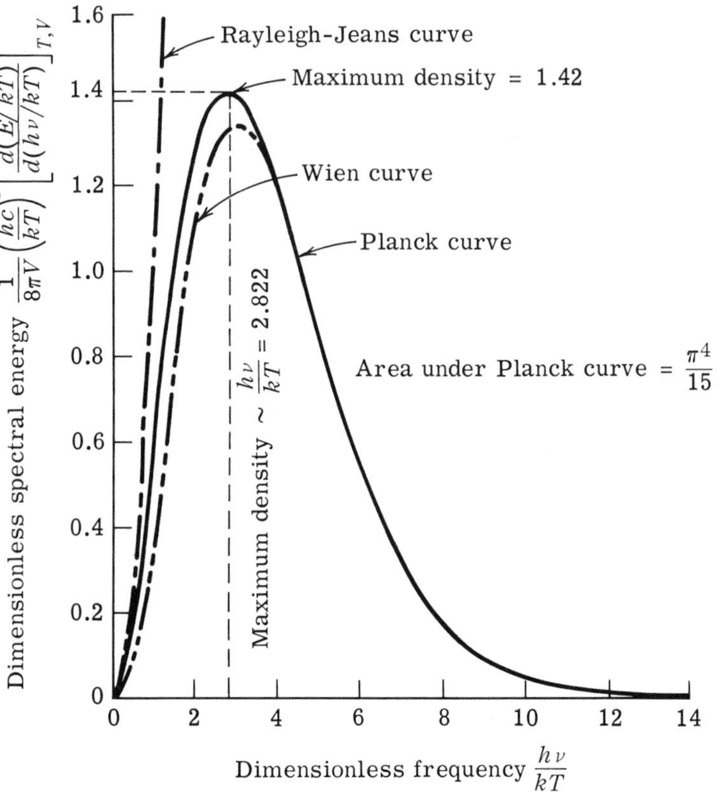

Figure 10-4 *Spectral energy density as a function of frequency.*

whereas if $h\nu/kT << 1$ (that is, if the temperature is relatively high), then

$$\left[\frac{d\,(E/kT)}{d\,(h\nu/kT)}\right]_{T,V} \approx 8\pi V\left(\frac{kT}{hc}\right)^3 \left(\frac{h\nu}{kT}\right)^2 \tag{10-24}$$

These limiting forms, called sometimes the **Wien formula** ($h\nu/kT >> 1$) and the **Rayleigh-Jeans formula** ($h\nu/kT << 1$), are plotted in Figure 10-4 for comparison with the Planck formula (10-20′). The Wien curve compares favorably with the Planck curve at high frequencies but predicts energy densities which are too low at low frequencies; the Rayleigh-Jeans curve is a good approximation at low frequencies but increases indefinitely as the dimensionless frequency increases.

The equivalent of Equation (10-23) was proposed by Wien as an empirical law, before the introduction of the quantum theory. Equation (10-24), which may be written in the form

$$\left(\frac{dE}{d\nu}\right)_{T,V} \approx \frac{8\pi V\nu^2}{c^3}kT$$

was derived first by Rayleigh using concepts of classical mechanics. Note that this form of the Rayleigh-Jeans formula does not contain the quantum constant h and that it may be obtained by assigning, according to classical mechanics, the energy kT to each degree of freedom of the system, i.e., by multiplying Equation (10-10) by kT. The failure of this equation at high frequencies is consistent with the general observation that quantum-mechanical methods must be used whenever the energy quanta ($h\nu$) are of the order of magnitude of or larger than the thermal energy (kT). Equation (10-20′) was derived initially by Planck as an empirical interpolation between Equations (10-23) and (10-24); the quantum constant h appeared for the first time in this equation.

Much of the discussion of the past several paragraphs could have been in terms of wavelengths rather than in terms of frequencies. Since $\nu = c/\lambda$, it follows that

$$d\left(\frac{h\nu}{kT}\right) = -\frac{d\,(\lambda kT/hc)}{(\lambda kT/hc)^2} \tag{10-25}$$

As a typical example, Equation (10-20′) may be written

$$\left[\frac{d\,(E/kT)}{d\,(\lambda kT/hc)}\right]_{T,V} = 8\pi V\left(\frac{kT}{hc}\right)^3 \frac{(hc/\lambda kT)^5}{e^{hc/\lambda kT}-1} \tag{10-26}$$

where the minus sign of Equation (10-25) has been omitted for convenience. The maximum value of the factor $(hc/\lambda kT)^5/(e^{hc/\lambda kT} - 1)$ occurs at (see Problem 10-7)

$$\frac{hc}{\lambda kT} = 4.965 \tag{10-27}$$

The fact that the right-hand side of Equation (10-27) is larger than the right-hand side of Equation (10-22) is clarified by an examination of Equation (10-25), which reveals that a unit wavelength is equal to a larger frequency interval at small wavelengths than at large wavelengths.

Example

The normal eye is able to detect only that radiation which has wavelengths between approximately 3900 and 7800 Å. From Equation (10-27) the maximum value of the factor $(hc/\lambda kT)^5/(e^{hc/\lambda kT} - 1)$ occurs at these wavelengths for temperatures of

$$\frac{hc}{4.96\lambda k} = \frac{6.63 \times 10^{-27} \times 3.00 \times 10^{10} \text{ °K}}{4.96 \times 3.90 \times 10^{-5} \times 1.38 \times 10^{-16}} = 7450\text{°K}$$

and

$$\frac{hc}{4.96\lambda k} = \frac{6.63 \times 10^{-27} \times 3.00 \times 10^{10} \text{ °K}}{4.96 \times 7.80 \times 10^{-5} \times 1.38 \times 10^{-16}} = 3725\text{°K}$$

Hence, for temperatures greater than about 7450°K, most of the radiation occurs in the (invisible) ultraviolet region, whereas for temperatures less than about 3725°K, most of the radiation occurs in the (invisible) infrared region.

In a slight extension of the analysis of the present chapter, one might examine the flux of energy crossing, in one direction, an arbitrary plane in a blackbody radiation field. (This flux provides an upper bound to the thermal radiation emitted by the surface of a body.) For a discussion of this extension, see Appendix I.

PROBLEMS

10-1 Recall from Chapter 7 the time-independent Schrödinger wave equation for a system with negligible potential energy:

$$\nabla^2 \psi_k = -\frac{2m\varepsilon_k}{\hbar^2}\psi_k$$

Show that this equation may be written also in the form

$$\nabla^2 \psi_k = -\left(\frac{p_k}{\hbar}\right)^2 \psi_k$$

where p_k is momentum associated with the kth quantum state. Written in this form, the wave equation is applicable also to a photon. Show that for a photon,

$$\nabla^2 \psi_k = -\left(\frac{2\pi\nu_k}{c}\right)^2 \psi_k$$

Consider now a photon in a cubic box with walls of infinite electrical conductivity. Then ψ_k must vanish at the walls. Show that

$$\psi_k = \left(\frac{8}{l^3}\right)^{1/2} \sin\left(k_1\pi\frac{x}{l}\right) \sin\left(k_2\pi\frac{y}{l}\right) \sin\left(k_3\pi\frac{z}{l}\right)$$

satisfies the time-independent wave equation and boundary conditions provided that

$$\left(\frac{2\pi\nu_k}{c}\right)^2 = \left(\frac{\pi}{l}\right)^2 (k_1^2 + k_2^2 + k_3^2)$$

where l is length of edge of box. (Let origin of coordinate system coincide with one corner of box.) Compare this result with that which was derived beginning with the result of Problem 7-1.

10-2 Show that the quadratic energy-momentum relation $\varepsilon = p^2/2m$ (for nonrelativistic particles) and the linear energy-momentum relation $\varepsilon = pc$ (for photons), used in the derivation of Equation (10-6) from Equation (8-2), are special cases of the more general relation

$$\varepsilon = \sqrt{(mc^2)^2 + (pc)^2} - mc^2$$

where ε is kinetic energy (not including energy mc^2 associated with rest mass) and m is rest mass (represented in some texts by m_0). (HINT: For nonrelativistic particles, $pc << mc^2$.)

10-3 From Equation (10-6) the translational energy level of a photon (with zero rest mass) in its kth quantum state is proportional to the negative one-third power of the volume of the box, that is,

$$\varepsilon_k = \frac{b_k}{V^{\frac{1}{3}}}$$

where b_k is a proportionality constant. Proceeding as in Problem 7-3, show that for a system of photons

$$\langle p \rangle V = \frac{1}{3} \langle E \rangle$$

Note that this result depends on the fact that photons have zero rest mass but does not depend on the fact that a system of photons is a Bose-Einstein system. Compare this result with the result of Problem 7-3.

10-4 Calculate the value of the radiation pressure at the temperature of (*a*) a typical room (300°K), and (*b*) an atomic-bomb explosion (10^5°K). Is radiation pressure significant in comparison with molecular pressure in most physical systems?

10-5 Derive Equation (10-20) beginning with

$$\langle E \rangle = -\left(\frac{\partial \ln \Xi}{\partial \beta}\right)_V \qquad \ln \Xi = \frac{8\pi V}{3(\beta hc)^3} \int_0^\infty \frac{(\beta h\nu)^3 \, d(\beta h\nu)}{e^{\beta h\nu} - 1}$$

rather than beginning with Equation (10-16).

10-6 Beginning with Equation (10-20′), verify Equations (10-21) and (10-22).

10-7 Verify Equation (10-27).

10-8 Does "constant-pressure heat capacity" have meaning for a photon gas? Justify your answer.

10-9 At what temperature does the maximum energy density of blackbody radiation occur at the midpoint of the wavelength region which is visible to the normal eye?

10-10 How is the temperature ratio related to the volume ratio in a reversible adiabatic expansion of a photon gas? Compare this result with the result of Problem 8-10.

chapter 11
perfect electron gas

An essential distinction between language and experience is that language separates out from the living matrix little bundles and freezes them; in doing this it produces something totally unlike experience, but nevertheless useful
P. W. Bridgman, 1936 †

In the past three chapters, the fundamentals of statistical thermodynamics have been applied to a perfect monatomic gas (an example of a Maxwell-Boltzmann system of indistinguishable particles), an Einstein monatomic crystal (an example of a system of independent distinguishable subsystems), and blackbody radiation (an example of a Bose-Einstein system). In the present chapter, the quartet of simple examples of the fundamentally different types of systems is rounded out by a discussion of the perfect electron gas (an example of a Fermi-Dirac system).

Many of the properties of metals are described qualitatively by a simplified model, of volume V, which contains outer valence electrons and associated positive metallic ions, the ions forming a lattice through which the electrons move freely. Effects of interparticle forces are neglected. (Hence the methods of Chapter 6 may be applied.) The use of this model is based in part upon the observations that (1) an electric current in a metal involves a flow of electrons but no flow of ions, and (2) the electric conductivity of a metal decreases as temperature increases (implying that negligible "activation energy" is required to free an electron from its equilibrium position). However, the most satisfactory basis for the use of this model is perhaps the realized agreement between the predictions based upon its use and the results of experiments.

Since effects of interparticle forces are neglected in this model, the elec-

† P. W. Bridgman, "The Nature of Physical Theory," p. 24, Dover Publications, Inc., New York.

trons move in a potential field which is constant except at the system walls (where, as a result of the attractions between electrons and positive ions, the potential increases of the order of several electron volts for an electron attempting to pass from inside the system to outside the system). If the potential energy of an electron in a dilute gas phase is set equal to zero, the potential within the system is negative (see Figure 11-1).

The quantitative application of the results of an analysis of a perfect electron gas in a metal requires knowledge of the number of free electrons per metal atom. Since the perfect electron gas is only a crude model for

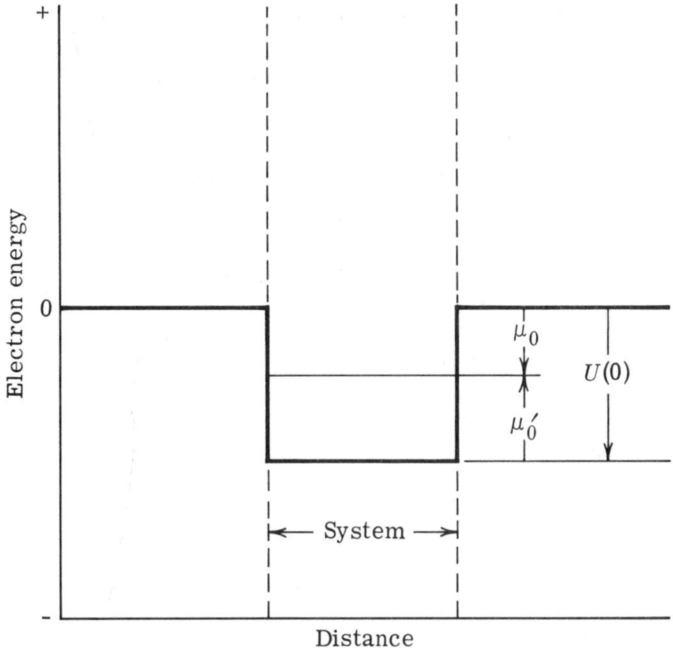

Figure 11-1 *Electron energies in simplified model of a metal. [U (0) is potential energy, μ_0' is maximum translational energy at 0° K.]*

most metals (the electrons *do* interact with the ion lattice), no simple recipe for predicting an effective number of free electrons exists. Some generalizations have been inferred, however, from measurements of physical properties (optical constants, Hall coefficient, soft X-ray emission, magnetic susceptibility, electrical conductivity, electronic specific heat, etc.). The alkali metals (Li, Na, K, Rb, and Cs) and the noble metals (Cu, Ag, and Au), with one electron outside complete closed shells, exhibit approximately one free electron per atom. Those divalent metals with hexagonal (close-packed) crystal structure (Be, Mg, β-Ca, Zn, and Cd) have less than two effective free electrons per atom. The other divalent metals (α-Ca, Sr, Ba, and Hg), the trivalent metals (Al, Ga, In, and Tl), and the quadrivalent metals (Sn, Pb, Ti, Zr, and Hf) exhibit, respectively, more than two, more than three, and more than four effective free electrons per atom. The number of effective free electrons of pentavalent metals (As, Sb, and Bi) appears to be small in comparison with their valence. Transition metals (V, Cr, Mn, Fe, Co, Ni, Nb, Mo, Ma, Ru, Rh, Pd, Ta, W, Re, Os, Ir, and Pt), particularly the ferromagnetic ones, are the most complicated of the metals; their relatively large electronic heat capacity is evidence that the concept of free electrons is not applicable to them. The most important deficiency in the free-electron model is that the allowed electron quantum states in the model are those states allowed for an electron moving freely in a box; in a more realistic model, certain bands of electron quantum states are not allowed as a consequence of electron-ion interactions. Discussions of the band model are beyond the scope of this book, however.

An electron exhibits a spin of 1/2, that is, an angular-momentum magnitude of $\hbar/2$. Hence electrons have antisymmetrical wave functions; no more than one electron in a system can be in a given particle quantum state at one time, and a system of electrons is a Fermi-Dirac system. Consequently, taking into account also those features of the model discussed in preceding paragraphs, the model being considered here may be studied using the methods developed for a grand canonical ensemble of Fermi-Dirac members containing particles with negligible effects of interparticle forces.

From Equation (6-7), the appropriate expression for the logarithm of the partition function is

$$\ln \Xi_{\mathrm{FD}} = \sum_k \ln (1 + e^{-\beta\varepsilon_k - \gamma}) \tag{6-7}$$

(For convenience, the subscript FD is omitted in the remainder of this chapter.) The allowed energy levels are the allowed energy levels for a particle in a box; from Equation (8-2), for a rectangular box,

$$\varepsilon_k = U(0) + \frac{h^2}{8m}\left[\left(\frac{k_1}{l_1}\right)^2 + \left(\frac{k_2}{l_2}\right)^2 + \left(\frac{k_3}{l_3}\right)^2\right] \tag{11-1}$$

where $U(0)$ is the potential energy (with negative value) of an electron at rest within the system relative to the potential energy of an electron in a dilute gas phase (see Figure 11-1), k_1, k_2, k_3 are quantum numbers, and l_1, l_2, l_3 are lengths of edges of the box. For each energy level, two different orientations of spin are possible, i.e., the degeneracy is 2. In principle, one could substitute now into Equation (6-7), evaluate $\ln \Xi$, and calculate values of thermodynamic properties from suitable operations on $\ln \Xi$. Calculations at this level of generality are tedious, however.

Calculations would be simplified if one could approximate the Fermi-

Dirac system by a Maxwell-Boltzmann system. The sufficient condition given in Chapter 8,

$$\left(\frac{2\pi mkT}{h^2}\right)^{3/2}\frac{V}{N} >> 1 \qquad (8\text{-}23)$$

or, in terms of the thermal de Broglie wavelength,

$$\frac{1}{\Lambda^3}\frac{V}{N} >> 1 \qquad (8\text{-}26)$$

provides also an order-of-magnitude necessary condition for use of the Maxwell-Boltzmann approximation. As a typical example, consider copper at its normal melting point. The volume per electron V/N is the volume per metal atom divided by the valence. Hence, for copper (with an atomic weight of 63.57, a specific gravity of about 8.94, and a valence of 1), V/N equals about $1.18 \times 10^{-23}\,\text{cm}^3$, so that at its normal melting point (1356°K),

$$\frac{1}{\Lambda^3}\frac{V}{N} = \left(\frac{2\pi mkT}{h^2}\right)^{3/2}\frac{V}{N} \approx 1.42 \times 10^{-3} << 1 \qquad (11\text{-}2)$$

Values of the same order of magnitude exist for other metals, so that, for free electrons in metals, the value of this dimensionless parameter is small (rather than large) in comparison with unity; the thermal de Broglie wavelength is about ten times the distance between neighboring ions. This situation arises because of the small values of the electron mass m and the volume per electron V/N. Hence quantum effects are large and the Maxwell-Boltzmann approximation may not be used.

The results of the preceding paragraph do motivate, however, a useful approximate calculation procedure. Equation (11-2) may be rearranged to show that normal melting temperatures of metals are much lower than the values of a parameter of the system of electrons having units of temperature. Hence consider the limiting case in which $T \to 0$.

If $T \to 0$, then any given term on the right-hand side of Equation (6-7) either vanishes or approaches infinity depending on the sign of $\beta\varepsilon_k + \gamma$. Hence a satisfactory procedure for calculating expected values of mechanical quantities is to operate upon $\ln \Xi$ first and to let $T \to 0$ later. [Alternatively, the second lines of Equations (11-3) to (11-5) could be written immediately.] One obtains

$$\langle E_0\rangle = -\lim_{T\to 0}\left(\frac{\partial \ln \Xi}{\partial \beta}\right)_{\gamma, V} = \lim_{T\to 0}\sum_k \langle N_k\rangle\, \varepsilon_k \qquad (11\text{-}3)$$

$$\langle N_0\rangle = -\lim_{T\to 0}\left(\frac{\partial \ln \Xi}{\partial \gamma}\right)_{\beta, V} = \lim_{T\to 0}\sum_k \langle N_k\rangle \qquad (11\text{-}4)$$

$$\langle p_0\rangle = \lim_{T\to 0}\frac{1}{\beta}\left(\frac{\partial \ln \Xi}{\partial V}\right)_{\beta, \gamma} = -\lim_{T\to 0}\sum_k \langle N_k\rangle \frac{d\varepsilon_k}{dV} \qquad (11\text{-}5)$$

where, in agreement with Equation (6-10),

$$\langle N_k \rangle = \frac{1}{e^{\beta \varepsilon_k + \gamma} + 1}$$

or, in the nomenclature of classical thermodynamics,

$$N_k = \frac{1}{\exp[(\varepsilon_k - \mu)/kT] + 1}$$

[Because of the relative ease with which $(\varepsilon_k - \mu)/kT$ can be handled as $T \to 0$, the nomenclature of classical thermodynamics will be used in the remainder of this chapter.] Since, according to Equation (11-1), the translational energy level of the kth quantum state of a particle is proportional to the negative two-thirds power of volume V, Equation (11-5) may be written, in agreement with Problem 7-3, in the form

$$p_0 V = \lim_{T \to 0} \frac{2}{3} \sum_k N_k \varepsilon_k' \qquad (11\text{-}5')$$

where ε_k' $(\equiv \varepsilon_k - U(0))$ is the allowed energy level relative to the potential energy, that is, ε_k' is the translational-energy level. Hence E_0 may be calculated immediately once p_0 is known; i.e., only Equations (11-4) and (11-5′) need to be evaluated here. In analogy with the procedures of the preceding chapter, it is convenient to transform, at this point, from a sum over quantum states to a sum over energy levels so that

$$p_0 V = \lim_{T \to 0} \frac{2}{3} \sum_{\varepsilon'} G_{\varepsilon'} N_k \varepsilon'$$

$$N_0 = \lim_{T \to 0} \sum_{\varepsilon'} G_{\varepsilon'} N_k$$

where $G_{\varepsilon'}$ is the number of quantum states with energy ε'. These sums may be replaced, to good approximation, by integrals provided that the difference between consecutive values of N_k is small in comparison with unity. Since, in agreement with Figure 6-2 and Table 6-3,

$$\lim_{T \to 0} \frac{1}{\exp[(\varepsilon_k' - \mu')/kT] + 1} = \begin{cases} 1 & \varepsilon_k' < \mu_0' \\ 0 & \varepsilon_k' > \mu_0' \end{cases}$$

where μ_0' $(\equiv \mu_0 - U(0))$ is the chemical potential at 0°K relative to the potential energy, it is seen that this condition is satisfied. Hence one may write

$$p_0 V = \frac{2}{3} \int_0^{\mu_0'} \varepsilon' G(\varepsilon')\, d\varepsilon' \qquad (11\text{-}6)$$

$$N_0 = \int_0^{\mu_0'} G(\varepsilon')\, d\varepsilon' \qquad (11\text{-}7)$$

where $G(\varepsilon')\,d\varepsilon'$ is the number of quantum states with energies between ε' and $\varepsilon' + d\varepsilon'$. The evaluation of $G(\varepsilon')\,d\varepsilon'$ is facilitated, without loss in generality, by considering a cubic box. Then, from Equation (11-1),

$$\varepsilon_k' = \frac{h^2}{8ml^2}(k_1^2 + k_2^2 + k_3^2)$$

whereas $G(\varepsilon')\,d\varepsilon'$ is twice the number of points with coordinates k_1, k_2, k_3 in one-eighth the spherical shell with radius $(8ml^2\,\varepsilon'/h^2)^{1/2}$ and thickness $(2ml^2/\varepsilon'\,h^2)^{1/2}\,d\varepsilon'$ (see Figure 10-3). The factor of 2 enters because, as discussed previously, two different quantum states are possible for each energy level. Since a unit volume is associated with each point in quantum-number space, one obtains

$$G(\varepsilon')\,d\varepsilon' = 4\pi\left(\frac{2m}{h^2}\right)^{3/2} V\varepsilon'^{1/2}\,d\varepsilon'$$

where $V\,(\equiv l^3)$ is volume. Substituting into Equations (11-6) and (11-7),

$$p_0 V = \frac{16\pi}{15}\left(\frac{2m}{h^2}\right)^{3/2} V\mu_0'^{5/2} \tag{11-8}$$

$$N_0 = \frac{5}{2}\frac{p_0 V}{\mu_0'} \tag{11-9}$$

$$E_0 = N_0\,U(0) + \frac{3}{2}p_0 V \tag{11-10}$$

Since, at 0°K, only one system quantum state is possible (the N_0 electrons fill, one electron per electron quantum state, all electron quantum states with $\varepsilon_k' < \mu_0'$), it follows that

$$\frac{S_0}{k} = 0$$

Although these equations are written with independent variables T, μ', and V in mind, the independent variables T, N, and V are more convenient in many cases. Then

$$A_0 = NU(0) + \frac{3}{40}N\frac{h^2}{m}\left(\frac{3N}{\pi V}\right)^{2/3} \tag{11-11}$$ ◀

$$E_0 = A_0 \tag{11-12}$$ ◀

$$p_0 = \frac{2}{3}\frac{A_0 - NU(0)}{V} \tag{11-13}$$ ◀

$$S_0 = 0 \tag{11-14}$$ ◀

$$\mu_0 = \frac{5}{3}\frac{A_0}{N} - \frac{2}{3}U(0) \tag{11-15}$$ ◀

The fundamental equations for these two choices of independent variables are, respectively, Equations (11-8) and (11-11). By simple differentiations,

$$N_0 = \left(\frac{\partial p_0 V}{\partial \mu_0'}\right)_{T,V} \tag{11-9'}$$

$$p_0 = -\left(\frac{\partial A_0}{\partial V}\right)_{T,N} \tag{11-13'}$$

$$\mu_0 = \left(\frac{\partial A_0}{\partial N}\right)_{T,V} \tag{11-15'}$$

Expressions for E_0 and S_0 are not obtained by differentiations of Equations (11-8) and (11-11); these differentiations are with respect to temperature and must be made before the limit $T \to 0$ is taken.

Since the energy μ_0' plays such an important role in the thermodynamics of an electron gas, it is given a special name—the **Fermi energy**. It is evaluated, in practice, using the expression for the number of electrons in the system; from Equation (11-9), with $p_0 V$ given by fundamental equation (11-8),

▶ $$\mu_0' = \frac{h^2}{8m}\left(\frac{3N}{\pi V}\right)^{2/3} \tag{11-16}$$

Hence the Fermi energy is a function of only the electron density in the system; its value is fixed physically by the fact that the N electrons fill, one electron per electron quantum state, all electron quantum states with $\varepsilon_k' < \mu_0'$. Typical values of μ_0' are of the order of several electron volts. Since, from Equations (11-9) and (11-10),

$$\frac{p_0 V}{N} = \frac{2}{5}\mu_0' \tag{11-17}$$

$$\frac{E_0'}{N} = \frac{3}{5}\mu_0' \tag{11-18}$$

it follows that typical values of $p_0 V/N$ and E_0'/N, where $E_0' \equiv E_0 - NU(0)$, are also of the order of several electron volts. [In more conventional units, p_0 is of the order of 10^6 atm (see Problem 11-3).] The extremely large values of p_0 and E_0 are a direct consequence of the Pauli exclusion principle. The extremely large force which is required to balance this extremely large pressure force is provided almost entirely by the electrostatic Coulomb attraction between the free electrons and the positive metallic ions.

The work required to remove an electron from a metal at 0°K is related to the Fermi energy by

▶ $$w_0 = -\mu_0 = -\mu_0' - U(0) \tag{11-19}$$

where μ_0 is the energy of the most energetic electron in the metal relative to the energy of an electron in a dilute gas phase at 0°K, whereas μ_0' is the energy of this same electron relative to the potential energy of an electron in the metal (see Figures 11-1 and 11-2). Since the electrons do not escape from the metal at 0°K, it follows that μ_0' is always less than the magnitude of $U(0)$.

The preceding several paragraphs were devoted to the limiting case in which $T \to 0$ so that N_k equals unity for $\varepsilon_k' < \mu_0'$ and equals zero for $\varepsilon_k' > \mu_0'$. Consider now the case in which $T \neq 0$. Values of N_k have already been plotted as a function of $\varepsilon_k - \mu$ for temperatures of 1000°K and 2000°K (Figure 6-2). In an alternative presentation, values of

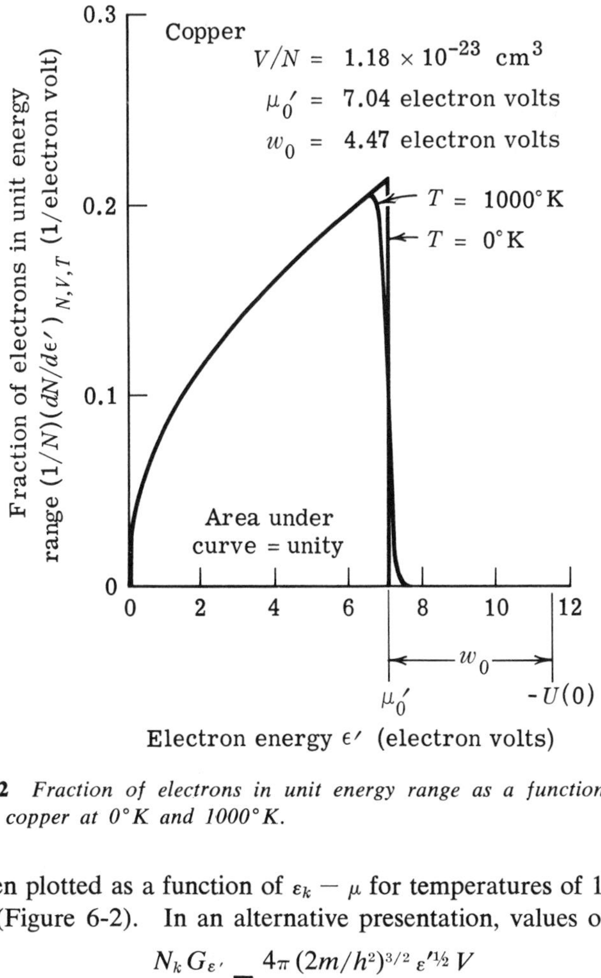

Figure 11-2 *Fraction of electrons in unit energy range as a function of electron energy for copper at 0°K and 1000°K.*

$$\frac{N_k G_{\varepsilon'}}{N} = \frac{4\pi (2m/h^2)^{3/2} \varepsilon'^{1/2}}{e^{(\varepsilon' - \mu')/kT} + 1} \frac{V}{N} \qquad (11\text{-}20)$$

or, using an alternative nomenclature, of

$$\frac{1}{N}\left(\frac{dN}{d\varepsilon'}\right)_{N,V,T} = \frac{4\pi (2m/h^2)^{3/2} \varepsilon'^{1/2}}{e^{(\varepsilon' - \mu')/kT} + 1} \frac{V}{N} \qquad (11\text{-}20') ◀$$

where $N_k G_{\varepsilon'}/N$ and $(1/N)(dN/d\varepsilon')_{N,V,T}$ are alternative symbols for the fraction of electrons in unit energy range, are plotted as a function of ε' for temperatures of 0°K and 1000°K in Figure 11-2. It is seen that the energy range over which deviations from the curve for 0°K occur is of the order of the thermal energy kT; that is, deviations from the curve for 0°K are small for all temperatures at which metals exist in the solid state. This observation explains why the free electrons in a metal (which play a major role in the theory of thermal and electrical conduction in a metal) play such a minor role in the theory of heat capacity of a metal; only a small fraction of the electrons (only those with translational energies near μ_0') are excited to higher energies at those temperatures of interest to engineers and scientists.

If a series analysis is carried out in which one retains the lowest-order terms in kT/μ_0' that appear (an analysis which requires much more effort than the analysis for $T \to 0$), then one finds that (for independent variables T, N, and V) the fundamental equation may be written

$$A' = A_0'\left[1 - \frac{5\pi^2}{12}\left(\frac{kT}{\mu_0'}\right)^2 + \cdots\right] \tag{11-21}$$

so that, by appropriate differentiations of the fundamental equation,

$$E' = \left(\frac{\partial (A'/kT)}{\partial (1/kT)}\right)_{V,N} = E_0'\left[1 + \frac{5\pi^2}{12}\left(\frac{kT}{\mu_0'}\right)^2 + \cdots\right] \tag{11-22}$$

$$p = -\left(\frac{\partial A'}{\partial V}\right)_{T,N} = p_0\left[1 + \frac{5\pi^2}{12}\left(\frac{kT}{\mu_0'}\right)^2 + \cdots\right] \tag{11-23}$$

$$S = -\left(\frac{\partial A'}{\partial T}\right)_{V,N} = \frac{\pi^2}{2} Nk\frac{kT}{\mu_0'} + \cdots \tag{11-24}$$

$$\mu' = \left(\frac{\partial A'}{\partial N}\right)_{T,V} = \mu_0'\left[1 - \frac{\pi^2}{12}\left(\frac{kT}{\mu_0'}\right)^2 + \cdots\right] \tag{11-25}$$

$$C_V = \left(\frac{\partial E}{\partial T}\right)_{V,N} = \frac{\pi^2}{2} Nk\frac{kT}{\mu_0'} + \cdots \tag{11-26}$$

For copper at its normal melting point, the dimensionless parameter kT/μ_0' has the value 0.017. Hence in most applications the temperature-dependent parts of A, E, p, and μ are negligible in comparison with the temperature-independent parts, and the free-electron contributions to S and C_V are negligible in comparison with the vibrating-ion contributions (see Chapter 9). The prediction of negligibly small electronic heat capacities for metals at room temperatures (in agreement with experimental results) was one of the greatest accomplishments of the quantum theory of metals.

Example

Consider the electronic heat capacity of silver (with an atomic weight of 107.88, a specific gravity of 10.50, and a valence of 1). The volume per free electron is

$$\frac{V}{N} = \frac{107.88 \times 1.66 \times 10^{-24}}{10.50}\,\text{cm}^3 = 1.70 \times 10^{-23}\,\text{cm}^3$$

From Equation (11-16)

$$\mu_0' = \frac{6.63 \times 10^{-27} \times 6.63 \times 10^{-27} \times 6.24 \times 10^{11}}{8 \times 9.11 \times 10^{-28}} \left(\frac{3}{\pi \times 1.70 \times 10^{-23}}\right)^{2/3} \text{ev}$$

$$= 5.51\ \text{ev}$$

In the standard method of presenting electronic heat capacities, a temperature-independent property is achieved by dividing C_V by T. Hence, applying Equation (11-26) to one mole of silver,

$$\frac{C_V}{T} = \frac{\pi^2}{2}\,\frac{6.02 \times 10^{23} \times 1.38 \times 10^{-16} \times 1.38 \times 10^{-16} \times 6.24 \times 10^{11}}{5.51 \times 10^{7}}$$

$$= 6.40 \times 10^{-4}\ \text{joule/mole-}^\circ\text{K}^2$$

This predicted value is 5 percent greater than the measured value 6.11×10^{-4} joule/mole-°K².

In order to compare the electronic contribution with the vibrating-ion contribution, note that, at 300°K, the electronic contribution is

$$C_V = \frac{\pi^2}{2}\,\frac{1.38 \times 10^{-16} \times 300 \times 6.24 \times 10^{11}}{5.51} Nk$$

$$= 0.0231\,Nk$$

This contribution is less than 1 percent of the vibrating-ion contribution (of the order of $3Nk$).

In order to place the free-electron contributions to the thermodynamic functions of the system in better perspective, results of exact calculations of the dimensionless ratios S/Nk, pV/NkT, and $2C_V/3Nk$ are plotted, for a free-electron gas, as functions of the dimensionless temperature kT/μ_0' in Figure 11-3. Note that at temperatures below the normal melting temperature of copper the free-electron contributions to S and C_V are extremely small, whereas the pressure is extremely large in comparison with the pressure in a Maxwell-Boltzmann system.

Nonzero temperatures do have a significant effect, however, on the ability of the electrons to escape from the metal. As indicated previously, electrons do not escape from the metal at 0°K; that is, at 0°K the translational energy of the most energetic electron is less than the magnitude of the potential energy $U(0)$. As the temperature is increased, however, some of the electrons acquire a translational energy greater than μ_0' (see Figure 11-2). At any given nonzero temperature, a fraction of the electrons have translational energy greater than the magnitude of $U(0)$, that is, translational energy sufficient to escape from the metal. Emission of electrons from a metal due to nonzero temperature is known as **thermionic emission**. A discussion of the rate of thermionic emission is included in Appendix I.

The value of the **work function**

$$w = -\mu = -\mu' - U(0)$$

may be established experimentally by observing the electron emission when either the metal is heated or a monochromatic light is shined on the metal surface. The first method is discussed in Appendix I; the second method

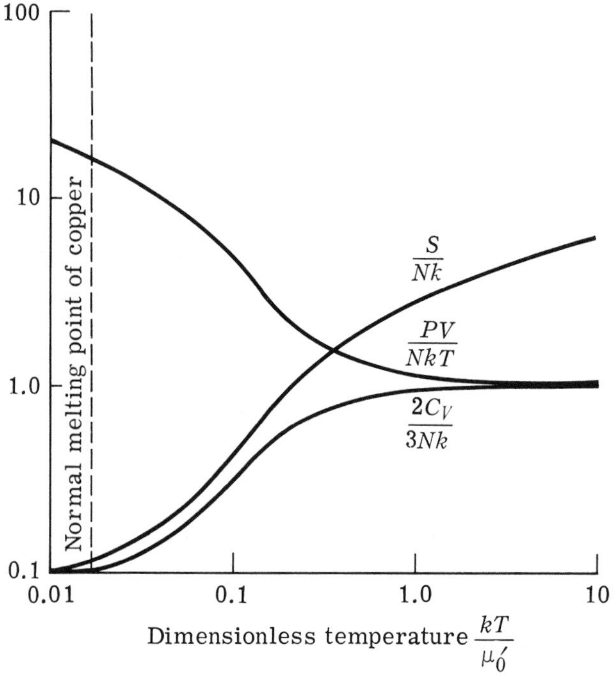

Figure 11-3 *Dimensionless entropy, heat capacity, and pressure as functions of dimensionless temperature for free-electron gas.*

is discussed briefly here. Free electrons in a metal are able to absorb the energy $h\nu$ of incident photons and to use this energy to augment their translational energy. At relatively low radiation frequencies, such that $h\nu < w$, relatively few electrons are excited to translational energies sufficient to escape from the metal; whereas at relatively high radiation frequencies, such that $h\nu > w$, relatively many electrons are excited to translational energies sufficient to escape from the metal. The frequency range associated with the transition from low emission rate to high emission rate decreases as the metal temperature is lowered (see Figure 11-2). Emission of electrons from a metal due to incident photons is known as **photoelectric emission.**

The fact that unfilled energy levels are available immediately above the filled energy levels plays an important role in the theory of electrical conduction in a metal. (This feature distinguishes a metal from an insulator.) Electrical conduction occurs when an electric field accelerates electrons to unfilled quantum states with higher energy levels.

Although the perfect electron gas is the only example of a Fermi-Dirac system discussed explicitly in this book, other valuable applications (e.g., the Fermi-Thomas model of the atom and the Fermi nucleon-gas model of the nucleus) exist. These applications, as well as further details of the theory of the perfect electron gas, are described in more specialized writings.

PROBLEMS

11-1 Show that a system of electrons in a typical metal may be approximated by a Maxwell-Boltzmann system only for temperatures of the order of, or greater than, 10^6 °K.

11-2 Using the methods of this chapter, show that the variances $\sigma^2(E)$, $\sigma^2(N)$, and $\sigma^2(p)$ vanish for a perfect electron gas as $T \to 0$.

11-3 Calculate, for electrons in copper, the value of the Fermi energy μ_0', the pressure p_0, and the energy E_0'/N_0.

11-4 Calculate, for electrons in copper at 0°K, the average speed of the electrons. Why is this average speed not zero?

11-5 The expression

$$\frac{C_V}{T} = 6.11 \times 10^{-4}\,\text{joule/mole-°K}^2$$

describes, to good approximation, the results of measurements of the electronic heat capacity of silver. Calculate, using this expression, the value of the Fermi energy and the effective number of free electrons per atom for silver. (The atomic weight and the specific gravity of silver are, respectively, 107.88 and 10.50.)

11-6 In a metal with one free electron per atom, what is the ratio of the de Broglie wavelength to the distance between neighboring ions for an electron with energy equal to the Fermi energy? At 0°K, do the electrons with energy not equal to the Fermi energy have smaller or larger wavelengths?

11-7 Recall that only a small fraction of the free electrons (only those free electrons with energies near μ_0') are excited to higher energies as the temperature of a metal is increased. If each excited free electron had a heat capacity of $3k/2$, what fraction of the free electrons would be excited at temperatures for which $kT << \mu_0'$? Compare your result with Figure 11-2.

11-8 Recall that the Fermi energy μ_0' is fixed by the condition that, at 0°K, the free electrons fill, one electron per electron quantum state, all electron quantum states with $\varepsilon_k' < \mu_0'$. Keeping this condition in mind, discuss the dependence of (*a*) the number of free electrons, (*b*) the number of electron quantum states, and (*c*) the value of the Fermi energy on the size of a piece of metal.

11-9 Recall that for a perfect monatomic gas, E/V varies linearly with N for fixed V. For a perfect electron gas in a metal, however, E_0'/V varies as $N^{5/3}$ for fixed V, even though effects of interparticle forces are neglected. Why?

chapter **12**

perfect adsorbed gas

It is a recurring experience of scientific progress that what was yesterday an object of study, of interest in its own right, becomes today something to be taken for granted, something understood and reliable, something known and familiar—a tool for further research and discovery.
J. R. Oppenheimer, 1953 †

In the past four chapters, the fundamentals of statistical thermodynamics have been applied to four simple examples of four fundamentally different types of systems (a Maxwell-Boltzmann system of indistinguishable particles, a system of independent distinguishable subsystems, a Bose-Einstein system, and a Fermi-Dirac system). The remaining chapters are devoted to additional relatively simple examples, chosen either because (in the case of the perfect adsorbed gas) the model differs greatly from those discussed previously or because (in the case of the diatomic perfect gas and the Debye monatomic crystal) the model extends significantly a model discussed previously. All seven examples satisfy the additional requirement of usefulness to engineers and scientists.

Consider a model of an adsorbed gas on a crystal in which the number of adsorbed particles per unit area of the crystal is sufficiently small so that the particles may be considered to act independently. Let the adsorbed particles be bound to the crystal by forces which are small in comparison with those which hold the atoms of the crystal together. (Then effects of the adsorbed particles on the atoms of the crystal may be neglected; the crystal serves only to provide a potential for "holding" the adsorbed particles.) Effects of internal degrees of freedom of the adsorbed particles will be neglected. Each adsorbed particle has three degrees of freedom which may be considered, for convenience, to be either normal to or parallel to

† J. R. Oppenheimer, "Science and the Common Understanding," p. 22, Simon and Schuster, Inc., New York, 1953.

the crystal surface. The particle vibrates in the degree of freedom normal to the surface; if the temperature is relatively low, it vibrates (in the vicinity of a potential minimum) also in the two degrees of freedom parallel to the surface, and if the temperature is relatively high, it moves freely in the two degrees of freedom parallel to the surface.

The potential field which holds the adsorbed particle near the surface (and, if the temperature is relatively low, near a potential minimum) is the sum of contributions from several crystal atoms (see Figure 12-1). If the crystal atoms are spaced regularly, this resultant potential field is doubly periodic in the two directions parallel to the crystal surface. The nature of this periodic potential field is indicated schematically in Figure 12-2,

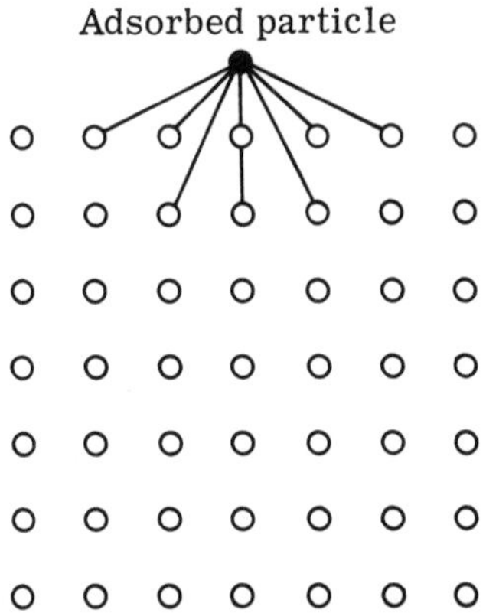

Figure 12-1 *Cross section of cubic crystal and adsorbed particle. (Connecting lines indicate representative crystal atoms which contribute to potential field of adsorbed particle.)*

where the potential energy of an adsorbed particle above a row of crystal atoms is plotted as a function of distance parallel to a crystal surface and above a row of crystal atoms. The nature of the variation of the potential field in the direction normal to the surface is indicated schematically in Figure 12-3, where the potential energy of an adsorbed particle above a crystal atom is plotted as a function of distance normal to a crystal surface. If vibrational amplitudes are small, the vibrations may be described by harmonic oscillations with frequencies determined by the curvature of the potential-energy curve at the point of minimum potential energy. Typical frequencies are usually of the order of 10^{12} cycles/sec for vibrations normal to the crystal surface and a little less for vibrations parallel to the crystal surface.

In order to facilitate discussions of equilibrium between an adsorbed phase and a gas phase, a consistent zero-energy level must be chosen. For convenience, set the potential energy of a particle in a dilute gas at a large distance from the crystal equal to zero. If the three degrees of freedom coincide with the three axes of a rectangular coordinate system located with origin at the equilibrium position of an adsorbed particle, with the z axis normal to the crystal surface, and with the x and y axes parallel to rows of crystal atoms, then the potential energy of an adsorbed particle may be written, for the case in which the temperature is relatively low,

$$U(x, y, z) = U(0) + \frac{a}{2}(x^2 + y^2) + \frac{b}{2} z^2 \tag{12-1}$$

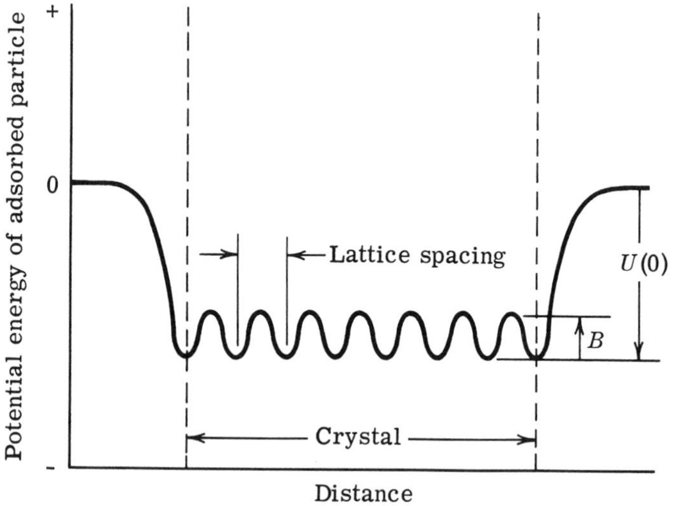

Figure 12-2 *Schematic diagram of potential energy as a function of distance parallel to a crystal surface, for adsorbed particle above a row of crystal atoms.*

and, for the case in which the temperature is relatively high,

$$U(x, y, z) = U(0) + \frac{b}{2} z^2 \tag{12-2}$$

where $U(0)$ is potential energy at the equilibrium position (see Figures 12-2 and 12-3), and a and b are the force constants

$$a = \left.\frac{\partial^2 U}{\partial x^2}\right|_0 = \left.\frac{\partial^2 U}{\partial y^2}\right|_0$$

$$b = \left.\frac{\partial^2 U}{\partial z^2}\right|_0$$

Terms of odd orders in x, y, and z do not appear since the potential is taken to be a symmetrical function of x, y, and z (a symmetrical function of z is a good approximation if the vibration amplitude in the z direction is not large); terms of fourth and higher orders are omitted since the vibration amplitudes are considered to be small; the force constants for displacements in the x and y directions are equal since the lattice spacings in these two directions are considered to be equal. The potential energy $U(0)$ is related to the heat of adsorption per molecule at 0°K by

$$Q_{\text{adsorption}} = -U(0) - \frac{1}{2}h(2\nu_a + \nu_b) \tag{12-3}$$

where the last term represents the ground-state energies of three oscillators with frequencies ν_a, ν_a, and ν_b (see Problem 7-2).

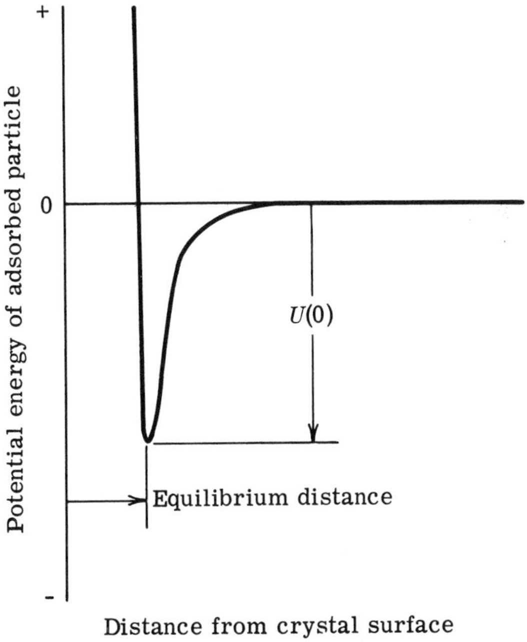

Figure 12-3 *Schematic diagram of potential energy as a function of distance normal to a crystal surface, for adsorbed particle above a crystal atom.*

The meanings of the phrases "temperature is relatively low" and "temperature is relatively high," used in the preceding paragraphs, may be clarified by an examination of Figure 12-2. The doubly periodic nature of the potential field in an xy plane near the crystal surface results in a two-dimensional array of potential wells separated by potential barriers, the significance of which depends on the thermal energy of the adsorbed particles. The phrase "temperature is relatively low" means that the thermal energy kT of the adsorbed particles is much smaller than the magnitude B of the potential barriers, so that particle motions in the two degrees of freedom parallel to the crystal surface are limited, in the main, to vibrational motions in the vicinity of potential minima; this limiting case will be called **localized adsorption**. The phrase "temperature is relatively high" means, on the other hand, that the thermal energy kT of the adsorbed particles is much larger than the magnitude B of the potential barriers, so that the particles may move freely in the two degrees of freedom parallel to the crystal surface; this limiting case will be called **mobile adsorption**.

First consider localized adsorption of independent indistinguishable particles on M equivalent distinguishable sites, with no more than one particle adsorbed at a given site. Since the maximum number of particles in the system is finite, one of the chief motivations for using a grand canonical ensemble is lost. [See the discussion of the effect of the maximum allowed number of particles in a system which follows Equation (6-3).] Furthermore, advantages accrue from using a procedure similar to that used for the Einstein monatomic crystal. Hence a canonical ensemble of members (with independent variables β, N, and M) of indistinguishable particles and independent distinguishable sites will be analyzed.

For the special case in which the number of particles equals the number of sites (that is, $N = M$), the particles may be considered to be distinguishable and the results of Chapter 9 may be adapted with only modest changes. In analogy with Equation (9-3),

$$E_j = NU(0) + \sum_{n=1}^{3N} \varepsilon_{nj} \tag{12-4}$$

The first term on the right-hand side of this equation does not contain the factor 1/2 since the N particles considered in this equation interact only with crystal atoms, so that each interparticle interaction is counted only once. In analogy with Equation (9-5),

$$Q = e^{-N\beta U(0)} \prod_{n=1}^{3N} q_n \tag{12-5}$$

Since two-thirds of the oscillators have force constants a, whereas one-third of the oscillators have force constants b, one may write alternatively

$$Q = e^{-N\beta U(0)}\, q_a^{2N}\, q_b^{N} \tag{12-6}$$

where

$$q_a = \sum_l e^{-\beta\varepsilon_{al}} \tag{12-7a}$$

$$q_b = \sum_l e^{-\beta\varepsilon_{bl}} \tag{12-7b}$$

or, in analogy with Equation (9-9),

$$q_a = \frac{1}{2\sinh(\beta h\nu_a/2)} \tag{12-8a}$$

$$q_b = \frac{1}{2\sinh(\beta h\nu_b/2)} \tag{12-8b}$$

Substituting from Equation (12-8) into Equation (12-6), one may calculate expected values of mechanical quantities, for the special case in which $N = M$, by appropriate differentiations of Equation (12-6).

In general, however, $N \leqq M$. For a given value of N, more system quantum states are possible if $N < M$ than if $N = M$. For every system quantum state which is possible for $N = M$,

$$G_N = \frac{M!}{N!\,(M-N)!} \tag{12-9}$$

system quantum states are possible for $N < M$, as may be seen by examining the series of M s's and N o's

$$s_9\ o\ s_6\ s_2\ s_7\ s_M\ o\ \cdots\ s_3\ o\ s_8\ s_1\ o\ s_4\ s_5$$

where each s corresponds to a distinguishable site and each o indicates that the preceding site contains an indistinguishable particle. (The first member of the series must be an s.) If the o's were distinguishable, they could be assigned $M!/(M-N)!$ different ways. Since the o's are not distinguishable, one must divide by the number of possible permutations of N distinguishable symbols, that is, by $N!$. Hence *each* term of the partition function must be multiplied by G_N. Multiplying the right-hand side of Equation (12-6) by G_N, one obtains for the case in which $N \leqq M$,

$$Q = \frac{M!}{N!\,(M-N)!}\, e^{-N\beta U(0)}\, q_a^{2N}\, q_b^{N} \tag{12-10}$$

or, using Stirling's approximation (see Appendix A),

$$\ln Q = M \ln M - N \ln N - (M-N)\ln(M-N) - N\beta U(0) + 2N \ln q_a + N \ln q_b \tag{12-11}$$

Substituting from Equation (12-8) into Equation (12-11), expected values of mechanical quantities may be calculated now, for the more general case in which $N \leqq M$, by appropriate differentiations of Equation (12-11).

The appropriate fundamental equation for the adsorbed phase is

$$dA = -S\,dT - \Phi\,dM + \mu\,dN \tag{12-12}$$

where M acts as the generalized displacement and Φ (with units of energy) is the generalized force conjugate to M. In dimensionless form,

$$d\left(\frac{A}{kT}\right) = E\,d\left(\frac{1}{kT}\right) - \frac{\Phi}{kT}\,dM + \frac{\mu}{kT}\,dN \tag{12-13}$$

Hence

$$\langle E \rangle = -\left(\frac{\partial \ln Q}{\partial \beta}\right)_{M,N}$$

$$= N\left(U(0) + h\nu_a \coth\frac{\beta h\nu_a}{2} + \frac{h\nu_b}{2}\coth\frac{\beta h\nu_b}{2}\right) \tag{12-14}$$ ◀

$$\langle\Phi\rangle = \frac{1}{\beta}\left(\frac{\partial \ln Q}{\partial M}\right)_{\beta, N} = -\frac{1}{\beta}\ln\left(1 - \frac{N}{M}\right) \tag{12-15}$$

$$\langle\gamma\rangle = \left(\frac{\partial \ln Q}{\partial N}\right)_{\beta, M}$$

$$= -\beta U(0) - \ln\left(2\sinh\frac{\beta h\nu_a}{2}\right)^2\left(2\sinh\frac{\beta h\nu_b}{2}\right) - \ln\frac{N/M}{1 - N/M} \tag{12-16}$$

$$\frac{S}{k} \sim \beta(\langle E\rangle - \langle A\rangle) \sim N\left[\beta h\nu_a \coth\frac{\beta h\nu_a}{2} + \frac{\beta h\nu_b}{2}\coth\frac{\beta h\nu_b}{2}\right.$$

$$\left. - \ln\left(2\sinh\frac{\beta h\nu_a}{2}\right)^2\left(2\sinh\frac{\beta h\nu_b}{2}\right)\right] + \ln\frac{M!}{N!\,(M-N)!} \tag{12-17}$$

Compare Equations (12-14) and (12-17) with Equations (9-15) and (9-20) for an Einstein monatomic crystal. Note that Equation (12-17) contains a configurational contribution for $N < M$.

If $N/M << 1$, then Equation (12-15) may be written, using the nomenclature of classical thermodynamics,

$$\Phi M \approx NkT \tag{12-18}$$

This equation is the analog of the thermal equation of state $pV = NkT$ for a thermally perfect gas phase.

If the adsorbed phase is in equilibrium with a gas phase, then μ/kT must be uniform in the two phases. For a thermally perfect gas phase,

$$\frac{\mu}{kT} = \frac{\mu^o(T)}{kT} + \ln\frac{p}{p^o} \tag{12-19}$$

where $\mu^o(T)$ is a function of temperature only and p^o is an arbitrary constant with units of pressure. [See Equation (8-22) for the special case of a perfect monatomic gas.] Equating μ/kT from Equations (12-16) and (12-19), one obtains

$$\frac{N(p, T)}{M} = \frac{\chi(T)\,p/p^o}{1 + \chi(T)\,p/p^o} \tag{12-20}$$

where
$$\chi(T) = \frac{e^{[\mu^o(T) - U(0)]/kT}}{[2\sinh(h\nu_a/2kT)]^2[2\sinh(h\nu_b/2kT)]} \tag{12-21}$$

When used at a given temperature, Equation (12-20) gives the amount of gas adsorbed as a function of pressure; it is known as the **Langmuir adsorption isotherm**. Note that

$$\lim_{p\to 0}\frac{N(p, T)}{M} \to \chi(T)\frac{p}{p^o} \qquad \lim_{p\to\infty}\frac{N(p, T)}{M} \to 1$$

Equation (12-20) describes many adsorption systems to good approximation. If $U(0)$, ν_a, and ν_b are given, then $\chi(T)$ may be calculated immediately from Equation (12-21) and the appropriate equation for $\mu^o(T)$.

Consider now mobile adsorption of indistinguishable particles with negligible effects of forces between adsorbed particles. Since no restriction is placed on the number of particles in the adsorbed phase, one may use a grand canonical ensemble of members; if the temperature is not too low and the number of adsorbed particles per unit area of surface is not too great, one may use the Maxwell-Boltzmann approximation. (A quantitative sufficient condition for use of the Maxwell-Boltzmann approximation is given in a later paragraph.) Hence consider a grand canonical ensemble of Maxwell-Boltzmann members with independent variables, β, γ, and $\mathcal{A}$, where $\mathcal{A}$ is the area of the adsorbed phase. The appropriate grand partition function may be obtained from Equation (6-9), deleting the subscript i, with the result

$$\ln \Xi_{\mathrm{MB}} = e^{-\gamma} \sum_k e^{-\beta \varepsilon_k} \tag{12-22}$$

(For convenience, the subscript MB will be omitted in the remainder of this chapter.) If effects of excitations of internal degrees of freedom of the adsorbed particles are neglected, the allowed energy levels result from considerations of translational motions in the two degrees of freedom parallel to the surface and vibrational motions in the degree of freedom normal to the surface. One obtains, for a surface with length l_1 and width l_2,

$$\varepsilon_k = U(0) + \frac{h^2}{8m}\left[\left(\frac{k_1}{l_1}\right)^2 + \left(\frac{k_2}{l_2}\right)^2\right] + h\nu\left(l + \frac{1}{2}\right) \tag{12-23}$$

where the first term on the right-hand side is the potential energy at the equilibrium position (see Figures 12-2 and 12-3), the second term is the translational energy (see results of Problem 7-1 with $k_3 = 0$), and the third term is the vibrational energy (see results of Problem 7-2). Substitution from Equation (12-23) into Equation (12-22) yields

$$\ln \Xi = e^{-\gamma - \beta U(0)} \sum_{k_1, k_2, l} \exp\left\{-\frac{\beta h^2}{8m}\left[\left(\frac{k_1}{l_1}\right)^2 + \left(\frac{k_2}{l_2}\right)^2\right] - \beta h\nu\left(l + \frac{1}{2}\right)\right\} \tag{12-24}$$

where (for consistency with the analysis of Chapter 9 and the preceding analysis of a perfect localized adsorbed gas) the degeneracy g_e of the internal quantum states of the adsorbed particle has been set equal to unity. Since the value of each of the three quantum numbers appearing here may be chosen independently of the values chosen for the other two quantum numbers, and since the exponential appearing in Equation (12-24) is factorable, one may factor the series appearing here into a product of three series,

$$\ln \Xi = e^{-\gamma-\beta U(0)} \sum_{k_1=1}^{\infty} \exp\left[-\frac{\beta h^2}{8m}\left(\frac{k_1}{l_1}\right)^2\right] \sum_{k_2=1}^{\infty} \exp\left[-\frac{\beta h^2}{8m}\left(\frac{k_2}{l_2}\right)^2\right] \sum_{l=0}^{\infty} \exp\left[-\beta h\nu\left(l+\frac{1}{2}\right)\right] \quad (12\text{-}25)$$

These three series may be evaluated using the methods established in Chapter 8 (for the first two series) and in Chapter 9 (for the third series). One obtains

$$\ln \Xi = e^{-\gamma-\beta U(0)} \frac{2\pi m \mathcal{A}}{\beta h^2} \frac{1}{2\sinh(\beta h\nu/2)} \quad (12\text{-}26)$$

Equation (12-26) relates explicitly the logarithm of the partition function Ξ with the independent variables β, γ, and $\mathcal{A}$.

The appropriate fundamental equation for the adsorbed phase is

$$d(\Phi^\dagger \mathcal{A}) = S\,dT + \Phi^\dagger\,d\mathcal{A} + N\,d\mu \quad (12\text{-}27)$$

where $\mathcal{A}$ acts as the generalized displacement and $\Phi^\dagger$ (with units of force per unit length) is the generalized force conjugate to $\mathcal{A}$. In dimensionless form

$$d\left(\frac{\Phi^\dagger \mathcal{A}}{kT}\right) = -E\,d\left(\frac{1}{kT}\right) + \frac{\Phi^\dagger}{kT}\,d\mathcal{A} + N\,d\left(\frac{\mu}{kT}\right) \quad (12\text{-}28)$$

Hence

$$\langle E\rangle = -\left(\frac{\partial \ln \Xi}{\partial \beta}\right)_{\mathcal{A},\gamma} = \left(U(0) + \frac{1}{\beta} + \frac{h\nu}{2}\coth\frac{\beta h\nu}{2}\right)\ln \Xi \quad (12\text{-}29)$$

$$\langle N\rangle = -\left(\frac{\partial \ln \Xi}{\partial \gamma}\right)_{\mathcal{A},\beta} = \ln \Xi \quad (12\text{-}30)$$

$$\langle \Phi^\dagger\rangle = \frac{1}{\beta}\left(\frac{\partial \ln \Xi}{\partial \mathcal{A}}\right)_{\beta,\gamma} = \frac{\ln \Xi}{\beta \mathcal{A}} \quad (12\text{-}31)$$

$$\frac{S}{k} \sim \ln \Xi + \beta\langle E\rangle + \gamma\langle N\rangle = \left(2 + \gamma + \beta U(0) + \frac{\beta h\nu}{2}\coth\frac{\beta h\nu}{2}\right)\ln \Xi \quad (12\text{-}32)$$

or, in the language of classical thermodynamics,

▶ $$\Phi^\dagger \mathcal{A} = \frac{\pi m \mathcal{A}(kT)^2}{h^2 \sinh(h\nu/2kT)} \exp\left(\frac{\mu}{kT} - \frac{U(0)}{kT}\right) \quad (12\text{-}26')$$

▶ $$E = \left(\frac{U(0)}{kT} + 1 + \frac{h\nu}{2kT}\coth\frac{h\nu}{2kT}\right)\Phi^\dagger \mathcal{A} \quad (12\text{-}29')$$

▶ $$N = \frac{\Phi^\dagger \mathcal{A}}{kT} \quad (12\text{-}30')$$

▶ $$\frac{S}{k} = \left(2 - \frac{\mu}{kT} + \frac{U(0)}{kT} + \frac{h\nu}{2kT}\coth\frac{h\nu}{2kT}\right)\frac{\Phi^\dagger \mathcal{A}}{kT} \quad (12\text{-}32')$$

Compare these four equations with Equations (8-5′) to (8-7′) and (8-12′) for a perfect monatomic gas. Note particularly the complete analogy between Equation (12-30′) and the thermal equation of state $pV = NkT$ for a thermally perfect gas phase.

The sufficient condition

$$e^{\beta\varepsilon_k + \gamma} >> 1$$

given in Chapter 6 for applicability of the Maxwell-Boltzmann approximation may be written now, for a perfect mobile adsorbed gas, in a more meaningful form. Combining Equations (12-26) and (12-30), and solving for $e^{\beta U(0)+\gamma}$, one obtains, for a perfect mobile adsorbed gas,

$$e^{\beta U(0)+\gamma} = \frac{2\pi m}{\beta h^2} \frac{\mathcal{A}}{\langle N \rangle} \frac{1}{2 \sinh(\beta h\nu/2)}$$

Since $\beta\varepsilon_k \geqq \beta U(0)$, the given inequality is satisfied certainly if

$$\frac{2\pi m}{\beta h^2} \frac{\mathcal{A}}{\langle N \rangle} \frac{1}{2 \sinh(\beta h\nu/2)} >> 1$$

or, using the nomenclature of classical thermodynamics, if

$$\frac{2\pi mkT}{h^2} \frac{\mathcal{A}}{N} \frac{1}{2 \sinh(h\nu/2kT)} >> 1 \qquad (12\text{-}33)$$

Equation (12-33) (applicable to a perfect mobile adsorbed gas) is the analog of Equation (8-23) (applicable to a perfect gas with three translational degrees of freedom). It is seen that the Maxwell-Boltzmann approximation is applicable provided the temperature is not too low and the number of adsorbed particles per unit area of surface is not too great.

The adsorption isotherm for a perfect mobile adsorbed gas may be derived by equating μ/kT from Equation (12-19) and from Equation (12-26′). One obtains

$$\frac{N(p, T)}{\mathcal{A}} = \chi^{\dagger}(T) \frac{p}{p^o} \qquad (12\text{-}34)$$

where

$$\chi^{\dagger}(T) = \frac{\pi mkT/h^2}{\sinh(h\nu/2kT)} \exp\left[\frac{\mu^o(T) - U(0)}{kT}\right] \qquad (12\text{-}35)$$

These equations (applicable to mobile adsorption) are the analogs of Equations (12-20) and (12-21) (applicable to localized adsorption).

Example

Consider the adsorption of argon (with an atomic weight of 39.94 and a gas-phase ground-state degeneracy of 1) on a solid at 100°K in the presence of an argon gas phase. Take $\nu = 5 \times 10^{12}\ \text{sec}^{-1}$ and $-U(0) = 1{,}500$ cal/mole. Setting, arbitrarily, $p^o = 1$ atm, one obtains, from Equations (8-18) and (8-22),

$$\frac{\mu^{\circ}(T)}{kT} = -\ln\left[g_e\left(\frac{2\pi mkT}{h^2}\right)^{3/2}\frac{kT}{p^{\circ}}\right]$$

$$= -\ln\left[\left(\frac{2\pi \times 39.94 \times 1.66 \times 10^{-24} \times 1.38 \times 10^{-16} \times 100}{6.63 \times 10^{-27} \times 6.63 \times 10^{-27}}\right)^{3/2} \times \frac{1.38 \times 10^{-16} \times 100}{1.01 \times 10^{6}}\right] = -13.36$$

For the given conditions,

$$\frac{-U(0)}{kT} = \frac{1{,}500}{1.38 \times 10^{-16} \times 100 \times 2.39 \times 10^{-8} \times 6.02 \times 10^{23}} = 7.55$$

$$\sinh\frac{h\nu}{2kT} = \sinh\frac{6.63 \times 10^{-27} \times 5 \times 10^{12}}{2 \times 1.38 \times 10^{-16} \times 100} = \sinh 1.20 = 1.51$$

Hence, from Equation (12-35),

$$\chi^{\dagger}(T) = \frac{\pi mkT/h^2}{\sinh(h\nu/2kT)}\exp\left[\frac{\mu^{\circ}(T) - U(0)}{kT}\right]$$

$$= \frac{\pi \times 39.94 \times 1.66 \times 10^{-24} \times 1.38 \times 10^{-16} \times 100 \times e^{-5.81}}{6.63 \times 10^{-27} \times 6.63 \times 10^{-27} \times 1.51}\ \frac{\text{atoms}}{\text{cm}^2}$$

$$= 1.30 \times 10^{14}\ \text{atoms/cm}^2$$

so that, from Equation (12-34),

$$\frac{N}{\mathcal{A}} = \chi^{\dagger}(T)\frac{p}{p^{\circ}} = 1.30 \times 10^{14}\, p\ \text{atoms/cm}^2$$

where p is in atmospheres. If one eliminates $N/\mathcal{A}$ and $\chi^{\dagger}$ from Equations (12-33) to (12-35), the sufficient condition for application of the Maxwell-Boltzmann approximation may be written

$$\frac{p}{p_0} << \exp\left[-\frac{\mu^{\circ}(T) - U(0)}{kT}\right]$$

so that, for the given conditions, the Maxwell-Boltzmann approximation is applicable for $p << 335$ atm.

Adsorption isotherms for localized adsorption and for mobile adsorption are compared schematically in Figure 12-4. The relative magnitudes of the slopes of these two isotherms as $p \to 0$ [that is, the relative magnitudes of $\chi(T)$ and $\chi^{\dagger}(T)$] depend on temperature (see Problem 12-1).

PROBLEMS

12-1 Show that

$$\lim_{p\to 0}\frac{N_{\text{mobile}}}{N_{\text{localized}}} = \frac{2\pi mkT}{h^2}\left(2\sinh\frac{h\nu_a}{2kT}\right)^2\frac{\mathcal{A}}{M}$$

What is the limit of this ratio as $T \to 0$? As $T \to \infty$? Compute the value of this ratio for argon adsorbed on graphite at 100°K. Take $\nu_a = 5 \times 10^{12}$ sec^{-1} and $\mathcal{A}/M = 4 \times 10^{-16}$ cm^2.

12-2 Using Equation (12-20), calculate N/M for argon adsorbed on a solid at 100°K in the presence of an argon gas phase at 10^{-3} atm. Take $\nu_a = \nu_b = 5 \times 10^{12}$ sec^{-1} and $-U(0) = 1{,}500$ cal/mole.

12-3 An adsorbent, with a surface area of 10^6 m^2 and at 300°K initially, is in equilibrium with 10 liters of argon, at 10^{-6} torr initially (1 torr $\equiv$ 1 mm Hg). If the adsorbent is cooled to 100°K, what is the final equilibrium pressure in the system? Consider the case in which $\nu = 5 \times 10^{12}$ sec^{-1}, $-U(0) = 1{,}500$ cal/mole, and the adsorbate is mobile.

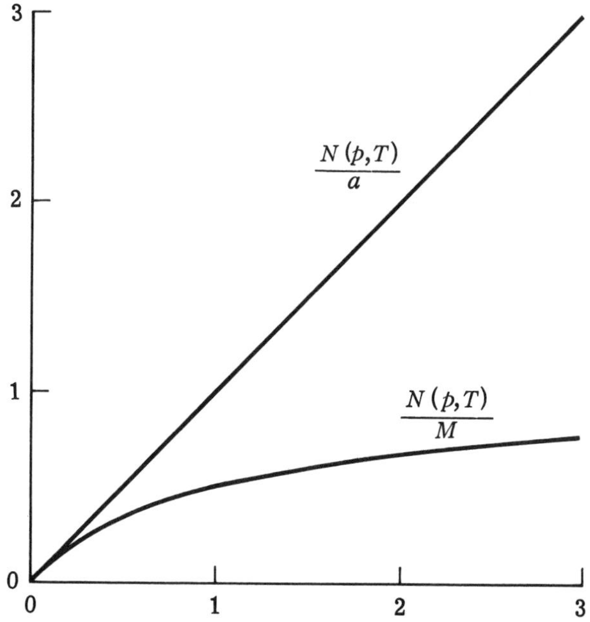

Figure 12-4 *Schematic comparison of adsorption isotherms for localized adsorption and for mobile adsorption.*

12-4 Show that if $N >> 1$, $M >> 1$, and $M - N >> 1$ (so that Stirling's approximation is applicable), the configurational contribution to the entropy of a perfect localized adsorbed gas may be written

$$\left(\frac{S}{k}\right)_{\text{configuration}} = -M\left[\frac{N}{M}\ln\frac{N}{M} + \left(1 - \frac{N}{M}\right)\ln\left(1 - \frac{N}{M}\right)\right]$$

Sketch the value of this entropy contribution as a function of N/M for $0 < N/M < 1$.

chapter **13**

perfect diatomic gas

For the sake of persons of different types, scientific truth should be presented in different forms and should be regarded as equally scientific, whether it appears in the robust form and vivid coloring of a physical illustration, or in the tenuity and paleness of a symbolic expression.
J. C. Maxwell †

As an extension of the discussion of the perfect monatomic gas presented in Chapter 8, consider now the perfect diatomic gas. Consider particularly a model in which all molecules are indistinguishable (i.e., only one type of molecule is present), the effects of interparticle forces and external fields are negligible, and the temperature is limited to the range in which effects of electron excitations are negligible. (If electron excitations are negligible, nucleus excitations are negligible certainly.) Represent the molecule by two distinguishable nuclei held together by a chemical bond (see Figures 13-1 and 13-2). Consider the six degrees of freedom (three translational, one vibrational, and two rotational) of the molecule to be independent, and approximate the vibrations by harmonic oscillations. An analysis based on this model predicts, to good approximation, the behavior of most diatomic gases at most temperatures and pressures of interest to engineers and scientists.

Brief comments on the nature and magnitude of interatomic forces might be useful at this point. The forces which hold the atoms of crystals together (Chapter 9) and which lead to physical adsorption (Chapter 12) may be considered, for purposes of the present comments, to be van der Waals forces, whereas the forces which hold the atoms of diatomic molecules together are the result of chemical bonds. Van der Waals forces are due largely to dipole attractions, which lead to bond energies of the order of 10 kcal/mole, interparticle distances of the order of several angstroms, and vibration frequencies of the order of 10^{12} cycles/sec. Chemical bonds,

† Quoted by M. Rukeyser in "Willard Gibbs," p. 439, Doubleday & Company, Inc., Garden City, N.Y., 1942.

on the other hand, are due frequently to either covalent or electrostatic bonding which leads to bond energies of the order of 100 kcal/mole, interparticle distances of the order of an angstrom, and vibration frequencies of the order of 10^{13} cycles/sec.

As indicated in Chapter 8, any atomic or molecular gas with temperature sufficiently high and pressure sufficiently low so that effects of interparticle forces may be neglected (i.e., any thermally perfect atomic or molecular gas) is described adequately by a Maxwell-Boltzmann system. Hence (using for convenience a grand canonical ensemble), the appropriate grand partition function is given by Equation (8-1):

$$\ln \Xi_{\mathrm{MB}} = e^{-\gamma} \sum_k e^{-\beta \varepsilon_k} \tag{8-1}$$

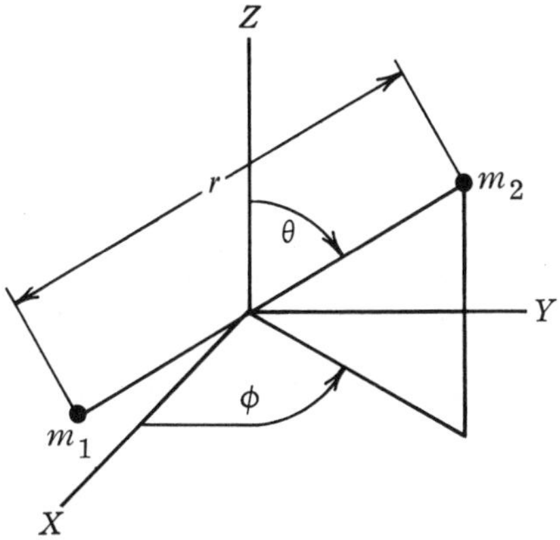

Figure 13-1 *Coordinate system used in discussions of vibrational and rotational degrees of freedom of diatomic molecule. (Origin of coordinate system is located at center of mass of molecule.)*

(For convenience, the subscript MB will be omitted in the remainder of this chapter.) Since effects of electron excitations are considered to be negligible in this example also, the allowed molecular energy levels result from considerations of translational, rotational, and vibrational motions only. Since, for the model being considered, the several degrees of freedom of the model are independent, the molecular energy may be written as a sum over energies associated with the several degrees of freedom, that is,

$$\varepsilon_k = \varepsilon_{k_1} + \varepsilon_{k_2} + \varepsilon_{k_3} + \varepsilon_{mj} + \varepsilon_l - D_e \tag{13-1}$$

where $\varepsilon_{k_1}, \varepsilon_{k_2}, \varepsilon_{k_3}$ are translational energies, ε_{mj} is rotational energy, ε_l is vibrational energy, and $-D_e$ is the potential energy at the equilibrium distance r_e for the case of no electron excitations. (Note that the symbol $-D_e$ used here is equivalent to the symbol $U(0)$ used in Chapters 9 and 12.) The zero of energy is taken to be the potential energy at infinite separation of the two atoms (see Figure 13-2). As in Chapter 8, designate the degeneracy of the ground state (with energy $-D_e + h\nu/2$) by g_e. Then, substituting from Equation (13-1) into Equation (8-1) and performing the summation over allowed ground states,

$$\ln \Xi = e^{-\gamma} g_e \exp(\beta D_e) \sum_{k_1, k_2, k_3, m, j, l} \exp[-\beta(\varepsilon_{k_1} + \varepsilon_{k_2} + \varepsilon_{k_3} + \varepsilon_{mj} + \varepsilon_l)] \tag{13-2}$$

It will be found, later in this chapter, that the allowed rotational energy levels may be specified uniquely by the quantum number j, so that the

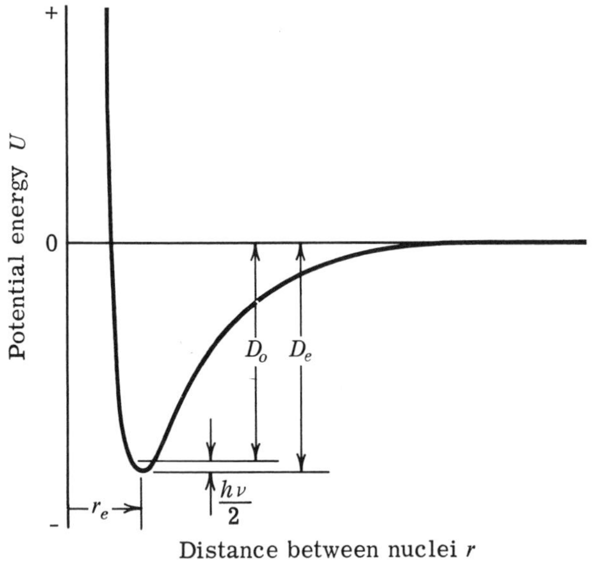

Figure 13-2 *Schematic diagram of potential energy as a function of distance between the nuclei in a diatomic molecule.*

quantum number m specifies only the allowed quantum states for each allowed energy level; for each allowed energy level ε_j, it will be found that $2j + 1$ quantum states are allowed. Hence Equation (13-2) may be written

$$\ln \Xi = e^{-\gamma} g_e e^{\beta D_e} \sum_{k_1, k_2, k_3, j, l} (2j + 1) \exp[-\beta(\varepsilon_{k_1} + \varepsilon_{k_2} + \varepsilon_{k_3} + \varepsilon_j + \varepsilon_l)] \tag{13-3}$$

Since the allowed values of each of the five quantum numbers k_1, k_2, k_3, j, and l may be assigned independently, and the exponential appearing in Equation (13-3) is factorable, one may factor the series appearing in Equation (13-3) into a product of five series and write

$$\ln \Xi = e^{-\gamma} g_e e^{\beta D_e} \sum_{k_1} \exp(-\beta\varepsilon_{k_1}) \sum_{k_2} \exp(-\beta\varepsilon_{k_2}) \sum_{k_3} \exp(-\beta\varepsilon_{k_3}) \sum_{j} (2j + 1) e^{-\beta\varepsilon_j} \sum_{l} e^{-\beta\varepsilon_l} \tag{13-4}$$

The problem is to evaluate now the five series appearing here.

The first three series have been evaluated already in Chapter 8. From Equation (8-5),

$$\sum_{k_1} \exp(-\beta\varepsilon_{k_1}) \sum_{k_2} \exp(-\beta\varepsilon_{k_2}) \sum_{k_3} \exp(-\beta\varepsilon_{k_3}) = \left(\frac{2\pi m}{\beta h^2}\right)^{3/2} V \quad (13\text{-}5)$$

The molecular mass m is, in the present case, the sum of the atomic masses m_1 and m_2. [In this chapter, excepting Equation (13-5), m represents a quantum number in the material up to the end of the discussion of Figure 13-3; excepting Problems 13-2 and 13-3, m represents molecular mass in the material following the discussion of Figure 13-3.]

Since the internal degrees of freedom of the considered model are independent, one may analyze the rotational quantum states using a constant value of the distance between the atoms, the rational choice of this distance being the equilibrium distance r_e. Locate the origin of the coordinate system at the center of mass of the molecule (see Appendix H for a discussion of the center-of-mass coordinate system). The appropriate wave equation is the time-independent wave equation in center-of-mass spherical polar coordinates for a single particle of reduced mass $\mu\,[\equiv m_1 m_2/(m_1 + m_2)]$ with $r = r_e$, $\partial\psi/\partial r = 0$, and $U(r) = 0$. By either separating out the time-independent equation from Equation (7-4) or transforming Equation (7-13) into spherical polar coordinates, one obtains, for the considered model,

$$\frac{1}{\sin\theta}\frac{\partial}{\partial\theta}\left(\sin\theta\frac{\partial\psi}{\partial\theta}\right) + \frac{1}{\sin^2\theta}\frac{\partial^2\psi}{\partial\phi^2} + \frac{2I_e\,\varepsilon}{\hbar^2} = 0 \quad (13\text{-}6)$$

where $I_e\,(\equiv \mu r_e^2)$ is the moment of inertia about the center of mass (see Problem 13-1). The wave function appearing here may be separated into two factors; let

$$\psi(\theta, \phi) = \Theta(\theta)\,\Phi(\phi) \quad (13\text{-}7)$$

Then, substituting into Equation (13-6) and dividing by $\Theta\Phi$, one obtains

$$\frac{1}{\Theta\sin\theta}\frac{d}{d\theta}\left(\sin\theta\frac{d\Theta}{d\theta}\right) + \frac{1}{\Phi\sin^2\theta}\frac{d^2\Phi}{d\phi^2} + \frac{2I_e\,\varepsilon}{\hbar^2} = 0$$

or, after rearranging,

$$\frac{\sin\theta}{\Theta}\frac{d}{d\theta}\left(\sin\theta\frac{d\Theta}{d\theta}\right) + \frac{2I_e\,\varepsilon}{\hbar^2}\sin^2\theta = -\frac{1}{\Phi}\frac{d^2\Phi}{d\phi^2}$$

Since the left-hand side is independent of ϕ and the right-hand side is independent of θ, each side must equal a constant. For convenience, designate this constant by m^2. Then

$$\frac{d^2\Phi}{d\phi^2} = -m^2\Phi \quad (13\text{-}8)$$

$$\frac{1}{\sin\theta}\frac{d}{d\theta}\left(\sin\theta\frac{d\Theta}{d\theta}\right) - \frac{m^2}{\sin^2\theta}\Theta + \frac{2I_e\,\varepsilon}{\hbar^2}\Theta = 0 \quad (13\text{-}9)$$

Solutions to Equation (13-8) are given by

$$\Phi_m(\phi) = \frac{1}{\sqrt{2\pi}} e^{im\phi} \tag{13-10}$$

where m may have values 0, ±1, ±2, . . . (see Problem 13-2). Solutions to Equation (13-9) are given by

$$\Theta_{mj}(\theta) = \left(\frac{(2j+1)(j-|m|)!}{2(j+|m|)!}\right)^{1/2} \frac{(-\sin\theta)^{|m|}}{2^j j!} \frac{d^{j+|m|}(\cos^2\theta - 1)^j}{d(\cos\theta)^{j+|m|}} \tag{13-11}$$

for

$$\frac{2I_e \varepsilon_j}{\hbar^2} = j(j+1) \tag{13-12}$$

where j may have values 0, 1, 2, . . . but must satisfy

$$|m| \leq j \tag{13-13}$$

(see Problem 13-3). Equation (13-12) indicates that the allowed rotational energy levels are specified uniquely by the quantum number j. Hence the quantum number m specifies only the allowed quantum states for each allowed rotational-energy level. Equation (13-13) indicates that, for a given value of j, the quantum number m may have one of the $2j + 1$ values $-j$, $-j + 1$, . . . , 0, . . . , $j - 1$, j; that is, $2j + 1$ quantum states are allowed for each allowed energy level. The degeneracies implied by Equation (13-13) have been used already in Equation (13-3); the allowed values of ε_j given by Equation (13-12) will be used in the evaluation of the fourth series appearing in Equation (13-4).

Although not essential in the analysis which follows, a physical interpretation of the quantum numbers j and m is provided here for the appeal it might have to the reader. They are related to the total angular momentum L and the angular momentum L_z about the z axis by

$$L = \sqrt{2I_e \varepsilon_j} = \sqrt{j(j+1)}\,\hbar \qquad \text{and} \qquad L_z = m\hbar$$

The possible relationships are indicated in Figure 13-3 for the case in which $j = 2$; the possible values of L_z are represented as projections of L on the z axis. Projections of L on the plane normal to the z axis have magnitudes $\sqrt{j(j+1) - m^2}\,\hbar$ but undefined direction. Hence all longitudinal angles ϕ occur with equal probability, and the vector L lies with equal probability on any generator of the cone with half angle given by

$$\cos\theta = \frac{m}{\sqrt{j(j+1)}}$$

Furthermore, none of the allowed positions of the vector L coincide with the z axis (although it does approach the z axis for $m = j$ and $j \rightarrow \infty$), so that the direction of the vector L is never defined completely. These uncertainties are typical of the descriptions provided by quantum mechanics.

The quantum number j is called frequently the **total angular momentum quantum number**, and m is called frequently the **azimuthal quantum number**. The $2j + 1$ degenerate quantum states (quantum states with the same energy level) for a given value of j may be distinguished by interactions with a magnetic field.

If one substitutes for ε_j from Equation (13-12) into the fourth series appearing in Equation (13-4), then

$$\sum_j (2j+1)\,e^{-\beta\varepsilon_j} = \sum_j (2j+1)\exp\left[-\frac{\beta\hbar^2}{2I_e}j(j+1)\right]$$
$$\sim \sum_j (2j+1)\exp\left[-\frac{\theta_r}{T}j(j+1)\right]$$

where $\theta_r\,(\equiv \hbar^2/2I_e k)$ is the **characteristic temperature for rotation**. If the difference between consecutive terms of this series is small in comparison

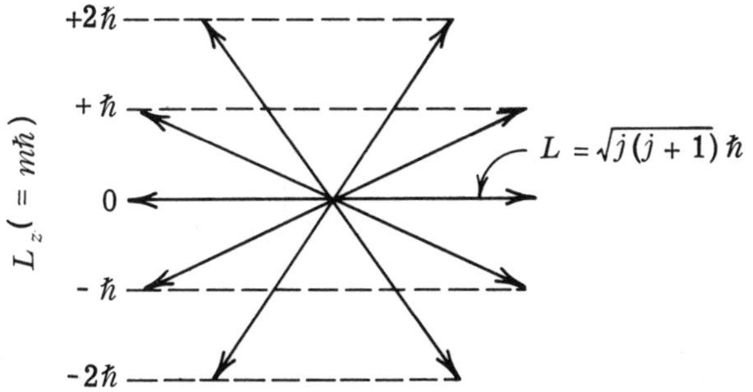

Figure 13-3 *Vector model of angular momentum for the case in which $j = 2$, in which case $L = \sqrt{6}\,\hbar$ and L_z may have values $-2\hbar$, $-\hbar$, 0, $\hbar$, $2\hbar$.*

with unity, then the series may be replaced by an integral. This condition is met if $\theta_r << T$. Values of θ_r (proportional inversely to I_e) are given in Table 13-1 for several diatomic gases, including those with the largest value of θ_r. It is seen that, except for hydrogen, deuterium, and their compounds, the characteristic temperature for rotation is so low that $\theta_r << T$ for most applications of interest. Hence replace the sum by an integral (see Figure 13-4) with the result

$$\sum_j (2j+1)\,e^{-\beta\varepsilon_j} \sim \int_0^\infty (2j+1)\exp\left[-\frac{\theta_r}{T}j(j+1)\right]dj$$
$$\sim \int_0^\infty \exp\left[-\frac{\theta_r}{T}j(j+1)\right]dj\,(j+1) = \frac{T}{\theta_r} \sim \frac{2I_e}{\beta\hbar^2} \qquad (13\text{-}14a)$$

This result is valid, of course, only for the case in which the nuclei are distinguishable and $T >> \theta_r$.

Table 13-1 Characteristic temperatures and dissociation energies for several diatomic molecules

Molecule	θ_r, °K	θ_V, °K	D_0, ev
H_2	87.5	6320	4.476
HD	65.8	5500	4.511
D_2	43.8	4490	4.553
HCl	15.2	4330	4.430
HBr	12.2	3820	3.75
N_2	2.89	3390	9.76
CO	2.78	3120	9.14
NO	2.45	2745	5.29
O_2	2.08	2278	5.08
Cl_2	0.351	814	2.48
Br_2	0.116	465	1.97
I_2	0.0537	309	1.54

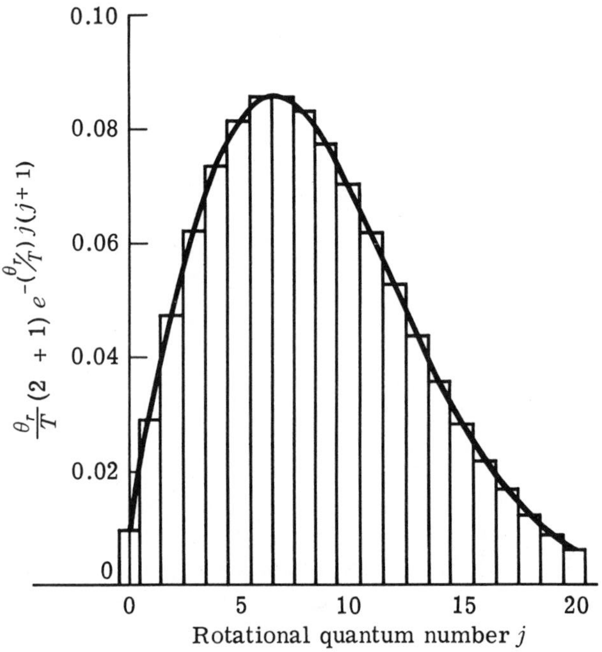

Figure 13-4 *Comparison of the sum* $(\theta_r/T)\sum_j (2j+1)\exp[-(\theta_r/T)j(j+1)]$ *with the integral* $(\theta_r/T)\int_0^\infty (2j+1)\exp[-(\theta_r/T)j(j+1)]\,dj$, *for the case in which* $\theta_r/T = 0.01$, *normalized so that area under smooth curve is unity.*

If the two nuclei are indistinguishable (i.e., if they are the same isotope of the same element), then interchanging the two nuclei either leaves the rotational wave function unchanged (a symmetrical rotational wave function) or changes its sign (an antisymmetrical rotational wave function).

[Since both the rotational wave function and the wave function associated with the nuclear spins must be considered when relating, according to the methods of Chapter 6, the symmetry of the total molecular wave function to the nuclear spins, the symmetry of the rotational wave function cannot be related uniquely to the nuclear spins (see the example at the end of this paragraph)]. A detailed examination of the rotational wave function $\psi(\theta, \phi) = \Theta(\theta)\,\Phi(\phi)$ reveals that interchanging the two nuclei (that is, replacing ϕ by $\phi + \pi$, and θ by $\pi - \theta$) leaves ψ unchanged if j is even, and changes its sign if j is odd. Hence regardless of whether the rotational wave function is symmetrical or antisymmetrical, only about half as many rotational quantum states are allowed for indistinguishable nuclei as for distinguishable nuclei. Therefore Equation (13-14a) may be written in the more general form

$$\sum_j (2j+1)\, e^{-\beta\varepsilon_j} = \frac{2I_e}{\sigma\beta\hbar^2} \tag{13-14b}$$

where $\sigma = 1$ for distinguishable nuclei ($j = 0, 1, 2, 3, \ldots$) and $\sigma \doteq 2$ for indistinguishable nuclei (j either even or odd).

Example

In an illustration of the role of symmetry and antisymmetry in an exchange of the nuclei in a diatomic molecule with two indistinguishable nuclei, consider H_2. As indicated in Table 6-1, the nucleus of the hydrogen atom has a spin of 1/2. Hence, according to the methods of Chapter 6, the total molecular wave function of the hydrogen molecule must be antisymmetrical in an exchange of the nuclei. Consequently, in an exchange of the nuclei if the wave function describing the nuclear spins is symmetrical (**ortho-H_2**), then the rotational wave function must be antisymmetrical; whereas if the wave function describing the nuclear spins is antisymmetrical (**para-H_2**), then the rotational wave function must be symmetrical. If the rotational degrees of freedom are excited completely ($T >> \theta_r$), then the three different symmetrical and the single antisymmetrical nuclear-spin wave functions are populated equally; that is, 75 percent of the molecules are ortho-H_2 and 25 percent of the molecules are para-H_2. (The calculation of the number of different symmetrical and antisymmetrical nuclear-spin wave functions requires a slight extension of the methods of Chapter 7.) Since the transition from ortho-H_2 to para-H_2 requires (in the absence of a catalyst) a time large in comparison with the time of a typical experiment, this composition is observed also in most experiments in which T is of the order of or less than θ_r.

If one writes Equations (13-5) and (13-4b) in the forms

$$\sum_{k_1} \exp(-\beta\varepsilon_{k_1}) \sum_{k_2} \exp(-\beta\varepsilon_{k_2}) \sum_{k_3} \exp(-\beta\varepsilon_{k_3}) = \left(\frac{2\pi m}{\beta h^2}\right)^{3/2} V$$

$$\sum_j (2j+1)\, e^{-\beta\varepsilon_j} = \frac{1}{\sigma}\left(\frac{2\pi I_e}{\beta h^2}\right)^{2/2} 4\pi$$

then the analogy which exists (for $T >> \theta_r$) between translational and rotational motions is emphasized. Note that the mass m and volume V are analogous to the moment of inertia I_e and the solid angle 4π; the factor $2\pi m/\beta h^2$ or $2\pi I_e/\beta h^2$, as the case may be, is raised in each case to a power equal to the number of degrees of freedom divided by 2. The translational analog of the symmetry number σ is unity. This analogy is associated closely with the equipartition of energy among the translational and rotational degrees of freedom which occurs for $T >> \theta_r$.

Consider finally the fifth series appearing in Equation (13-4), the series associated with the vibrational degree of freedom. If the amplitude of vibration is not too large, the expression for the potential energy due to relative displacement of the two nuclei may be written

$$U'(r - r_e) = U(r - r_e) + D_e = \frac{1}{2} a (r - r_e)^2 \qquad (13\text{-}15)$$

where r is the distance between the two nuclei (see Figures 13-1 and 13-2) and a is the force constant

$$a = \left.\frac{d^2 U'}{dr^2}\right|_{r=r_e} = \left.\frac{d^2 U}{dr^2}\right|_{r=r_e} \qquad (13\text{-}16)$$

In agreement with the convention established in Equation (13-1), the zero of vibrational energy is taken to be the potential energy at equilibrium distance r_e. The frequency of oscillation is related to the force constant by the classical equation

$$\nu = \frac{1}{2\pi}\left(\frac{a}{\mu}\right)^{1/2} \qquad (13\text{-}17)$$

where μ is reduced mass (see Appendix H). Hence, from Problem 7-2, the allowed vibrational energy levels are

$$\varepsilon_l = h\nu\left(l + \frac{1}{2}\right) \qquad (13\text{-}18)$$

where $l = 0, 1, 2, \cdots$; that is, the allowed vibrational energy levels are spaced equally with spacing $h\nu$. Hence, from Equations (9-6) and (9-9),

$$\sum_l e^{-\beta\varepsilon_l} = \sum_l e^{-\beta h\nu(l+1/2)} = \frac{1}{2\sinh(\beta h\nu/2)} \qquad (13\text{-}19)$$

As indicated earlier in this chapter, the frequency ν for molecular vibrations (with chemical bonding) is an order of magnitude greater than the frequency for atomic vibrations in a crystal (with van der Waals bonding). Typical values of this frequency are given in Table 13-1, where values of the **characteristic temperature for vibration** θ_V ($\equiv h\nu/k$) are tabulated for the same diatomic gases considered in the discussion of the characteristic temperature for rotation. It is seen that, for some gases, θ_V is of the order of magnitude of room temperature; whereas, for many gases, θ_V is an order of magnitude higher (e.g., of the order of magnitude of typical flame temperatures).

An examination of the effect of the value of θ_V/T on the distribution of the molecules among the several allowed vibrational energy levels might be instructive. It can be shown easily (see Problem 13-9), that the fraction

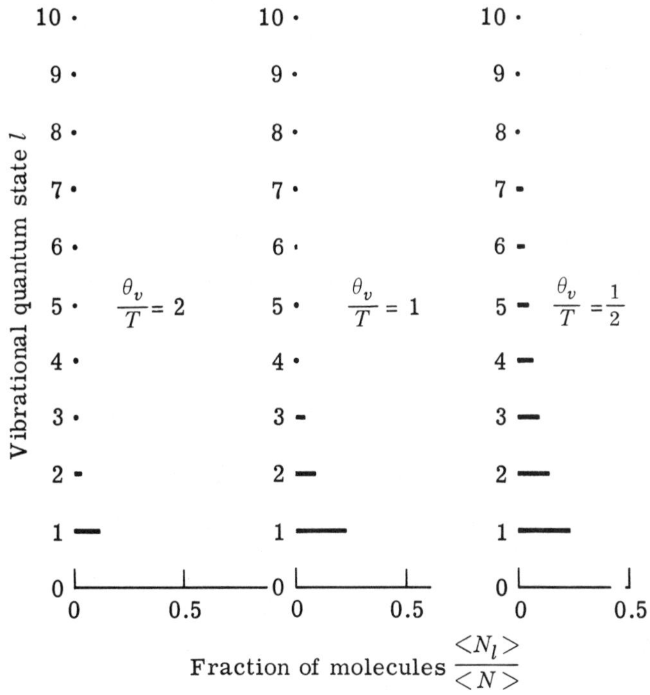

Figure 13-5 *Fraction of diatomic molecules in lth vibrational quantum state for several values of θ_V/T.*

of diatomic molecules in the lth vibrational quantum state may be given by

$$\frac{\langle N_l \rangle}{\langle N \rangle} \sim (1 - e^{-\theta_V/T})\, e^{-l\theta_V/T}$$

Values of this fraction are indicated in Figure 13-5 as a function of the vibrational quantum state l for the cases in which θ_V/T equals 2, 1, and 1/2. This figure emphasizes the shifting of molecules from ground states to excited energy levels as temperature increases.

Note that a value of $\langle N_l \rangle / \langle N \rangle$ near unity does not violate the condition necessary for use of the Maxwell-Boltzmann approximation. Recall, from Chapter 6, that the Maxwell-Boltzmann approximation is applicable for cases in which the probability of finding more than one particle in a given particle quantum state is negligible. The quantum state of a diatomic molecule is determined by the translational, rotational, vibrational, and electronic quantum numbers. Since the number of available translational states is much greater than the number of available internal states, the magnitude of the probability of finding more than one particle in a given particle quantum state is established primarily by the probabilities associated with the translational degrees of freedom. Hence the Maxwell-Boltzmann approximation may be applicable even if all the internal degrees of freedom of all the molecules are in their ground states.

The evaluation of the several series appearing in the grand partition function, Equation (13-4), is completed now. Substituting from Equations (13-5), (13-14b), and (13-19), one may write

$$\ln \Xi = e^{-\gamma} g_e e^{\beta D_e} \left(\frac{2\pi m}{\beta h^2}\right)^{3/2} V \frac{2I_e}{\sigma\beta\hbar^2} \frac{1}{2\sinh(\beta h\nu/2)} \tag{13-20}$$

Hence numerical values of thermodynamic functions of a thermally perfect diatomic gas may be calculated now (for the case in which electronic excitations are negligible and $T >> \theta_r$). (The words "perfect" and "thermally perfect" are applied synonymously in this chapter to a model with negligible effects of interparticle forces. This model is not calorically perfect, however; its heat capacity is, in general, a function of temperature.)

Using the methods of Chapters 4 and 5, one obtains

$$\langle E\rangle = -\left(\frac{\partial \ln \Xi}{\partial \beta}\right)_{\gamma, V} = \left(-D_e + \frac{5}{2\beta} + \frac{h\nu}{2}\coth\frac{\beta h\nu}{2}\right)\ln \Xi \tag{13-21}$$

$$\langle N\rangle = -\left(\frac{\partial \ln \Xi}{\partial \gamma}\right)_{\beta, V} = \ln \Xi \tag{13-22}$$

$$\langle p\rangle = \frac{1}{\beta}\left(\frac{\partial \ln \Xi}{\partial V}\right)_{\beta, \gamma} = \frac{\ln \Xi}{\beta V} \tag{13-23}$$

$$\frac{S}{k} \sim \ln \Xi + \beta\langle E\rangle + \gamma\langle N\rangle$$

$$\sim \left(-\beta D_e + \frac{7}{2} + \frac{\beta h\nu}{2}\coth\frac{\beta h\nu}{2} + \gamma\right)\ln \Xi \tag{13-24}$$

In the nomenclature of classical thermodynamics, one may write alternatively (for independent variables T, μ, and V)

▶ $$pV = e^{\mu/kT} g_e e^{D_e/kT} \left(\frac{2\pi mkT}{h^2}\right)^{3/2} VkT \frac{2I_e kT}{\sigma\hbar^2} \frac{1}{2\sinh(h\nu/2kT)} \tag{13-20$'$}$$

▶ $$E = \left(-\frac{D_e}{kT} + \frac{5}{2} + \frac{h\nu}{2kT}\coth\frac{h\nu}{2kT}\right) pV \tag{13-21$'$}$$

▶ $$N = \frac{pV}{kT} \tag{13-22$'$}$$

$$\frac{S}{k} = \left(-\frac{D_e}{kT} + \frac{7}{2} + \frac{h\nu}{2kT}\coth\frac{h\nu}{2kT} - \frac{\mu}{kT}\right)\frac{pV}{kT} \tag{13-24'}$$ ◀

or (for independent variables T, N, and V)

$$A = -NkT\ln\left[g_e e^{D_e/kT}\left(\frac{2\pi mkT}{h^2}\right)^{3/2}\frac{V}{N}\frac{2I_e kT}{\sigma\hbar^2}\frac{e}{2\sinh(h\nu/2kT)}\right] \tag{13-25}$$ ◀

$$E = \left(-\frac{D_e}{kT} + \frac{5}{2} + \frac{h\nu}{2kT}\coth\frac{h\nu}{2kT}\right)NkT \tag{13-26}$$ ◀

$$p = \frac{NkT}{V} \tag{13-27}$$ ◀

$$\frac{S}{k} = -\frac{A}{kT} + \left(-\frac{D_e}{kT} + \frac{5}{2} + \frac{h\nu}{2kT}\coth\frac{h\nu}{2kT}\right)N \tag{13-28}$$ ◀

$$\frac{\mu}{kT} = \frac{A}{NkT} + 1 \tag{13-29}$$ ◀

or (for independent variables T, N, and p)

$$G = -NkT\ln\left[g_e e^{D_e/kT}\left(\frac{2\pi mkT}{h^2}\right)^{3/2}\frac{kT}{p}\frac{2I_e kT}{\sigma\hbar^2}\frac{1}{2\sinh(h\nu/2kT)}\right] \tag{13-30}$$ ◀

$$E = \left(-\frac{D_e}{kT} + \frac{5}{2} + \frac{h\nu}{2kT}\coth\frac{h\nu}{2kT}\right)NkT \tag{13-31}$$ ◀

$$V = \frac{NkT}{p} \tag{13-32}$$ ◀

$$\frac{S}{k} = -\frac{G}{kT} + \left(-\frac{D_e}{kT} + \frac{7}{2} + \frac{h\nu}{2kT}\coth\frac{h\nu}{2kT}\right)N \tag{13-33}$$ ◀

$$\frac{\mu}{kT} = \frac{G}{NkT} \tag{13-34}$$ ◀

where $A\,(\equiv E - TS)$ is the Helmholtz function and $G\,(\equiv E + pV - TS)$ is the Gibbs function. Equations (13-20′), (13-25), and (13-30) are fundamental equations, i.e., the other equations may be obtained by appropriate differentiations of these equations (see Chapter 8). The zero of energy in these equations is the energy of the atoms at infinite separation and at rest; the zero of entropy is the entropy of a system with only a single quantum state, e.g., a crystal of identical atoms at 0°K.

Note that the energy D_e which appears here cannot be measured directly. Its value may be obtained, however, from

$$D_e = D_0 + \frac{h\nu}{2} = D_0 + \frac{k\theta_V}{2}$$ ◀

where D_0 is the dissociation energy of the diatomic molecule at 0°K (see

Figure 13-2). Values of D_0 and θ_V are given in Table 13-1 for several diatomic molecules.

As indicated in Equation (12-19), the separation of the chemical potential for a thermally perfect gas into

$$\frac{\mu}{kT} = \frac{\mu^o(T)}{kT} + \ln \frac{p}{p^o} \tag{12-19}$$

is convenient frequently. From Equations (13-30) and (13-34), one obtains, for the model being considered,

$$\frac{\mu^o(T)}{kT} = -\ln\left[g_e e^{D_e/kT}\left(\frac{2\pi mkT}{h^2}\right)^{3/2}\frac{kT}{p^o}\frac{2I_e kT}{\sigma h^2}\frac{1}{2\sinh(h\nu/2kT)}\right] \tag{13-35}$$

The Langmuir adsorption isotherm, Equation (12-20), is a typical application of this separation of the chemical potential into temperature-dependent and pressure-dependent parts. As a second application, consider the necessary condition for chemical equilibrium,

$$\sum_i \nu_i \mu_i = 0 \tag{13-36}$$

where ν_i is the **stoichiometric coefficient** for the ith type of particle appearing in the mass-conservation equation

$$\sum_i \nu_i m_i = 0 \tag{13-37}$$

If μ_i is chemical potential per molecule, then m_i is mass per molecule; by convention, ν_i is positive for products and negative for reactants. Substituting from Equation (12-19) into Equation (13-36), one obtains

$$\sum \nu_i \ln \frac{p_i}{p^o} + \frac{\sum_i \nu_i \mu_i^o(T)}{kT} = 0$$

or

$$\ln \prod_i \left(\frac{p_i}{p^o}\right)^{\nu_i} = -\frac{\sum_i \nu_i \mu_i^o(T)}{kT}$$

where $\Pi(p_i/p^o)^{\nu_i}$ is the continued product defined by

$$\prod_i \left(\frac{p_i}{p^o}\right)^{\nu_i} = \left(\frac{p_1}{p^o}\right)^{\nu_1}\left(\frac{p_2}{p^o}\right)^{\nu_2}\cdots$$

If one defines now an **equilibrium constant** by

$$K_p \equiv \prod_i \left(\frac{p_i}{p^o}\right)^{\nu_i} \tag{13-38}$$

then this equilibrium constant (a function of temperature only) may be evaluated from

$$\ln K_p = -\frac{\sum_i \nu_i \mu_i^o(T)}{kT} \tag{13-39}$$

by substituting from Equation (13-35) for diatomic molecules and from

$$\frac{\mu^o(T)}{kT} = -\ln\left[g_e\left(\frac{2\pi mkT}{h^2}\right)^{3/2}\frac{kT}{p^o}\right] \qquad (13\text{-}40)$$

for monatomic molecules (atoms). The more complicated case involving polyatomic molecules is mentioned briefly late in the present chapter.

Example

In an application of the results of the preceding paragraph, the equilibrium composition of hydrogen at 1/2 atm and 4000°K is computed here. If the dissociation of H_2 is described by

$$H_2 \leftrightarrows 2H$$

then the stoichiometric coefficients for H_2 and H are, respectively, -1 and $+2$ so that Equation (13-39) may be written

$$\ln K_p = \frac{\mu_{H_2}{}^o(T)}{kT} - 2\frac{\mu_H{}^o(T)}{kT}$$

The required values of the chemical potentials are calculated using Equations (13-35) and (13-40). Since the hydrogen atom has one electron, with spin direction either parallel to or antiparallel to an arbitrary direction, its ground-state degeneracy g_e is 2. Since the hydrogen molecule has two electrons, with spin directions antiparallel, its ground-state degeneracy g_e is 1. From Table 13-1, for H_2,

$$\theta_r \equiv \frac{\hbar^2}{2I_e k} = 87.5°\text{K}$$

$$\theta_V \equiv \frac{h\nu}{k} = 6320°\text{K}$$

$$D_e \equiv D_0 + \frac{k\theta_V}{2} = (4.476 + 0.272)\ \text{ev}$$

Since the nuclei of H_2 are indistinguishable, $\sigma = 2$. Hence, for $T = 4000°$K, from Equation (13-35),

$$\frac{\mu_{H_2}{}^o(T)}{kT} = -34.44$$

and, from Equation (13-40),

$$\frac{\mu_H{}^o(T)}{kT} = -17.74$$

where p^o has been assigned, for convenience, the value 1 atm. (Note that any value may be assigned to p^o as long as this value is used consistently.) Hence

$$\ln K_p = 1.04 \qquad \text{or} \qquad K_p = 2.83$$

From Equation (13-38), with $p^o = 1$ atm,

$$2.83 = \frac{p_H{}^2}{p_{H_2}} = \frac{p_H{}^2}{\frac{1}{2} - p_H}$$

Solving for p_H, one obtains

$$p_H = 0.434\ \text{atm} \qquad p_{H_2} = 0.066\ \text{atm}$$

or, in mole fractions,

$$x_H = 0.868 \qquad x_{H_2} = 0.132$$

Note that effects of translational, vibrational, and rotational degrees of freedom have been taken into account in this computation.

It is to be kept in mind that Equation (13-20), and all equations derived from it, are valid only for the case in which $T >> \theta_r$. If T/θ_r is not quite large enough for use of Equation (13-14*b*), then a series expression for $\sum_j (2j + 1) \exp(-\beta\varepsilon_j)$, in powers of $\theta_r/T (\equiv \beta\hbar^2/2I_e)$ with $\theta_r/T < 1$ and the first term given by Equation (13-14*b*), is convenient. After some algebra, the first two terms are found to be

$$\sum_j (2j + 1) e^{-\beta\varepsilon_j} = \frac{1}{\sigma}\frac{T}{\theta_r}\left(1 + \frac{1}{3}\frac{\theta_r}{T}\right)$$

This equation is to be substituted into Equation (13-4) for the case in which T/θ_r is not quite large enough for use of only $T/\sigma\theta_r$.

Recall that a further restriction on Equation (13-20), and all equations derived from it, is that effects of electron excitations are negligible. If electron excitations are not negligible, then the factor $g_e e^{\beta D_e}$ in Equation (13-20) must be replaced by a series of the form $\sum_e e^{-\beta\varepsilon_e}$, where the sum is over the allowed electronic quantum states. In most applications, all terms with $\beta\varepsilon_e > 5$ may be neglected. If only the ground energy level and the first excited energy level are important, then

$$\sum_e e^{-\beta\varepsilon_e} = g_{e1} e^{-\beta\varepsilon_{e1}} + g_{e2} e^{-\beta\varepsilon_{e2}}$$

where subscripts 1 and 2 refer, respectively, to the ground energy level and to the first excited energy level. (Note that $\varepsilon_{e1} = -D_e$.) Examples of diatomic gases for which electron excitations must be taken into account sometimes include NO and O_2 (see Table 13-2). For all other gases listed in Table 13-1, $(\varepsilon_{e2} - \varepsilon_{e1})/k$ exceeds 17,000°K and $g_{e1} = 1$.

Table 13-2 Electronic data for NO and O_2

Molecule	g_{e1}	g_{e2}	$\frac{\varepsilon_{e2} - \varepsilon_{e1}}{k}$, °K
NO	2	2	178
O_2	3	2	11,300

Since characteristic temperatures for excitations of the nucleus are of the order of millions of degrees Kelvin, excitations of the nucleus are neglected completely here. Furthermore, since the degeneracy of the nucleus occurs both in the monatomic gas and in all compounds of a given element, it also may be neglected (provided that it is done consistently) in most applications.

The most interesting thermodynamic derivative for a diatomic gas is perhaps the heat capacity. Differentiating Equation (13-26), one finds

$$C_V = \left(\frac{\partial E}{\partial T}\right)_{V,N} = \left\{\frac{5}{2} + \left[\frac{h\nu/2kT}{\sinh\,(h\nu/2kT)}\right]^2\right\} Nk \qquad (13\text{-}41)$$

Note that the first term on the right-hand side associates implicitly (for $T >> \theta_r$) a heat capacity of $Nk/2$ with each of the five translational and rotational degrees of freedom; at temperatures sufficiently high so that $h\nu/kT = \theta_V/T << 1$, the second term on the right-hand side approaches

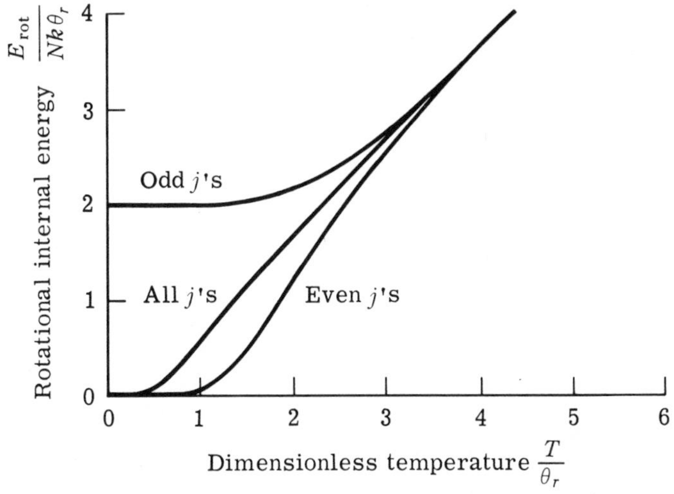

Figure 13-6a *Rotational contribution to internal energy of diatomic gas as a function of temperature.*

Nk, so that (for $T >> \theta_V$) a heat capacity of $Nk/2$ is associated with each of the two forms (potential and kinetic) of vibrational energy. It is seen that equipartition of energy among the several degrees of freedom and among the alternative forms of energy occurs only at sufficiently high temperatures.

The temperature dependence of the rotational and vibrational contributions to the internal energy, entropy, and heat capacity of a diatomic gas are displayed graphically in Figures 13-6*a* to 13-8. Consider first the rotational contributions, Figure 13-6*a*, *b*, and *c*. Recall that (1) if the two nuclei in a diatomic molecule are distinguishable, the series

$$\sum_j (2j + 1) \exp\left[-\frac{\theta_r}{T} j(j+1)\right]$$

must be summed over all j's; (2) if the two nuclei are indistinguishable and

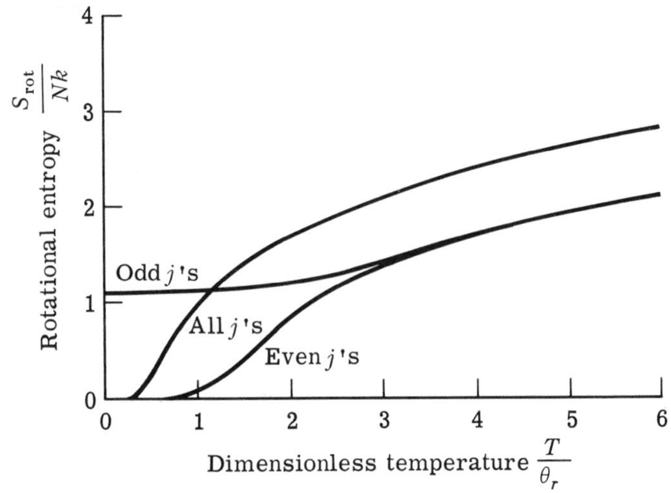

Figure 13-6b *Rotational contribution to entropy of diatomic gas as a function of temperature.*

the rotational wave function is symmetrical in an exchange of the nuclei, the series is summed only over even j's; and (3) if the two nuclei are indistinguishable and the rotational wave function is antisymmetrical in an exchange of the nuclei, the series is summed only over odd j's. From Figure 13-6*a*, it is seen that, for all j's and for even j's, the internal energy approaches

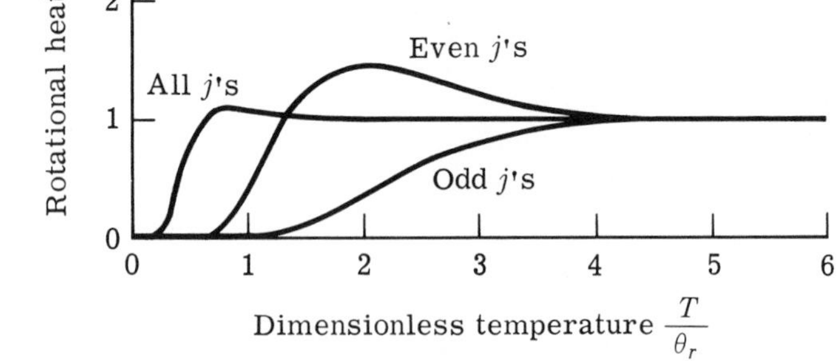

Figure 13-6c *Rotational contribution to heat capacity of diatomic gas as a function of temperature.*

zero as T/θ_r approaches zero—all molecules occupy the lowest rotational energy level, that is, the $j = 0$ energy level; for odd j's, the internal energy approaches $2Nk\theta_r$ as T/θ_r approaches zero—all molecules occupy the $j = 1$ energy level. The three energy curves differ negligibly for T/θ_r greater than about 4. Figure 13-6*b* emphasizes that, for all j's and for even j's, the entropy approaches zero as T/θ_r approaches zero—the $j = 0$ energy level is associated with only one quantum state ($m = 0$); for odd j's, the entropy approaches $Nk \ln 3$ as T/θ_r approaches zero—the $j = 1$ energy level is associated with three quantum states ($m = -1, 0, +1$). For T/θ_r greater than about 4, the entropy for all j's exceeds the entropy for the other two cases by $Nk \ln 2$—twice as many rotational quantum states are allowed for distinguishable nuclei (all j's) as for indistinguishable nuclei (j either even or odd). (Recall that this factor of 2 was handled in earlier discussions by introducing the factor σ with alternative values 1 and 2.) From Figure 13-6*c*, it is seen that the heat capacity approaches zero as T/θ_r approaches zero for all three cases; as T/θ_r increases, it approaches Nk (its classical value) at $T/\theta_r \approx 1.5$ for all j's and at $T/\theta_r \approx 5$ for the other two cases. The curve for all j's (including the maximum at $T/\theta_r \approx 0.8$) describes, to very good approximation, the observed heat capacities for HD; the curves for even j's and odd j's describe equally well the observed heat capacities for para- and ortho-H_2 and D_2. The condition $T >> \theta_r$ for applicability of many of the expressions used in this chapter is seen now to be equivalent to $T > 5\theta_r$.

Figure 13-7 indicates that, as T/θ_V approaches zero, the vibrational contributions to the entropy and heat capacity approach zero, whereas the internal energy approaches $Nk\,\theta_V/2$—the ground-state energy level (nondegenerate) is $h\nu/2$. As T/θ_V increases, the heat capacity attains 90 percent of Nk (its classical value) at $T/\theta_V = 0.9$. According to Table 13-1, typical values of θ_r are so small, and values of θ_V so large, relative to room temperature, that most diatomic gases have, at room temperature, a heat capacity of $5Nk/2$ (with contributions from translational and rotational degrees of freedom).

Figure 13-8 compares typical heat-capacity measurements with predictions made using the methods of the present chapter for temperatures near θ_V. For temperatures less than about $0.5\theta_V$, the agreement is seen to be excellent—the vibration amplitudes are small enough so that, to good approximation, (1) the vibrations are harmonic and (2) the vibrations and rotations are independent. For higher temperatures, anharmonicity of vibrations and interactions between vibrations and rotations become significant. Values of C_p for Cl_2 which exceed $4.5Nk$ contain perhaps electronic contributions; the temperatures at which these high values were measured were of the order of 10 percent of the characteristic temperature for excitation to the first excited electronic energy level.

Note that in the classical limits ($T >> \theta_r$ and $T >> \theta_V$) the rotational and vibrational contributions to the internal energy and heat capacity of a diatomic gas ($E_{\text{rot}} = E_{\text{vib}} = NkT$ and $C_{\text{rot}} = C_{\text{vib}} = Nk$) do not depend on the nature of the gas. In the same limit, however, the rotational and vibra-

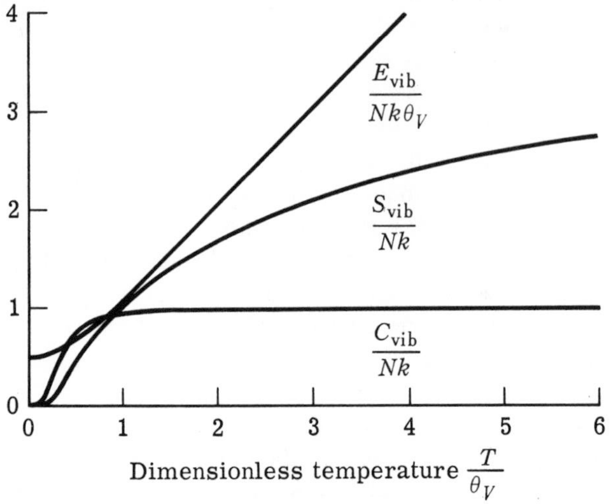

Figure 13-7 *Vibrational contributions to internal energy, entropy, and heat capacity of diatomic gas as functions of temperature.*

tional contributions to the entropy (hence also the Helmholtz and Gibbs functions) of a diatomic gas

$$\left(\frac{S_{\text{rot}}}{Nk}\right)_{T>>\theta_r} = 1 + \ln\left(\frac{T}{\sigma\theta_r}\right) \qquad \left(\frac{S_{\text{vib}}}{Nk}\right)_{T>>\theta_V} = 1 + \ln\left(\frac{T}{\theta_V}\right)$$

depend on σ, θ_r, and θ_V, that is, on the distinguishability (or indistinguishability) of the two nuclei and the moment of inertia and frequency of vibration of the molecule. For a given temperature, the greater the moment of inertia and the lower the frequency of vibration, the greater the number of quantum states occupied significantly and the greater the entropy [see, for example, Equations (13-30) and (13-33) and Figures 13-5, 13-6*b*, and 13-7].

A summary discussion of characteristic temperatures and their use as criteria for excitation of the several degrees of freedom might be helpful at this point. Their definitions, as well as values for nitrogen, are given in Table 13-3. (Note that, for a given degree of freedom, the characteristic temperature is proportional to the difference between the two lowest allowed energy levels divided by Boltzmann's constant.) For a given degree of freedom, if $T << \theta$, the given degree of freedom is unexcited; if T is of the order of magnitude of θ, the quantum-mechanical description must be used; and if $T >> \theta$, the given degree of freedom is excited fully and the classical-mechanical description may be used.

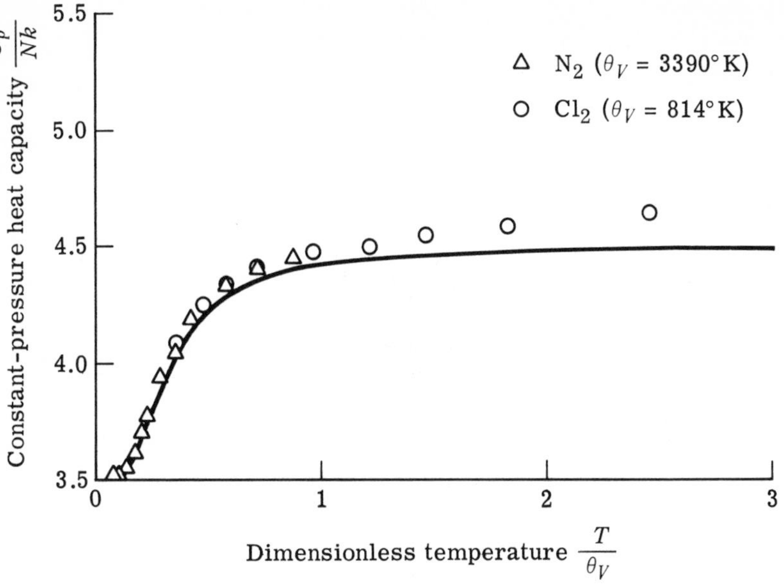

Figure 13-8 *Comparison of several experimental values of constant-pressure heat capacity with the curve $7/2 + C_{vib}/Nk$. (Experimental values are taken from Table 4e-2 of "American Institute of Physics Handbook," 2d Ed., edited by D. E. Gray, McGraw-Hill Book Company, New York, 1963.)*

In practice the thermodynamic functions of gases are evaluated usually from the actual energy levels deduced from spectroscopy. The methods of spectroscopy are based on the expression

$$h\nu_{ij} = \varepsilon_i - \varepsilon_j \qquad (13\text{-}42)$$

relating ν_{ij} (the frequency of the light quantum emitted in a radiative transition between two energy levels) with ε_i and ε_j (the values of these two energy levels). The data obtained by spectroscopy are presented usually in recip-

Table 13-3 Characteristic temperatures

Degree of freedom	*Characteristic temperature θ*	*Value for nitrogen, °K*
Translation†	$\frac{h^2}{8m V^{2/3} k}$	8.56×10^{-16}
Rotation	$\frac{\hbar^2}{2I_e k}$	2.89
Vibration	$\frac{h\nu}{k}$	3.39×10^3
Electronic	$\frac{D_{e2} - D_{e1}}{k}$	7.24×10^4

† The numerical value given here is based on $V = 1\ cm^3$.

rocal centimeters rather than in units of energy or frequency. Dividing Equation (13-42) by hc, where c is the speed of light, the spectroscopist writes

$$\omega_{ij} = \omega_i - \omega_j \tag{13-42'}$$

where ω_{ij} ($\equiv \nu_{ij}/c$), ω_i ($\equiv \varepsilon_i/hc$), and ω_j ($\equiv \varepsilon_j/hc$) are called **wave numbers.** Similarly, dividing Equation (13-12), rearranged, and Equation (13-18) by hc, he would write

$$\omega_j = B\, j(j+1) \tag{13-12'}$$

and

$$\omega_l = \omega\left(l + \frac{1}{2}\right) \tag{13-18'}$$

where B ($\equiv h/8\pi^2 I_e c$) is called the **band spectral constant** and ω ($\equiv \nu/c$) is called the **vibrational wave number**. Typical values of the ratio $\omega/B\,(=\theta_V/\theta_r)$ are of the order of 10^3 (see Table 13-1). A graphical example of the energy levels with which the spectroscopist deals is given in Figure 13-9, where several allowed rotational plus vibrational energy levels are given for a diatomic molecule with distinguishable nuclei (all j's allowed) and for the special case in which $\omega/B = 10^2$. This figure emphasizes that the spacing between adjacent rotational energy levels is nonlinear, whereas the spacing between adjacent vibrational energy levels is linear, and also that the spacing between adjacent lower rotational energy levels is much smaller than spacing between adjacent vibrational energy levels. Values of entropy, chemical potential, and equilibrium constant calculated from spectroscopic data agree well with values obtained, respectively, from calorimetric, vapor-pressure, and equilibrium-composition data. Although the use of spectroscopic data is more accurate than the use of the methods of the present chapter, the model used here (independent rotational and vibrational degrees of freedom, harmonic oscillations, etc.) includes all first-order effects for diatomic molecules.

Finally, consider polyatomic molecules (molecules with more than two atoms). If the molecule contains n atoms, then $3n$ coordinates must be specified in order to specify completely the position of the molecule. If the molecule is linear (i.e., if the atoms lie on a common straight line), then the translational and rotational motions may be specified using five coordinates, whereas if the molecule is nonlinear, then six coordinates are required to specify the translational and rotational motions. Hence the number of vibrational degrees of freedom equals $3n - 5$ for linear molecules and $3n - 6$ for nonlinear molecules; Equation (13-20) becomes, for a linear molecule,

$$\ln \Xi = e^{-\gamma} g_e e^{\beta D_e} \left(\frac{2\pi m}{\beta h^2}\right)^{3/2} V \frac{2I_e}{\sigma\beta\hbar^2} \prod_{i=1}^{3n-5} \frac{1}{2\sinh(\beta h\nu_i/2)} \tag{13-43}$$

and, for a nonlinear molecule,

$$\ln \Xi = e^{-\gamma} g_e e^{\beta D_e} \left(\frac{2\pi m}{\beta h^2}\right)^{3/2} \frac{V}{\sigma} \left(\frac{2}{\beta \hbar^2}\right)^{3/2} (\pi I_{ex} I_{ey} I_{ez})^{1/2} \prod_{i=1}^{3n-6} \frac{1}{2 \sinh (\beta h \nu_i/2)} \tag{13-44}$$

where ν_i is the frequency associated with the ith vibrational degree of freedom and I_{ex}, I_{ey}, and I_{ez} are the principal moments of inertia. (Justifica-

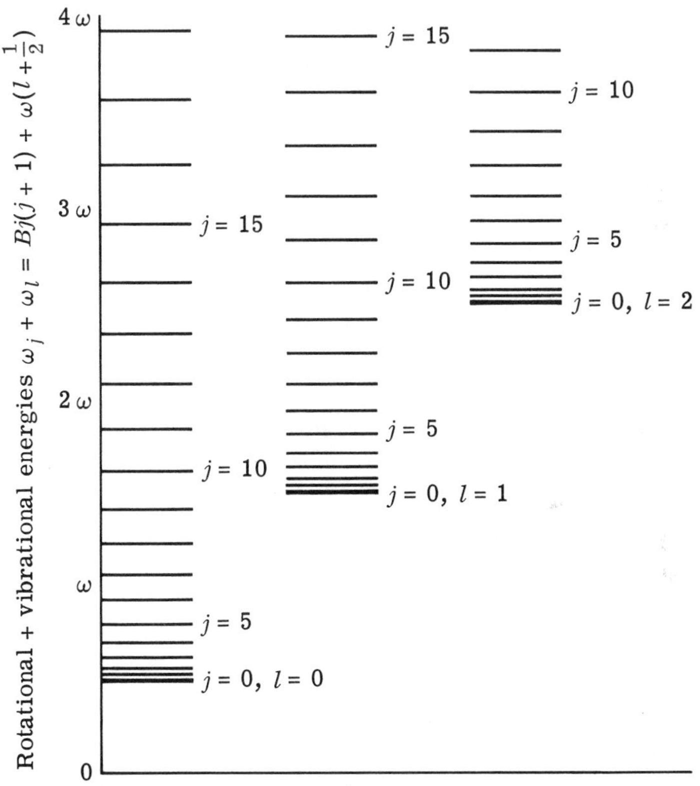

Figure 13-9 *Allowed rotational plus vibrational energy levels for diatomic molecule with distinguishable nuclei and for $\omega/B = 10^2$.*

tion of the rotational contribution of the latter equation is beyond the scope of the present text.) Values of band spectral constants and vibrational wave numbers are available from spectroscopic measurements for some of the more simple polyatomic molecules; as the molecule becomes more complicated, both the analytical and the spectroscopic studies become rapidly more difficult.

Example

In an example of the use of spectroscopic data, the heat capacity of carbon dioxide (a linear polyatomic molecule) at 300°K is computed here using vibrational frequencies determined from spectroscopic measurements. By appropriate differentiations of Equation (13-43),

$$C_V = \left\{\frac{5}{2} + \sum_{i=1}^{4}\left[\frac{h\nu_i/2kT}{\sinh(h\nu_i/2kT)}\right]^2\right\} Nk$$

Spectroscopic measurements yield the four vibrational wave numbers 2350 cm^{-1}, 668 cm^{-1}, 668 cm^{-1}, and 1351 cm^{-1} for the four fundamental modes of vibration. Substituting these wave numbers (equal to ν_i/c) into the equation for C_V, one obtains (for $T = 300$°K)

$$C_V = \left(\frac{5}{2} + 0.002 + 0.451 + 0.451 + 0.065\right) Nk = 3.47\, Nk$$

This value is in excellent agreement with experimental values.

PROBLEMS

13-1 By definition, in a center-of-mass coordinate system, $\sum_i m_i \mathbf{V}_i = 0$, where m_i and $\mathbf{V}_i$ are, respectively, the mass and velocity of the ith particle. Hence, show that for a diatomic molecule with atomic masses m_1 and m_2,

$$r_{1e} = \frac{m_2}{m_1 + m_2} r_e \qquad r_{2e} = \frac{m_1}{m_1 + m_2} r_e$$

where r_{1e} and r_{2e} are equilibrium distances from the center of mass to the atoms. Compare the moment of inertia calculated using these radii with the moment of inertia $I_e = \mu r_e^2$.

13-2 Verify, by substitution, that Equation (13-10) satisfies Equation (13-8). Note that Equation (13-10) is single-valued only for $m = 0, \pm 1, \pm 2, \ldots$. Verify that

$$\int_0^{2\pi} \Phi_m^* \Phi_m \, d\phi = 1.$$

What is the probability that the longitudinal angle is between ϕ and $\phi + d\phi$?

13-3 Determine, from Equation (13-11), the functions Θ_{00} and Θ_{11}. Verify, by substitution, that these two functions satisfy Equation (13-9) and

$$\int_0^{\pi} \Theta_{mj}^* \Theta_{mj} \sin\theta \, d\theta = 1.$$

For these two typical cases, what is the probability that the colatitudinal angle is between θ and $\theta + d\theta$?

13-4 Compute the value of j for which the ordinate of the smooth curve of Figure 13-4 has its maximum value. What energy is associated with this value of j? Compare this energy with the expected value of the rotational energy per molecule for $\theta_r << T$.

13-5 Using the data of Table 13-1, compare the value of the equilibrium distance r_e for HBr with the average value of the equilibrium distances for H_2 and Br_2. Using the data for H_2 and I_2, estimate the value of θ_r for HI.

13-6 Beginning with

$$\ln \Xi = \sum_j (2j+1) \exp\left[-\frac{\beta\hbar^2}{2I_e} j(j+1)\right] Z(\beta, V, \gamma)$$

where $Z(\beta, V, \gamma)$ represents factors in the right-hand side of Equation (13-4) which are not associated with the rotational degrees of freedom, compute (by summing over the appropriate number of terms) the value of the rotational contribution to the internal energy, of a diatomic gas with distinguishable nuclei and at $T = 1.5\theta_r$. Compare your results with Figure 13-6a.

13-7 Beginning with equations (6-11) and (6-14), compute, for a diatomic gas with distinguishable nuclei and at $T = 1.5\theta_r$, the fraction of molecules in the first four rotational-energy levels.

13-8 Using the data of Table 13-1, compare the value of the force constant a for HBr with the geometric mean of the force constants for H_2 and Br_2. Using the data for H_2 and I_2, estimate the value of θ_V for HI.

13-9 Beginning with Equations (6-11) and (6-14), show that the fraction of diatomic molecules in the lth vibrational quantum state is given by

$$\frac{\langle N_l \rangle}{\langle N \rangle} \sim (1 - e^{-\theta_V/T})\, e^{-l\theta_V/T}$$

Verify several values of this fraction indicated in Figure 13-5.

13-10 Compute the fraction of molecules in the lowest vibrational energy level ($l = 0$) at $T = 300°K$ for H_2, O_2, and I_2.

13-11 Calculate the value of the vibrational contribution to the heat capacity of H_2 and I_2 at 100°K, 1000°K, and 10,000°K.

13-12 From the data of Table 13-1, compute values of the moment of inertia I_e, the equilibrium distance r_e, the force constant a, and the energy D_e for H_2 and I_2.

13-13 Verify the numerical values given in Table 13-3. Express the associated energy changes in terms of wave numbers with reciprocal centimeters. (The first excited electronic energy level is observed at $D_{e2} - D_{e1} = 6.23$ ev.)

13-14 Indicate schematically the heat capacity of a diatomic gas (e.g., nitrogen; see Table 13-3) from 0 to 10^4 °K. For the purposes of this problem, neglect condensation into a liquid or solid at low temperatures and dissociation into atoms at high temperatures.

13-15 Calculate the value of the entropy S for 1 mole of N_2 at 25°C and 1 atm, using Equations (13-30) and (13-33). Compare the result of this calculation with the value 45.9 cal/mole-°K measured calorimetrically.

13-16 Compute the equilibrium composition of nitrogen at 5000°K and 0.2 atm. (The ground-state degeneracies g_e of N and N_2 are, respectively, 4 and 1.)

13-17 Discuss the role of symmetry and antisymmetry in the exchange of the nuclei in D_2. If six different (symmetrical) nuclear-spin wave functions exist for **ortho-D_2**, whereas three different (antisymmetrical) nuclear-spin wave functions exist for **para-D_2**, how would you predict the heat capacity of D_2 which has been cooled from room temperature to $T < \theta_r$ in the absence of a catalyst?

13-18 Compute the heat capacity of N_2O (a linear polyatomic molecule) at 300°K, for which spectroscopists measure fundamental vibrational wave numbers of 1,288 cm^{-1}, 588 cm^{-1}, 588 cm^{-1}, and 2,237 cm^{-1}.

13-19 Show that, for a reactive mixture of thermally perfect gases,

$$\frac{d \ln K_p}{dT} = \frac{\sum_i \nu_i h_i(T)}{kT^2}$$

where $h_i(T)$ is the enthalpy per particle of type i. [HINTS: Begin with Equation (13-39); recall that, for a thermally perfect gas, $\mu_i = g_i$, where g_i is the Gibbs function per particle of type i; use Equation (8-21').] For dissociation of a diatomic gas, express the right-hand side as a function of the energy D_e, the vibration frequency ν, the temperature T, and the appropriate natural constants.

13-20 Consider the isentropic compression of a mixture consisting of 1 mole of a thermally perfect monatomic gas and 1 mole of a thermally perfect diatomic gas. For convenience, examine the special case in which $\theta_r << T << \theta_V$. In this process, does the entropy change of the monatomic gas (alternatively, the diatomic gas) equal zero? Explain your answer, keeping in mind that the entropy change of the mixture equals zero.

chapter 14
debye monatomic crystal

It is the office of theoretical investigation to give the form in which the results of experiment may be expressed.
J. W. Gibbs, 1881 †

As a final example of the application of the methods of statistical thermodynamics, the model of a solid known as a Debye monatomic crystal is considered. This model was motivated in part by the failure of the Einstein monatomic crystal (see Chapter 9) to predict quantitatively the heat capacities of solids at low temperatures. Hence the discussion presented here may be considered to be an extension of the discussion presented in Chapter 9.

Recall that the Einstein model consists of $3N$ oscillators, where N is the number of atoms in the crystal, and that each of these oscillators vibrates at the frequency fixed by the mass of the atom and the force constant associated with the displacement of a given atom relative to neighboring atoms. This model neglects possible vibrations in which groups of atoms are displaced relative to the remainder of the crystal. Such possible vibrations are taken into account in the Debye model.

If a crystal contains N atoms and the electronic effects are negligible, it has a total of $3N$ degrees of freedom–three degrees of freedom for each atom. One may associate six of these degrees of freedom with translational and rotational displacements of the entire crystal, leaving $3N - 6$ degrees of freedom for vibrational displacements of groups of atoms within the crystal. For most crystals of interest, N is so large (of the order of 10^{20}) that one may neglect 6 in comparison with $3N$ and consider the crystal to have $3N$ vibrational degrees of freedom. This approximation is made in the remainder of this chapter.

In principle, the possible vibrations of the crystal (involving displacements of groups of atoms) may be described rigorously using independent

† Quoted by M. Rukeyser in "Willard Gibbs," p. 267, Doubleday & Company, Inc., Garden City, N. Y., 1942.

normal modes of vibration (see Figure 14-1). Since a given mode of vibration is distinguishable (by virtue of its wavelength and orientation), not even symmetry restrictions exist on the wave functions describing these vibra-

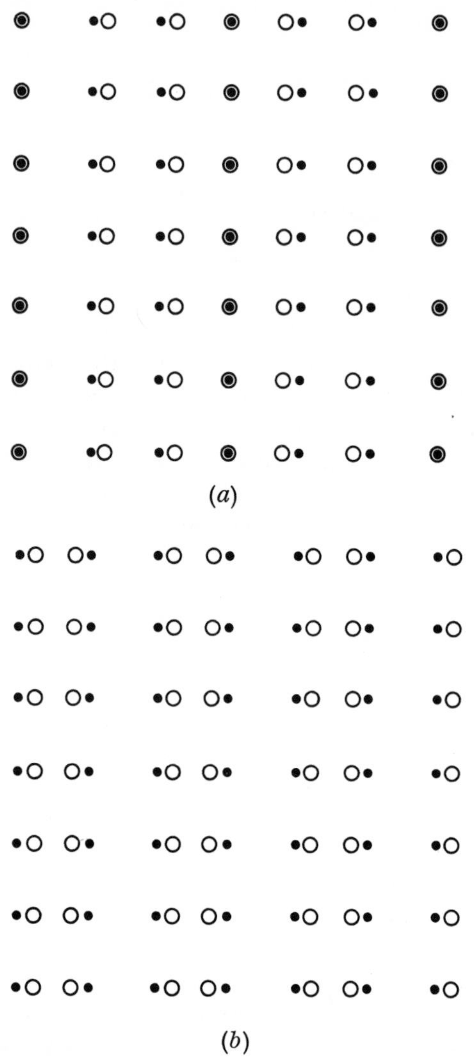

Figure 14-1 *Two possible normal modes of vibration for a crystal. (a) Wavelength $= 6\times$ atom spacing. (b) Wavelength $= 2\times$ atom spacing. (Dots and circles represent respectively equilibrium and displaced locations of atoms.)*

tions. If the vibration amplitudes are not too large, each of these normal modes of vibration may be considered to be a harmonic oscillation with frequency fixed by the appropriate effective mass and effective force constant. Hence the crystal may be treated as a system of $3N$ independent subsystems–each subsystem being a harmonic oscillator. As will be discussed in greater detail later, the most difficult problem is, in practice, the prediction of the frequencies of these harmonic oscillators.

Migrations of atoms will be considered negligible. Hence the following analysis will be of a canonical ensemble of members which contain independent distinguishable subsystems. (Recall that this category of systems is in addition to the categories of Fermi-Dirac, Maxwell-Boltzmann, and Bose-Einstein systems of indistinguishable particles.) As in Chapter 9, the partition function is given by

$$Q = e^{-N\beta U(0)/2} \prod_{n=1}^{3N} q_n \tag{9-5}$$

where

$$q_n = \sum_{l} e^{-\beta \varepsilon_{nl}} \tag{9-6}$$

Now, however, the frequencies of the several oscillators are not all equal, that is,

$$\varepsilon_{nl} = h\nu_n (l + 1/2)$$

where ν_n is the frequency of the nth oscillator. Both $U(0)$ and ν_n are functions of the atom spacing, i.e., functions of the number density N/V. Substituting from Equation (14-1) into Equation (9-6), one obtains (as was done in Chapter 9)

$$q_n = \frac{e^{-\beta h\nu_n/2}}{1 - e^{-\beta h\nu_n}} \tag{14-2}$$

Substituting now from Equation (14-2) into Equation (9-5) and taking the logarithm yields

$$-\ln Q = \frac{N\beta U(0)}{2} + \sum_{n=1}^{3N} \left[\ln(1 - e^{-\beta h\nu_n}) + \frac{\beta h\nu_n}{2} \right] \tag{14-3}$$

If the oscillators are distributed among the several oscillator frequencies in such a manner that the function describing this distribution is continuous to good approximation, then the sum over oscillators appearing here may be replaced by an integral over frequencies, i.e., one may write

$$\begin{aligned} -\ln Q &= \frac{N\beta U(0)}{2} + \sum_{\nu=0}^{\infty} G_\nu \left[\ln(1 - e^{-\beta h\nu}) + \frac{\beta h\nu}{2} \right] \\ &= \frac{N\beta U(0)}{2} + \int_0^\infty G(\nu) \left[\ln(1 - e^{-\beta h\nu}) + \frac{\beta h\nu}{2} \right] d\nu \end{aligned} \tag{14-4}$$

where G_ν is the number of oscillators with frequency ν and $G(\nu)\, d\nu$ is the number of oscillators with frequencies between ν and $\nu + d\nu$. Since the total number of oscillators is $3N$, the function $G(\nu)$ must satisfy

$$\int_0^\infty G(\nu)\, d\nu = 3N \tag{14-5}$$

The problem is reduced now to the problem of determining the nature of the function $G(\nu)$.

Debye motivated an expression for $G(\nu)$ by considerations of standing waves in an elastic continuum having the same elastic properties and density as the crystal. Since an infinite number of normal modes of vibration are possible in a continuum whereas only $3N$ normal modes are possible in a crystal with N atoms, some means for sorting out $3N$ normal modes from the infinite number of normal modes possible in a continuum is required. Debye noted that normal modes with wavelengths smaller than approximately twice the atomic spacing are unrealistic and suggested that one consider only those $3N$ normal modes (each mode different from the others) which have the greatest realizable wavelengths, i.e., those modes which have the lowest realizable frequencies. Use of this model is justified if it leads to useful predictions of thermodynamic properties of crystals.

In the derivation of the function $G(\nu)$ for this model, consider a rectangular parallelepiped with edge lengths l_1, l_2, and l_3 and containing an elastic continuum. Three modes of vibration (one longitudinal acoustic mode with propagation speed c_l and two orthogonal transverse modes with propagation speed c_t) are possible for each allowed wavelength. For the purposes of the present analysis, the boundary of the system may be either rigid (so that the standing wave must have a node at the boundary) or free (so that the standing wave has maximum amplitude at the boundary). For definiteness, consider the case in which the boundary is rigid. Then, if the three axes of the (rectangular) coordinate system coincide with three edges of the model, the displacements of the standing waves are proportional to

$$\sin\left(k_1\pi\frac{x}{l_1}\right)\sin\left(k_2\pi\frac{y}{l_2}\right)\sin\left(k_3\pi\frac{z}{l_3}\right)$$

where k_1, k_2, and k_3 are integers with possible values $1, 2, \cdots$. These standing waves are formed by superposing traveling waves with wavelength λ related to the integers k_1, k_2, and k_3 by

$$\lambda = \frac{2l_1}{k_1}\cos\alpha_1 = \frac{2l_2}{k_2}\cos\alpha_2 = \frac{2l_3}{k_3}\cos\alpha_3 \tag{14-6}$$

(see Figure 14-2). From $\cos^2\alpha_1 + \cos^2\alpha_2 + \cos^2\alpha_3 = 1$, it follows that

$$\left(\frac{\lambda k_1}{2l_1}\right)^2 + \left(\frac{\lambda k_2}{2l_2}\right)^2 + \left(\frac{\lambda k_3}{2l_3}\right)^2 = 1$$

or

$$\frac{1}{\lambda} = \left[\left(\frac{k_1}{2l_1}\right)^2 + \left(\frac{k_2}{2l_2}\right)^2 + \left(\frac{k_3}{2l_3}\right)^2\right]^{1/2} \tag{14-7}$$

so that the allowed frequencies are

$$\nu_l = \frac{c_l}{\lambda} = c_l\left[\left(\frac{k_1}{2l_1}\right)^2 + \left(\frac{k_2}{2l_2}\right)^2 + \left(\frac{k_3}{2l_3}\right)^2\right]^{1/2} \tag{14-8a}$$

$$\nu_t = \frac{c_t}{\lambda} = c_t\left[\left(\frac{k_1}{2l_1}\right)^2 + \left(\frac{k_2}{2l_2}\right)^2 + \left(\frac{k_3}{2l_3}\right)^2\right]^{1/2} \tag{14-8b}$$

where subscripts l and t refer, respectively, to longitudinal and transverse waves. (Note that $\nu_l \neq \nu_t$.) In analogy with the methods of Chapters 10 and 11, one could consider now (without loss in generality) a system with $l_1 = l_2 = l_3$. In order to show that the result is independent of the choice of the edge lengths, consider here the case in which $l_1 \neq l_2 \neq l_3$. Examine first the longitudinal modes. Each point k_1, k_2, k_3 (alternatively, each unit volume) of the positive octant of k_1, k_2, k_3 space represents one normal longitudinal mode of vibration of the system. Hence the number of longitudinal

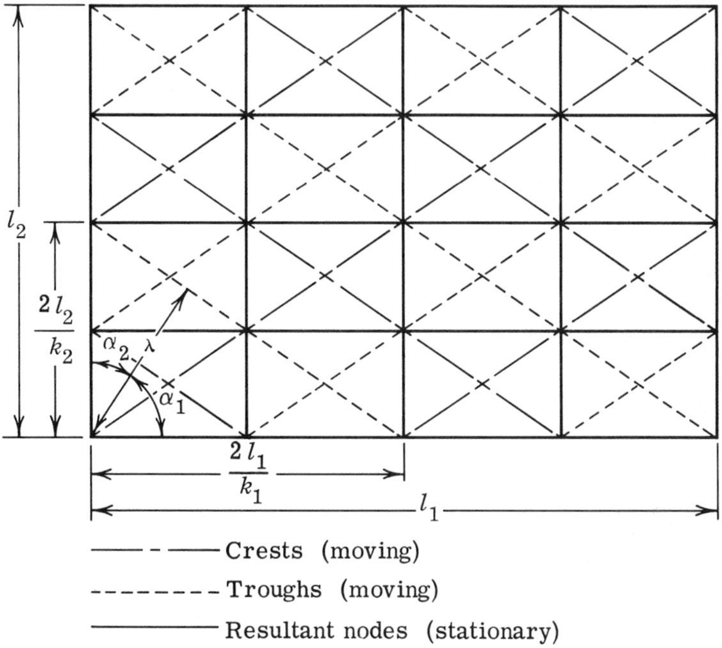

Figure 14-2 *Standing waves in a two-dimensional model at time of maximum displacement. (Note that a similar figure could have been used in discussions of standing matter waves for atoms or photons or electrons in a box.)*

modes with frequency less than ν is one-eighth the volume of the ellipsoid

$$\left(\frac{k_1}{2l_1\nu/c_l}\right)^2 + \left(\frac{k_2}{2l_2\nu/c_l}\right)^2 + \left(\frac{k_3}{2l_3\nu/c_l}\right)^2 = 1$$

that is, the number of longitudinal modes with frequency less than ν is

$$\frac{1}{8}\frac{4\pi}{3}\left(\frac{2l_1\nu}{c_l}\right)\left(\frac{2l_2\nu}{c_l}\right)\left(\frac{2l_3\nu}{c_l}\right)$$

so that the number of longitudinal modes with frequency between ν and $\nu + d\nu$ is

$$G_l(\nu)\,d\nu = \frac{d}{d\nu}\left(\frac{4\pi V\nu^3}{3c_l^3}\right)d\nu = 4\pi\frac{V\nu^2}{c_l^3}\,d\nu \qquad (14\text{-}9)$$

where $V \equiv l_1 l_2 l_3$. Similarly, keeping in mind that each point k_1, k_2, k_3 of the positive octant of k_1, k_2, k_3 space represents *two* normal transverse modes of vibration, one obtains for the number of transverse modes with frequency between ν and $\nu + d\nu$

$$G_t(\nu)\,d\nu = \frac{8\pi V \nu^2}{c_t^3}\,d\nu \tag{14-10}$$

Combining Equations (14-9) and (14-10) yields

$$G(\nu)\,d\nu = G_l(\nu)\,d\nu + G_t(\nu)\,d\nu = 4\pi V\left(\frac{1}{c_l^3} + \frac{2}{c_t^3}\right)\nu^2\,d\nu \tag{14-11}$$

which is the required expression for the total number of modes with frequency between ν and $\nu + d\nu$. Equation (14-11) is the analog (for standing waves in an elastic continuum) of Equation (10-10) (for standing matter waves in a box). It is seen now that the form of these equations is independent of the choice of the edge lengths.

Debye's suggestion is equivalent to using Equation (14-11) for $\nu < \nu_m$ and setting $G(\nu) = 0$ for $\nu > \nu_m$, where the **cutoff frequency** ν_m is defined, using Equation (14-5), by

$$3N = \int_0^{\nu_m} 4\pi V\left(\frac{1}{c_l^3} + \frac{2}{c_t^3}\right)\nu^2\,d\nu = \frac{4\pi}{3}V\left(\frac{1}{c_l^3} + \frac{2}{c_t^3}\right)\nu_m^3 \tag{14-12}$$

Eliminating the propagation speeds from Equations (14-11) and (14-12), the convenient form

$$G(\nu)\,d\nu = 9N\frac{\nu^2}{\nu_m^3}\,d\nu \tag{14-13}$$

may be written as an alternative form of Equation (14-11). For a given crystal type, the cutoff frequency ν_m is a function of the number density N/V.

The models of Einstein and Debye are compared in Figure 14-3, where the number of modes $G(\nu)$ per unit frequency is plotted as a function of frequency. Einstein's model is equivalent to using, for $G(\nu)$, a Dirac δ function, whereas Debye's model requires, for $G(\nu)$, a quadratic function with a cutoff at $\nu_m \equiv k\theta_D/h$. Debye's model is intermediate to Einstein's simple model and the more complicated models introduced more recently.

The range of frequencies in which Equation (14-13) applies rigorously (i.e., the range of frequencies in which a crystal acts as a continuum) may be established with the aid of Equation (14-12). From Equation (14-12), it is seen that the wavelength associated with the cutoff frequency ν_m is of the order of $(V/N)^{1/3}$, that is, of the order of the atom spacing. However, a crystal behaves as a continuum only if the wavelength of the vibration is greater than about ten times the atom spacing. Hence the range of frequencies in which Equation (14-13) applies rigorously is given approximately by

$$0 < \nu < \frac{\nu_m}{10} \tag{14-14}$$

It is found, however, that, in spite of the reservations expressed concerning the applicability of Equation (14-13) for $\nu_m/10 < \nu < \nu_m$, the use of Equation (14-13) in Equation (14-4) for $0 < \nu < \nu_m$ leads to predictions of heat capacities which are in good agreement with experimental results.

Using Debye's suggestion, one may now evaluate the partition function.

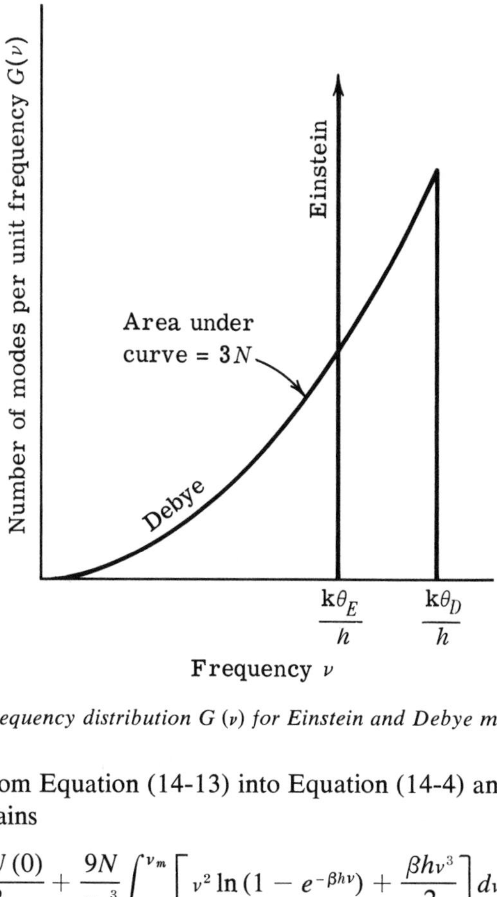

Figure 14-3 *Frequency distribution G (ν) for Einstein and Debye monatomic crystals.*

Substituting from Equation (14-13) into Equation (14-4) and integrating by parts, one obtains

$$\begin{aligned}
-\ln Q &= \frac{N\beta U(0)}{2} + \frac{9N}{{\nu_m}^3}\int_0^{\nu_m}\left[\nu^2 \ln(1 - e^{-\beta h\nu}) + \frac{\beta h\nu^3}{2}\right] d\nu \\
&= \frac{N\beta U(0)}{2} + \frac{9N}{(\beta h\nu_m)^3}\int_0^{\beta h\nu_m} x^2 \ln(1 - e^{-x})\, dx + \frac{9}{8}N\beta h\nu_m \\
&= \frac{N\beta U(0)}{2} + \frac{9}{8}N\beta h\nu_m + 3N\ln(1 - e^{-\beta h\nu_m}) \\
&\qquad - \frac{3N}{(\beta h\nu_m)^3}\int_0^{\beta h\nu_m} \frac{x^3\, dx}{e^x - 1}
\end{aligned} \tag{14-15}$$

where $x \equiv \beta h\nu$. Introducing the **Debye temperature** $\theta_D\,(\equiv h\nu_m/k)$, and the

Helmholtz function A, one may write alternatively (in the nomenclature of classical thermodynamics)

$$\frac{A}{kT} = \frac{NU(0)}{2kT} + \frac{9}{8}N\frac{\theta_D}{T} + 3N\ln(1 - e^{-\theta_D/T}) - 3N\left(\frac{T}{\theta_D}\right)^3 \int_0^{\theta_D/T} \frac{x^3\,dx}{e^x - 1} \tag{14-15'}$$

The integral

$$3\left(\frac{T}{\theta_D}\right)^3 \int_0^{\theta_D/T} \frac{x^3}{e^x - 1}\,dx$$

appearing here has been called frequently the Debye function. In recent literature, however, this name is reserved for another function which will be introduced in the following paragraph.

Absolute values of thermodynamic properties of a Debye monatomic crystal may be calculated now. Internal energy, entropy, and constant-volume heat capacity are given by

$$E = \left(\frac{\partial(A/kT)}{\partial(1/kT)}\right)_{V,N} = \frac{NU(0)}{2} + \frac{9}{8}Nk\,\theta_D + \frac{9NkT}{(\theta_D/T)^3}\int_0^{\theta_D/T} \frac{x^3\,dx}{e^x - 1} \tag{14-16}$$

$$\frac{S}{k} = \frac{E - A}{kT} = 9N\left(\frac{T}{\theta_D}\right)^3 \int_0^{\theta_D/T} \left[\frac{x^3}{e^x - 1} - x^2\ln(1 - e^{-x})\right]dx \tag{14-17}$$

$$\frac{C_V}{k} = \frac{1}{k}\left(\frac{\partial E}{\partial T}\right)_{V,N} = 3ND\left(\frac{T}{\theta_D}\right) \tag{14-18}$$

where

$$D\left(\frac{T}{\theta_D}\right) \equiv 3\left(\frac{T}{\theta_D}\right)^3 \int_0^{\theta_D/T} \frac{x^4 e^x}{(e^x - 1)^2}\,dx \tag{14-19}$$

is the **Debye function** referred to in the preceding paragraph. In the expression for the internal energy, the first term is the potential energy of the atoms in their equilibrium positions, the second term is the energy associated with the several modes of vibration even when unexcited, whereas the third term is the energy associated with the several modes of vibration as a consequence of excitation. If more than one quantum state is associated with the lowest possible energy level of the crystal, then an additional constant term (of no consequence in most applications) must be added to the expression for the entropy. (Since only one quantum state is associated with the lowest possible energy level of a pure monatomic crystal, this additional term occurs only for solid solutions, for some polyatomic crystals, and for glassy solids.) As in Chapter 9, expressions for chemical potential and pressure are not given here due to the complications introduced by the dependence of $U(0)$ and θ_D on either V with N held constant or N with V held constant. In principle, they would be calculated from

$$\mu = \left(\frac{\partial A}{\partial N}\right)_{V,T} \tag{14-20}$$

$$p = -\left(\frac{\partial A}{\partial V}\right)_{N,T} \tag{14-21}$$

Fortunately (and as indicated already in Chapter 9), thermodynamic functions (e.g., enthalpy and the Gibbs function) which involve both internal energy and a pV term may be evaluated, to good approximation, for many solids by neglecting the pV term in comparison with internal energy.

The variance of the internal energy is given by

$$\sigma^2(E) = \left(\frac{\partial^2 \ln Q}{\partial \beta^2}\right)_{V,N} = \frac{3ND(\beta h\nu_m)}{\beta^2} \tag{14-22}$$

so that

$$\frac{\sigma(E)}{\langle E\rangle - \dfrac{NU(0)}{2} - \dfrac{9}{8}Nk\theta_D} = \frac{(\beta h\nu_m)^{3/2}}{3\sqrt{N}} \frac{\left(\displaystyle\int_0^{\beta h\nu_m} \frac{x^4 e^x}{(e^x-1)^2}\,dx\right)^{1/2}}{\displaystyle\int_0^{\beta h\nu_m} \frac{x^3}{e^x-1}\,dx} \tag{14-23}$$

and

$$\sigma^2(E) = \frac{1}{\beta^2}\frac{\langle C_V\rangle}{k} \tag{14-24}$$

where $D(\beta h\nu_m)$ is the Debye function defined in Equation (14-19). Equation (14-23) is in agreement with similar equations written in preceding chapters to the extent that the relative deviations from expected values are proportional inversely to the square root of the number of particles or subsystems. As noted previously (see Problem 5-2), Equation (14-24) is a general relation for canonical ensembles.

For nonzero finite values of the upper limit, the integrals appearing in the preceding equations must be evaluated numerically. They are tabulated in the more comprehensive statistical-thermodynamics textbooks and handbooks; values of internal energy, entropy, and heat capacity are plotted as a function of temperature in Figure 14-4. Keep in mind that, for metals at temperatures sufficiently high that the electron-gas heat capacity is significant in comparison with $3Nk$ and for metals at temperatures sufficiently low that the Debye heat capacity is relatively small (see Problem 14-7), these values of thermodynamic properties must be supplemented by the values predicted for an electron gas in Chapter 11.

Heat capacities predicted by the Debye and Einstein models are compared with measured values of heat capacities in Figure 14-5. The measured values for Fe exceed the predicted values due largely to the fact that Fe is ferromagnetic and the models considered here do not include magnetic effects. Equally good agreement is realized for measured and predicted values of the entropy and the temperature-dependent part of the internal energy. The zero-point term $9Nk\theta_D/8$ in the expression for the internal energy is under suspicion, however; the integral from which it was evaluated weights relatively heavily those contributions for θ near θ_D.

Values of the Debye temperature may be deduced either from heat-

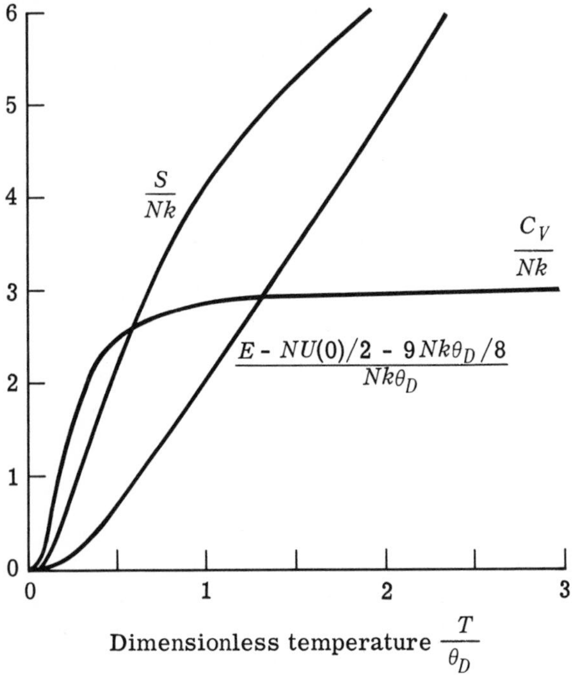

Figure 14-4 *Internal energy, entropy, and heat capacity of Debye monatomic crystal as functions of temperature.*

capacity data or from elastic constants. [When using heat-capacity data, one looks for a value of θ_D which correlates predicted and measured values; when using elastic constants, one first computes the propagation speeds from values of the isothermal compressibility and Poisson's ratio and then computes the cutoff frequency using Equation (14-12).] Values obtained using these two methods agree better than one might expect for such a crude model. Exceptions are observed, however. For example, slightly different values of θ_D are obtained frequently for measurements made at different temperatures. These exceptions are attributed largely to the inadequacy of Equation (14-13), particularly at high frequencies. Most current studies of the heat capacities of solids are concerned with these exceptions.

Periodic trends of the Debye temperature are brought out in Table 14-1,

Table 14-1 † Values of $\theta_D/100$ (°K) for the elements

Period	*Ia*	*IIa*	*IIIb*	*IVb*	*Vb*	*VIb*	*VIIb*	*VIII*			*Ib*	*IIb*	*IIIa*	*IVa*	*Va*	*VIa*
2	Li	Be											B	C	N	0
	3.7	11.6												22.3 (dia) 4.2 (graph)		
3	Na	Mg											Al	Si	P	S
	1.58	4.0											4.28	6.40		
4	K	Ca	Sc	Ti	V	Cr	Mn	Fe	Co	Ni	Cu	Zn	Ga	Ge	As	Se (vit)
	0.90	2.30		4.2	3.6	6.3	4.5	4.67	4.45	4.5	3.43	3.10	3.2	3.70		0.9
5	Rb	Sr	Y	Zr	Nb	Mo	Tc	Ru	Rh	Pd	Ag	Cd	In	Sn 1.99 (white) 2.1 (gray)	Sb	Te
	0.52	1.47		3.1	2.3	4.5		6.0	4.8	3.0	2.26	1.88	1.08		2.07	1.53
6	Cs	Ba	La	Hf	Ta	W	Re	Os	Ir	Pt	Au	Hg	Tl	Pb	Bi	Po
		1.10	1.42	2.6	2.4	4.0	4.3	5.0	4.2	2.40	1.64	0.8	0.87	1.1	1.19	
7	Fr	Ra	Ac				Dy	Th	U							
							1.4	1.7	2.0							

† Adapted from Dwight E. Gray (ed.), "American Institute of Physics Handbook," 2d ed., table 4e-12, McGraw-Hill Book Company, New York, 1963.

where the Debye temperatures of many of the elements are presented in the form of the periodic table. The most obvious trend is the decrease of θ_D as the atomic mass increases; this trend is explained by the fact that the frequency of vibration of a harmonic oscillator is proportional to $(a/m)^{1/2}$ where a is the force constant and m is the mass. Due to relatively small force constants and relatively large masses, typical values of θ_D are relatively low, frequently of the order of magnitude of room temperature or less. Associated cutoff frequencies are of the order of 6×10^{12} sec^{-1}, about an order of magnitude lower than the vibration frequency for a typical diatomic molecule.

Consider now the behavior of the aforementioned thermodynamic functions for limiting temperatures. If $T << \theta_D$, then

$$A \rightarrow \frac{NU(0)}{2} + \frac{9}{8}Nk\theta_D - \frac{\pi^4 NkT}{5}\left(\frac{T}{\theta_D}\right)^3 \tag{14-25}$$

$$E \rightarrow \frac{NU(0)}{2} + \frac{9}{8}Nk\theta_D + \frac{3\pi^4 NkT}{5}\left(\frac{T}{\theta_D}\right)^3 \tag{14-26}$$

$$\frac{S}{k} \rightarrow \frac{4\pi^4 N}{5}\left(\frac{T}{\theta_D}\right)^3 \tag{14-27}$$

$$\frac{C_V}{k} \rightarrow \frac{12\pi^4 N}{5}\left(\frac{T}{\theta_D}\right)^3 \tag{14-28}$$

whereas if $T >> \theta_D$, then

$$A \rightarrow \frac{NU(0)}{2} + 3NkT\left(\ln\frac{\theta_D}{T} - \frac{1}{3}\right) \tag{14-29}$$

$$E \rightarrow \frac{NU(0)}{2} + 3NkT \tag{14-30}$$

$$\frac{S}{k} \rightarrow 3N\left(\frac{4}{3} + \ln\frac{T}{\theta_D}\right) \tag{14-31}$$

$$\frac{C_V}{k} \rightarrow 3N \tag{14-32}$$

Figure 14-4 suggests that $T << \theta_D/3$ might be a better criterion for applicability of Equations (14-25) to (14-28), whereas $T >> \theta_D/3$ might be a better criterion for applicability of Equations (14-29) to (14-32). More specifically, Equations (14-28) and (14-18) agree within 1 percent for $T < \theta_D/12$, whereas Equations (14-32) and (14-18) agree within 1 percent for $T > 2\theta_D$. Equation (14-32), known as the law of Dulong and Petit, may be derived alternatively by applying classical mechanics to $3N$ harmonic oscillators.

Equation (14-16), with $T = 0$, is the negative of the heat of sublimation of a Debye monatomic crystal at 0°K. One obtains, for the heat of sublimation per atom,

$$Q_{\text{sublimation}} = -\frac{U(0)}{2} - \frac{9}{8}k\theta_D \tag{14-33}$$

However, as mentioned previously, the zero point term $9k\theta_D/8$ is under suspicion.

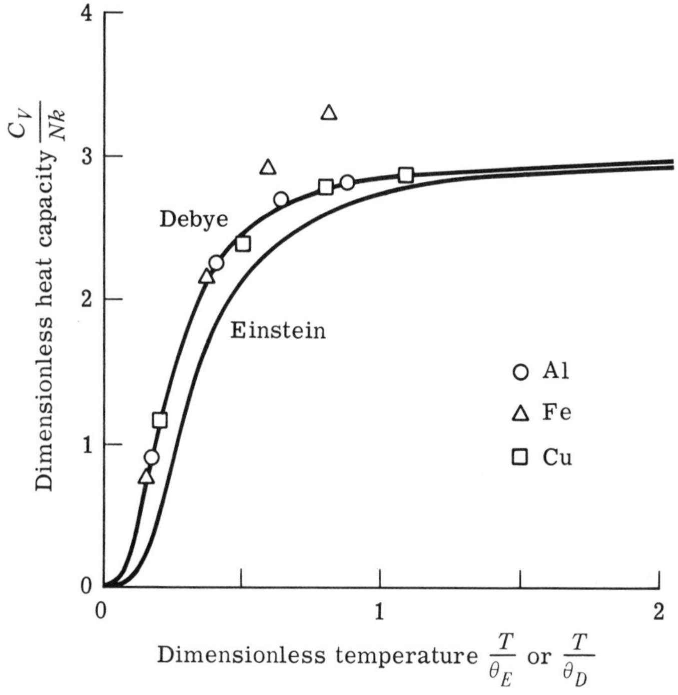

Figure 14-5 *Comparison of measured values of heat capacity with values for Einstein and Debye crystals. (Measured values are taken from Table 6-6 of A. H. Wilson, "Thermodynamics and Statistical Mechanics," Cambridge University Press, New York, 1957; temperatures associated with measured values are divided by values of θ_D taken from Table 14-1.)*

An expression for the vapor pressure of a monatomic crystal follows from the equality of the gas-phase and solid-phase chemical potentials at equilibrium. Combining Equations (8-18), (8-22), (14-16), (14-17), and (14-33), one obtains

$$\ln p = \frac{5}{2}\ln T - \frac{Q_{\text{sublimation}}}{kT} + 9\left(\frac{T}{\theta_D}\right)^3 \int_0^{\theta_D/T} x^2 \ln(1 - e^{-x})\,dx + \ln\left[g_e\left(\frac{2\pi mk}{h^2}\right)^{3/2} k\right] \tag{14-34}$$

where the pV term for the solid has been neglected in comparison with E [in agreement with comments following Equation (14-21)]. If $T << \theta_D$, then the upper limit of the integral is large in comparison with unity and

$$\ln p \approx \frac{5}{2} \ln T - \frac{Q_{\text{sublimation}}}{kT} - \frac{\pi^4}{5}\left(\frac{T}{\theta_D}\right)^3 + \ln\left[g_e\left(\frac{2\pi mk}{h^2}\right)^{3/2} k\right] \quad (14\text{-}35)$$

The last term (independent of temperature) is called the **vapor-pressure constant.** Values of this constant obtained from Equation (14-35) and measured values of vapor pressure, temperature, and heat of sublimation agree with the predicted value of this constant within experimental error. This agreement supports strongly the use of statistical thermodynamics of quantum-mechanical systems; neither classical thermodynamics nor statistical thermodynamics of classical-mechanical systems is able to predict values of this constant.

Example

Consider the vapor-pressure constant of argon (with an atomic weight of 39.94 and a gas-phase ground-state degeneracy of 1). From the preceding analysis, if p is in atmospheres and T is in degrees Kelvin, then the vapor-pressure constant is

$$\ln\left[g_e\left(\frac{2\pi mk}{h^2}\right)^{3/2} k\right] = \ln\left[\left(\frac{2\pi \times 39.94 \times 1.66 \times 10^{-24} \times 1.38 \times 10^{-16}}{6.63 \times 10^{-27} \times 6.63 \times 10^{-27}}\right)^{3/2} \times \frac{1.38 \times 10^{-16}}{1.01 \times 10^{6}}\right] = 1.86$$

Experiments yield 1.86 ± 0.05. Such agreement among predictions and measurements for vapor-pressure constants provided significant support for the use of statistical thermodynamics of quantum-mechanical systems.

The solid-vapor equilibrium discussed in the preceding paragraph provides an example of the relative roles of enthalpy $(E + pV)/N$ and entropy S/N in the equilibrium of two phases. The tendency of a particle to escape from a given phase (i.e., the chemical potential) increases with *increasing* enthalpy and with *decreasing* entropy. If the escaping tendencies are not equal initially, conversion of one phase into the other phase occurs until, at equilibrium, the escaping tendency is equal for the solid phase (with enthalpy and entropy both relatively low) and for the vapor phase (with enthalpy and entropy both relatively high).

For the case in which $T << \theta_D$, the Debye model of a crystal is referred to sometimes as a **phonon gas** (a gas composed of acoustical quanta). This name was coined in order to emphasize the similarities of this model and a photon gas. These similarities become apparent in a comparison of the photon-gas equations

$$\nu_k = \frac{c}{2l}(k_1^2 + k_2^2 + k_3^2)^{1/2} \tag{10-9}$$

$$G(\nu)\,d\nu = \frac{8\pi V\nu^2}{c^3}\,d\nu \tag{10-10}$$

$$E = \frac{8\pi^5}{15}\frac{V(kT)^4}{(hc)^3} \tag{10-12}$$

$$\frac{S}{k} = \frac{32\pi^5}{45}V\left(\frac{kT}{hc}\right)^3 \tag{10-18}$$

$$\frac{C_V}{k} = \frac{32\pi^5}{15}V\left(\frac{kT}{hc}\right)^3 \tag{10-19}$$

with the "phonon-gas" equations (for $l_1 = l_2 = l_3 = l$ and $T << \theta_D$)

$$\nu_l = \frac{c_l}{2l}(k_1^2 + k_2^2 + k_3^2) \tag{14-8a}$$

$$\nu_t = \frac{c_t}{2l}(k_1^2 + k_2^2 + k_3^2) \tag{14-8b}$$

$$G(\nu)\,d\nu = 4\pi V\left(\frac{1}{c_l^3} + \frac{2}{c_t^3}\right)\nu^2\,d\nu \tag{14-11}$$

$$E - \frac{NU(0)}{2} - \frac{9}{8}Nk\theta_D \to \frac{4\pi^5}{15}V\left(\frac{1}{c_l^3} + \frac{2}{c_t^3}\right)\frac{(kT)^4}{h^3} \tag{14-26$'$}$$

$$\frac{S}{k} \to \frac{16\pi^5}{45}V\left(\frac{1}{c_l^3} + \frac{2}{c_t^3}\right)\left(\frac{kT}{h}\right)^3 \tag{14-27$'$}$$

$$\frac{C_V}{k} \to \frac{16\pi^5}{15}V\left(\frac{1}{c_l^3} + \frac{2}{c_t^3}\right)\left(\frac{kT}{h}\right)^3 \tag{14-28$'$}$$

where the definition of θ_D and Equation (14-12) have been used to eliminate θ_D in the latter three equations. It is seen that the phonon gas differs from the photon gas chiefly in that it has a longitudinal acoustic mode of vibration in addition to the two orthogonal transverse modes of vibration. Also, the propagation speeds (sound speeds) c_l and c_t are smaller than the speed of light c.

The similarities of the phonon and photon gases could be extended by using for the phonon gas (as for the photon gas) a grand canonical ensemble with $\gamma = 0$. In this approach, each ensemble member would contain an indefinite number of **phonons** (excited normal modes of oscillation) rather than a definite number of normal modes of oscillation (most of which would not be excited). Use of the grand canonical ensemble would be justified since (for $T << \theta_D$) the expected value of the number of phonons is small in comparison with the maximum possible number ($3N$) of phonons; use of $\gamma = 0$ would be required since a given number of phonons (with a given total energy) can be converted into a different number of phonons (with the same total energy).

Although only the monatomic crystal has been discussed here, the results may be applied, with limitations, to more complicated crystals such as a crystal composed of molecules and an anisotropic crystal. If the crystal is relatively complicated, then the upper limit for applicability of Equations (14-25) to (14-28) is lowered and the crystal may melt before Equations (14-29) to (14-32) become applicable.

PROBLEMS

14-1 Heat-capacity measurements for copper at 100°K yield 3.85 cal/mole-°K. Using this value, compute the value of the Einstein and Debye temperatures for copper. Then, using these characteristic temperatures and the methods of Chapters 9 and 14, predict values of the heat capacity of copper at 25°K. Compare results of these two calculations with the measured value of 0.23 cal/mole-°K at 25°K. Which model (Einstein or Debye) is preferred?

14-2 Using the values of θ_D given in Table 14-1, estimate the values of C_V in cal/mole-°K for diamond, palladium, and rubidium at 300°K.

14-3 Using the thermodynamics relations between (*a*) A, E, and S, (*b*) E and C_V, and (*c*) S and C_V, check the consistency of Equations (14-25) to (14-28).

14-4 Show that, for a Debye monatomic crystal,

$$p = -\frac{N}{2}\left(\frac{\partial U(0)}{\partial V}\right)_{N,T} + \frac{\gamma}{V}\left(E - \frac{NU(0)}{2}\right)$$

where $\gamma \equiv -[(\partial \ln \theta_D/\partial \ln V)]_{N,T}$ is the **Grüneisen constant**. Hence, show that, if γ is independent of temperature, then the ratio of the **thermal expansion coefficient** β and the **isothermal compressibility** κ is related to γ by

$$\frac{\beta}{\kappa} = \frac{\gamma C_V}{V}$$

where $$\beta \equiv \frac{1}{V}\left(\frac{\partial V}{\partial T}\right)_{N,p} \quad \text{and} \quad \kappa \equiv -\frac{1}{V}\left(\frac{\partial V}{\partial p}\right)_{N,T}$$

Keep in mind that $U(0)$ is a function of N/V; note that the β used here is not related to the β introduced in Chapter 3.

14-5 Recall, from classical thermodynamics, that

$$C_p - C_V = \frac{pV}{T}\frac{(\beta T)^2}{\kappa p}$$

where $$\beta \equiv \frac{1}{V}\left(\frac{\partial V}{\partial T}\right)_{N,p} \quad \text{and} \quad \kappa \equiv -\frac{1}{V}\left(\frac{\partial V}{\partial p}\right)_{N,T}$$

Using the results of the preceding problem, show that one may write alternatively

$$\frac{C_p - C_V}{C_V} = \frac{\gamma^2 \kappa}{V} C_V T$$

Evaluate the right-hand side for copper at (*a*) $T/\theta_D = 1/12$ and (*b*) $T/\theta_D = 2$. Take

$\gamma = 2.1$, $\kappa = 7.5 \times 10^{-13}$ dyne^{-1} cm^2, and $V = 11.8 \times 10^{-24}$ cm^3/atom. Under what conditions may one write, to good approximation, $C_p \approx C_V$?

14-6 It has been suggested that the Grüneisen constant

$$\gamma \equiv -\left(\frac{\partial \ln \theta_D}{\partial \ln V}\right)_{N,T}$$

be evaluated using a Debye monatomic crystal with constant propagation speeds c_l and c_t. Compare the value obtained for this model with the value ($\gamma \approx 2$) obtained experimentally. Does the aforementioned model lead to an acceptable quantitative result?

14-7 Using Equations (11-26), (14-28), and (14-32), compute the temperatures at which the electron-gas contribution to the heat capacity is 10 percent of the Debye-crystal contribution to the heat capacity of copper.

14-8 Show that, for a Debye monatomic crystal at temperature T, the number of excited vibrational modes with frequencies between ν and $\nu + d\nu$ is

$$9N \frac{\nu^2}{\nu_m^3} e^{-h\nu/kT}\, d\nu$$

(HINT: First compute the number of unexcited vibrational modes, i.e., the number of vibrational modes in the ground state with frequencies between ν and $\nu + d\nu$.) At what frequency is this function a maximum?

chapter 15
summary and comparisons

The whole is simpler than its parts.
J. W. Gibbs †

The brief introduction to the viewpoints and methods given in Chapter 1 is supplemented here. An attempt is made to summarize and compare the essential features of Chapters 2 to 14 without the distractions of the details contained therein.

The starting point was provided by the fundamental postulates (Chapter 2):

> *Postulate* 1: The classical value of a mechanical-thermodynamic property of a system is analogous to the expected value computed from the most probable distribution of ensemble members among the possible ensemble-member quantum states.
>
> *Postulate* 2: The most probable distribution of ensemble members among possible ensemble-member quantum states is that distribution for which the number of possible quantum states of the ensemble and reservoir is a maximum.

The first postulate was motivated in part by the fact that, for macroscopic systems, the time required for the system to pass, at least once, through all allowed system quantum states is much larger than the time over which one averages when one makes measurements. Hence measurements on macroscopic systems are to be interpreted as averages over relatively short periods of time. These measurements are reproducible because a great majority of the allowed quantum states of a macroscopic system have macroscopic

† Quoted by M. Rukeyser in "Willard Gibbs," p. 431, Doubleday & Company, Inc., Garden City, N. Y., 1942.

properties which are indistinguishable with the instruments used. The second postulate provided a basis (see Appendix E) for analogs of the second law of classical thermodynamics and its consequences.

Discussions of "the most probable distribution of ensemble members among possible ensemble-member quantum states" were facilitated by use of the concept of an ensemble of independent members (a concept introduced by Boltzmann but used most effectively by Gibbs). Advantage was taken of the fact that most results of interest to thermodynamicists are independent of the ensemble which is used. Hence, the ensemble type may be chosen frequently, for mathematical convenience rather than for rigorous adherence to the nature of the system boundary conditions and the roles of the generalized displacements. The grand canonical ensemble (Chapter 3) and the canonical ensemble (Chapter 9) were found to be the most convenient ensembles, respectively, for systems of indistinguishable particles and for systems of distinguishable subsystems (or subsystem sites).

It was shown then (Chapter 4) that expected values of the mechanical quantities and variances of the extensive mechanical quantities may be calculated by operations upon the partition function; variances of the intensive mechanical quantities require, in addition to operations upon the partition function, a specific model of matter. As in the remaining pages of this book, these discussions used quantum-mechanical concepts and language (rather than classical-mechanical concepts and language). The application of probability theory to systems with discrete allowable energy levels is more simple in many respects than is the application of probability theory to systems with continuously variable energies. Furthermore, in a quantum-mechanical treatment, Planck's constant and the concept of indistinguishable particles are an integral part of the mechanics and do not have to be introduced artificially. In the first five chapters, the only quantum-mechanical concepts which were required were the concepts of discrete quantum states, discrete energy levels, and discrete mass quantities.

Classical thermodynamics and statistical thermodynamics were considered to be equally fundamental and equally valid; in all cases in which they describe the same phenomena, they were placed in correspondence. Correspondences of the mechanical quantities followed immediately from the fundamental postulate stated previously. Identifications of the nonmechanical properties of classical thermodynamics with the corresponding parameters of statistical thermodynamics were realized (Chapter 5) in term-by-term comparisons of two alternative forms of the appropriate fundamental equation of statistical thermodynamics with two alternative forms of the appropriate fundamental equation of classical thermodynamics. The laws of statistical thermodynamics were considered to differ from the laws of classical thermodynamics only in that the laws of statistical thermodynamics refer to expected values, whereas the laws of classical thermodynamics refer to exact values (i.e., classical thermodynamics does not acknowledge that fluctuations are possible).

In order to avoid giving the reader the impression that the results of the first five chapters depend on use of a specific model of matter, the most restricting postulate concerning the nature of matter made in these chapters was that only discrete energy levels and discrete particle numbers are allowed for a finite system in a stationary state. Additional restrictions were added later (Chapter 6) in order to reduce the quantum-mechanical problem of predicting allowed quantum states from a many-body problem to essentially a single-body (or few-body) problem. For cases in which the particles are indistinguishable, the analysis was restricted to those cases in which effects of interparticle forces may be neglected to good approximation–so that the energy of the system could be written as the sum of the energies of the microscopic particles of the system. (The particles were considered to interact sufficiently, nevertheless, to maintain all parts of the system in thermal equilibrium and to impose symmetry restrictions on the quantum-mechanical wave functions.) These systems were divided, in principle, into two categories: Fermi-Dirac systems (Pauli exclusion principle applicable) and Bose-Einstein systems (Pauli exclusion principle not applicable). It was shown, however, that if the expected value of the number of particles per particle quantum state is small for all particle quantum states, then both Fermi-Dirac and Bose-Einstein systems may be approximated by Maxwell-Boltzman systems (and many calculations may be simplified). For cases in which the subsystems (or subsystem sites) are distinguishable, both the energies due to subsystem interactions and the symmetry restrictions on the quantum-mechanical wave functions were neglected, so that the system partition function could be written as a simple product of subsystem partition functions. (The subsystems were considered to interact sufficiently, nevertheless, to maintain all parts of the system in thermal equilibrium.) Detailed discussions of systems with distinguishable subsystems (or subsystem sites) were reserved for the time at which applications were discussed.

Procedures for predicting the allowed quantum states (and associated energy levels) were presented then in a brief introduction to the principles of quantum mechanics (Chapter 7). The wave-mechanics formulation of Schrödinger was summarized in the form of five basic postulates in order to provide a "recipe" for treating relatively simple nonrelativistic systems. Although this discussion of quantum mechanics was extremely brief and very elementary, it was adequate for the prediction of the allowed quantum states and associated energy levels required in the applications of statistical thermodynamics contained in the subsequent chapters.

In these subsequent chapters (Chapters 8 to 14), the fundamentals outlined in the preceding chapters were applied to the series of relatively simple examples listed in Table 15-1. These applications are considered to be an essential part of this introduction to statistical thermodynamics; it is believed that they simultaneously clarify the fundamentals and illustrate the capability of statistical thermodynamics to provide physical interpretations and numerical values of thermodynamic properties. (Recall that classical thermodynamics provides neither physical interpretations nor numerical values.) Calculations for more complicated models differ from the calculations presented in these chapters chiefly in that they are more tedious.

Table 15-1 Summary of applications, Chapters 8–14

Application	*System*	*Ensemble*
Perfect monatomic gas	Maxwell-Boltzmann	Grand canonical
Einstein monatomic crystal	Independent distinguishable subsystems	Canonical
Blackbody radiation	Bose-Einstein	Grand canonical
Perfect electron gas	Fermi-Dirac	Grand canonical
Localized adsorption	Independent distinguishable sites	Canonical
Mobile adsorption	Maxwell-Boltzmann	Grand canonical
Perfect diatomic gas	Maxwell-Boltzmann	Grand canonical
Debye monatomic crystal	Independent distinguishable subsystems	Canonical

In agreement with the discussions of Chapter 6, the applications listed in Table 15-1 may be divided into two broad categories: applications to systems of indistinguishable particles and applications to systems of independent distinguishable subsystems or subsystem sites. In order to avoid unnecessary computational difficulties (Appendix D), the grand canonical ensemble was used for all systems of indistinguishable particles (perfect monatomic gas, blackbody radiation, perfect electron gas, mobile adsorption, and perfect diatomic gas), whereas the canonical ensemble was used for all systems of independent distinguishable subsystems or subsystem sites (Einstein monatomic crystal, localized adsorption, and Debye monatomic crystal). Additional simplifications in computations were realized for systems of indistinguishable particles by using whenever applicable (perfect monatomic gas, mobile adsorption, and perfect diatomic gas) the Maxwell-Boltzmann approximation. One example each of a Bose-Einstein system (blackbody radiation) and of a Fermi-Dirac system (perfect electron gas) was included. An attempt was made to unify the methods used in these examples as much as possible without introducing unnecessary mathematical complications.

The main body of the text is augmented by 12 appendixes. Background information is included in the following five:

A. Stirling's approximation

- B. Variance and gaussian distribution curve
- C. Fundamental equations of classical thermodynamics
- G. Generalized coordinates and conjugate momenta
- H. Center-of-mass coordinate system

More extensive information is provided as follows:

- D. Several ensembles of statistical thermodynamics
- E. Entropy according to maximum-term method
- F. Probabilities and entropy as functions of availabilities
- I. Emissions from surfaces
- J. Maxwell-Boltzmann velocity distribution

Values of natural constants and conversion factors are tabulated in Appendixes K and L, respectively.

appendix A

stirling's approximation

A convenient approximate expression for the natural logarithm of $x!$ is desired. Examine the discontinuous curve of $\ln x$ versus x (see Figure A-1). Since the height of each column is $\ln x$ and the width of each column is unity, it is seen that the area under the discontinuous curve from 1/2 to x + 1/2 equals $\ln x!$. If one approximates the discontinuous curve by the continuous curve, then

$$\ln x! \approx \int_{1/2}^{x+1/2} \ln x' \, dx' \tag{A-1}$$

Integrating by parts,

$$\begin{aligned} \ln x! &\approx x' \ln x' \Big|_{1/2}^{x+1/2} - x' \Big|_{1/2}^{x+1/2} \\ &\approx (x + 1/2) \ln (x + 1/2) - 1/2 \ln 1/2 - (x + 1/2) + 1/2 \end{aligned} \tag{A-2}$$

If x is so large that one may neglect 1/2 in comparison with x, then

$$\ln x! \approx x \ln x - x \tag{A-3}$$

This approximation is used in Chapter 2.

Equation (A-2) may be written alternatively in the form

$$x! \approx \left(\frac{x + 1/2}{e}\right)^{x+1/2} (2e)^{1/2} \approx (2x)^{1/2} \left(1 + \frac{1}{2x}\right)^{x+1/2} \left(\frac{x}{e}\right)^{x} \tag{A-4}$$

For large x,

$$\left(1 + \frac{1}{2x}\right)^{x+1/2} \approx \left(1 + \frac{1}{2x}\right)^{x} \approx e^{1/2}$$

Hence, to the approximation used here,

$$(x!)_{x>>1} \approx (2ex)^{1/2} \left(\frac{x}{e}\right)^{x} \tag{A-6}$$

A more refined calculation (requiring more effort than expended here) yields

$$(x!)_{x>>1} \approx (2\pi x)^{1/2} \left(\frac{x}{e}\right)^{x} \tag{A-7}$$

or $$(\ln x!)_{x>>1} \approx (1/2)\ln 2\pi x + x\ln x - x \qquad \text{(A-8)}$$

If x is so large that one may neglect $1/2$ in comparison with x, then Equation (A-8) reduces to Equation (A-3). Less than one percent error is made using either Equation (A-3) with $x > 100$ or Equation (A-8) with $x > 10$. Both equations are known as Stirling's approximation.

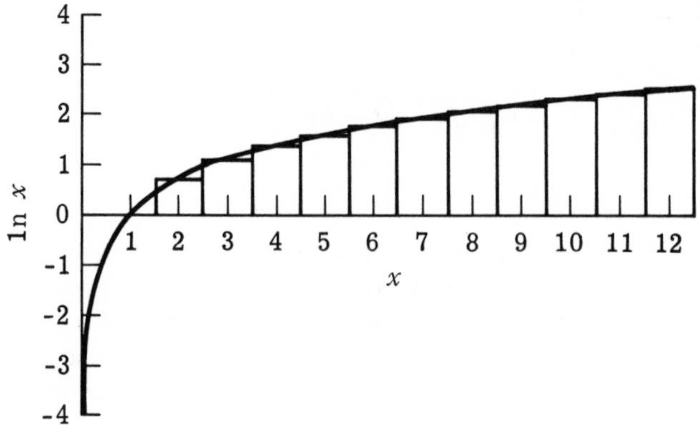

Figure A-1 *Exact representation (area under discontinuous curve) compared with approximate representation (area under continuous curve) of* $\ln x!$.

appendix B

variance and gaussian distribution curve

The comment that the gaussian (or normal) distribution curve "is characterized completely by the variance," made in Chapter 4, is elaborated on here. The equation for the **gaussian distribution curve** may be written

$$P = \frac{1}{\sqrt{2\pi\sigma^2(A)}} \exp\left[-\frac{(A - \langle A\rangle)^2}{2\sigma^2(A)}\right] \qquad \text{(B-1)}$$

In order to verify that $\langle A\rangle$ is the expected value of A, observe that

$$\begin{aligned}\langle A\rangle \equiv \int_{-\infty}^{+\infty} PA\,dA &= \int_{-\infty}^{+\infty} \frac{A}{\sqrt{2\pi\sigma^2(A)}} \exp\left[-\frac{(A-\langle A\rangle)^2}{2\sigma^2(A)}\right] dA \\ &= \sqrt{\frac{2\sigma^2(A)}{\pi}} \int_{-\infty}^{+\infty} \frac{A-\langle A\rangle}{\sqrt{2\sigma^2(A)}} \exp\left[-\frac{(A-\langle A\rangle)^2}{2\sigma^2(A)}\right] d\frac{A-\langle A\rangle}{\sqrt{2\sigma^2(A)}} \\ &\quad + \frac{\langle A\rangle}{\sqrt{\pi}} \int_{-\infty}^{+\infty} \exp\left[-\frac{(A-\langle A\rangle)^2}{2\sigma^2(A)}\right] d\frac{A-\langle A\rangle}{\sqrt{2\sigma^2(A)}} = 0 + \langle A\rangle \qquad \text{(B-2)}\end{aligned}$$

This result is a direct consequence of the symmetry of P about the point $A = \langle A\rangle$. In order to verify that $\sigma^2(A)$ is the variance of A, observe that

$$\begin{aligned}\sigma^2(A) \equiv \int_{-\infty}^{+\infty} P(A-\langle A\rangle)^2\,dA &= \int_{-\infty}^{+\infty} \frac{(A-\langle A\rangle)^2}{\sqrt{2\pi\sigma^2(A)}} \exp\left[-\frac{(A-\langle A\rangle)^2}{2\sigma^2(A)}\right] dA \\ &= \frac{2\sigma^2(A)}{\sqrt{\pi}} \int_{-\infty}^{+\infty} \frac{(A-\langle A\rangle)^2}{2\sigma^2(A)} \exp\left[-\frac{(A-\langle A\rangle)^2}{2\sigma^2(A)}\right] d\frac{A-\langle A\rangle}{\sqrt{2\sigma^2(A)}} \\ &= \sigma^2(A) \qquad \text{(B-3)}\end{aligned}$$

Note that $\sigma(A)$ is the root-mean-square deviation of A from $\langle A\rangle$. In order to verify that Equation (B-1) is normalized, observe that

$$\begin{aligned}1 \equiv \int_{-\infty}^{+\infty} P\,dA &= \int_{-\infty}^{+\infty} \frac{1}{\sqrt{2\pi\sigma^2(A)}} \exp\left[-\frac{(A-\langle A\rangle)^2}{2\sigma^2(A)}\right] dA \\ &= \frac{1}{\sqrt{\pi}} \int_{-\infty}^{+\infty} \exp\left[-\frac{(A-\langle A\rangle)^2}{2\sigma^2(A)}\right] d\frac{A-\langle A\rangle}{\sqrt{2\sigma^2(A)}} = 1 \qquad \text{(B-4)}\end{aligned}$$

Note that if P is normalized, then the probability that A has some value is unity. Since the variance $\sigma^2(A)$ is the only parameter which appears (in addition to the independent variable $A - \langle A \rangle$ and the dependent variable P) in Equation (B-1), it is seen that, as stated in Chapter 4, the curve P versus $A - \langle A \rangle$ is characterized completely by $\sigma^2(A)$. Gaussian curves for $\sigma^2(A) = 1/4$ and 4, with $\langle A \rangle = 2$, are given in Figure B-1. The inflection points occur at $A - \langle A \rangle = \pm\sigma(A)$; 68.3 and 99.7 percent of the area under a given curve are included, respectively, within $A - \langle A \rangle = \pm\sigma(A)$ and

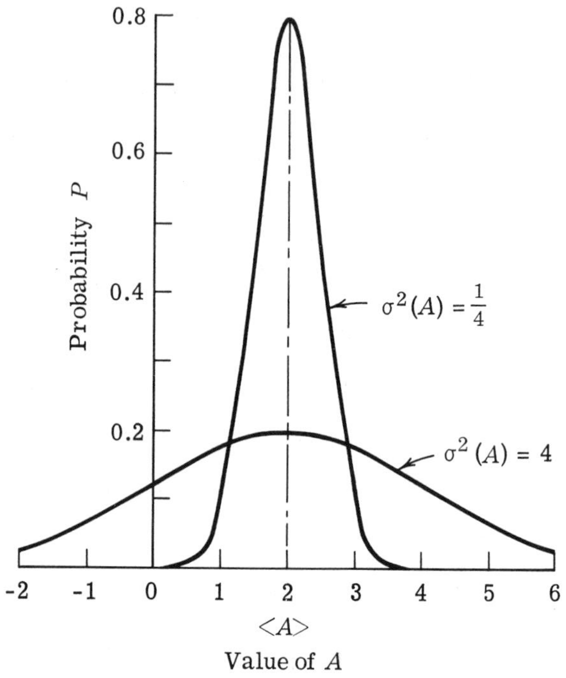

Figure B-1 *Gaussian (normal) distribution curves for $\sigma^2(A) = 1/4$ and 4, with $\langle A \rangle = 2$. (PdA is the probability that A lies in the range between A and $A + dA$.)*

within $A - \langle A \rangle = \pm 3\sigma(A)$. It is seen that if $\sigma(A) << \langle A \rangle$ (as is the case for many systems of interest to thermodynamicists), then the distribution is dominated by probabilities for A near $\langle A \rangle$.

The gaussian distribution curve is used frequently because (1) it describes the probability distribution for independent small deviations from an expected value and (2) it is simple mathematically. Distributions which are not described adequately by the gaussian curve (and which are not characterized completely by the variance) include broad distribution curves for cases in which the property A cannot have negative values.

appendix **C**

fundamental equations of classical thermodynamics

A **fundamental equation of thermodynamics** is an equation from which, with the aid of only definitions and *general* relations, the $K + 3$ independent relations between the $2K + 5$ thermodynamic variables E, S, V, N_i, T, p, and μ_i (with $i = 1, 2, \ldots, K$) may be deduced. (The number of independent variables is $K + 2$.) The most convenient fundamental equations are listed, for the convenience of the reader, in Table C-1. The dimensionless equations given on the right-hand side correspond to the fundamental equations of statistical thermodynamics given in Table 3-1; the variable (or combination of variables) appearing on the left-hand side of a dimensional equation is the product of kT and the variable (or combination of variables) appearing on the left-hand side of the associated dimensionless equation.

Of the listed fundamental equations, the reader is perhaps most familiar with

$$dE = T\,dS - p\,dV + \sum_i \mu_i\,dN_i \qquad \text{(C-1)}$$

The chemical potential μ_i may be considered to be defined by this equation, that is,

$$\mu_i \equiv \left(\frac{\partial E}{\partial N_i}\right)_{S,V,N_i'} \qquad \text{(C-2)}$$

where N_i' refers to all chemical species except the ith species. The equations for dH, dA, and dG follow from Equation (C-1) and the definitions

$$H \equiv E + pV \qquad \text{(C-3)}$$

$$A \equiv E - TS \qquad \text{(C-4)}$$

$$G \equiv H - TS \qquad \text{(C-5)}$$

As the first step in a derivation of the last dimensional equation, integrate Equation (C-1), holding the intensive properties constant, to obtain

$$E = TS - pV + \sum_i \mu_i N_i \qquad \text{(C-6)}$$

Table C-1 Several fundamental equations of classical thermodynamics
(All generalized forces except pressure equal zero.)

Dimensional equations	*Dimensionless equations*
$d(TS) = T\,ds + V\,dp - \sum_i N_i\,d\mu_i$	$d\left(\frac{S}{k}\right) = \frac{1}{kT}\,dE + \frac{p}{kT}\,dV - \sum_i \frac{\mu_i}{kT}\,dN_i$
$-dA = S\,dT + p\,dV - \sum_i \mu_i\,dN_i$	$-d\left(\frac{A}{kT}\right) = -E\,d\left(\frac{1}{kT}\right) + \frac{p}{kT}\,dV - \sum_i \frac{\mu_i}{kT}\,dN_i$
$dH = T\,dS + V\,dp + \sum_i \mu_i\,dN_i$	$d\left(\frac{H}{kT}\right) = \frac{1}{kT}\,dE + \frac{p}{kT}\,dV + \sum_i N_i\,d\left(\frac{\mu_i}{kT}\right)$
$d(pV) = S\,dT + p\,dV + \sum_i N_i\,d\mu_i$	$d\left(\frac{pV}{kT}\right) = -E\,d\left(\frac{1}{kT}\right) + \frac{p}{kT}\,dV + \sum_i N_i\,d\left(\frac{\mu_i}{kT}\right)$
$-d(pV - TS) = T\,dS - p\,dV - \sum_i N_i\,d\mu_i$	$-d\left(\frac{pV - TS}{kT}\right) = \frac{1}{kT}\,dE - V\,d\left(\frac{p}{kT}\right) - \sum_i \frac{\mu_i}{kT}\,dN_i$
$-dG = S\,dT - V\,dp - \sum_i \mu_i\,dN_i$	$-d\left(\frac{G}{kT}\right) = -E\,d\left(\frac{1}{kT}\right) - V\,d\left(\frac{p}{kT}\right) - \sum_i \frac{\mu_i}{kT}\,dN_i$
$dE = T\,dS - p\,dV + \sum_i \mu_i\,dN_i$	$d\left(\frac{E}{kT}\right) = \frac{1}{kT}\,dE - V\,d\left(\frac{p}{kT}\right) + \sum_i N_i\,d\left(\frac{\mu_i}{kT}\right)$
$0 = S\,dT - V\,dp + \sum_i N_i\,d\mu_i$	$0 = -E\,d\left(\frac{1}{kT}\right) - V\,d\left(\frac{p}{kT}\right) + \sum_i N_i\,d\left(\frac{\mu_i}{kT}\right)$

Differentiate, allowing both the intensive and the extensive properties to vary, to obtain

$$dE = T\,dS + S\,dT - p\,dV - V\,dp + \sum_i \mu_i\,dN_i + \sum_i N_i\,d\mu_i \qquad \text{(C-7)}$$

A comparison of Equations (C-1) and (C-7) yields the desired result, namely,

$$0 = S\,dT - V\,dp + \sum_i N_i\,d\mu_i \qquad \text{(C-8)}$$

(Note, incidentally, that the intensive variables T, p, and μ_i appearing here are those variables which must be uniform in a system in thermodynamic equilibrium.) The three remaining dimensional equations follow from Equation (C-8) and the identities

$$d(TS) \equiv T\,dS + S\,dT \qquad \text{(C-9)}$$

$$d(pV) \equiv p\,dV + V\,dp \qquad \text{(C-10)}$$

$$d(pV - TS) \equiv p\,dV + V\,dp - T\,dS - S\,dT \qquad \text{(C-11)}$$

The associated dimensionless equations may be obtained by appropriate manipulations and combinations of the dimensional equations.

Examine now the procedures for deriving the $K + 3$ independent relations between the $2K + 5$ relevant thermodynamic variables. The procedure applicable to the first seven listed fundamental equations is made apparent perhaps by an exemplary illustration: if $E(S, V, N_i)$ is known, then the $K + 3$ independent relations are

$$E = E(S, V, N_i) \qquad \text{(C-12)} ◀$$

$$T = \left(\frac{\partial E}{\partial S}\right)_{V, N_i} \qquad \text{(C-13)} ◀$$

$$p = -\left(\frac{\partial E}{\partial V}\right)_{S, N_i} \qquad \text{(C-14)} ◀$$

$$\mu_i = \left(\frac{\partial E}{\partial N_i}\right)_{S, V, N_i'} \qquad i = 1, 2, \ldots, K \qquad \text{(C-2)} ◀$$

where the last $K + 2$ equations follow from the fact that Equation (C-1) is a perfect differential, i.e., from the fact that the change in E is a unique function of the final and initial states of the system. The procedure applicable to the last listed fundamental equation differs slightly since T, p, and μ_i are all intensive properties. If $p(T, \mu_i)$ is known, then, from Equation (C-8),

$$\frac{S}{V} = \left(\frac{\partial p}{\partial T}\right)_{\mu_i} \qquad \text{(C-15)}$$

$$\frac{N_i}{V} = \left(\frac{\partial p}{\partial \mu_i}\right)_{T, \mu_i'} \qquad i = 1, 2, \ldots, K \qquad \text{(C-16)}$$

From Equation (C-6)

$$\frac{E}{V}(T, \mu_i) = \frac{S}{V}(T, \mu_i)\, T - p(T, \mu_i) + \sum_i \frac{N_i}{V}(T, \mu_i)\, \mu_i \qquad \text{(C-17)}$$

Hence the $K + 3$ independent relations are

▶ $$p = p(T, \mu_i) \qquad \text{(C-18)}$$

▶ $$S(T, V, \mu_i) = V\left(\frac{\partial p}{\partial T}\right)_{\mu_i} \qquad \text{(C-19)}$$

▶ $$N_i(T, V, \mu_i) = V\left(\frac{\partial p}{\partial \mu_i}\right)_{T, \mu_i'} \qquad i = 1, 2, \ldots, K \qquad \text{(C-20)}$$

▶ $$E(T, V, \mu_i) = TS(T, V, \mu_i) - p(T, \mu_i)V + \sum_i \mu_i N_i(T, V, \mu_i) \qquad \text{(C-21)}$$

The procedures for deriving the appropriate $K + 3$ independent relations from the associated dimensionless fundamental equations are similar.

Note that the $K + 3$ independent relations can be derived only from equations relating certain sets of variables. For example, these relations can be derived from $E(S, V, N_i)$ but not from $E(T, V, N_i)$, $E(S, p, N_i)$, or $E(T, p, N_i)$.

appendix D

several ensembles of statistical thermodynamics

As indicated in Chapter 3, many different types of ensembles of members (each type characterized by either the nature of the member boundary conditions and the roles of the generalized displacements or, alternatively, the independent variables) are possible. Eight of these many possible different types are identified in Table 3-1; two of these types (the grand canonical ensemble and the canonical ensemble) are used extensively in this book. In the present appendix, additional comments on and comparisons among these eight types of ensembles are made.

If one applies the methods of Chapter 3 to the eight types of ensembles listed in Table 3-1, then the eight associated partition functions listed in Table D-1 may be derived. From these partition functions, the expected

Table D-1 Several partition functions of statistical thermodynamics (All generalized forces except pressure equal zero.)

Independent variables	*Partition function* Q_z	*Analog of* $\ln Q_z$
E, V, N_i	$Q_1 = \Omega$	$\frac{S}{k}$
β, V, N_i	$Q_2 = \sum_j \exp(-\beta E_j)$	$-\frac{A}{kT}$
E, V, γ_i	$Q_3 = \sum_j \exp(-\sum_i \gamma_i N_{ij})$	$\frac{H}{kT}$
β, V, γ_i	$Q_4 = \sum_j \exp(-\beta E_j - \sum_i \gamma_i N_{ij})$	$\frac{pV}{kT}$
E, π, N_i	$Q_5 = \sum_j \exp(-\pi V_j)$	$-\frac{pV}{kT} + \frac{S}{k}$
β, π, N_i	$Q_6 = \sum_j \exp(-\beta E_j - \pi V_j)$	$-\frac{G}{kT}$
E, π, γ_i	$Q_7 = \sum_j \exp(-\sum_i \gamma_i N_{ij} - \pi V_j)$	$\frac{E}{kT}$
β, π, γ_i (except one)	$Q_8 = \sum_j \exp(-\beta E_j - \sum_i \gamma_i N_{ij} - \pi V_j)$	0

values and variances of the dependent variables may be calculated using the methods of Chapter 4. Valuable aid in the calculation of these expected values is provided by the fundamental equations of thermodynamics (see Table 3-1 and Appendix C).

Some of the partition functions listed in Table D-1 may be considered to be generalizations of other partition functions. For example, the last seven Q's may be considered to be generalizations of Q_1; Q_4 may be considered to be a generalization of either Q_2 or Q_3; Q_6 may be considered to be a generalization of either Q_2 or Q_5; Q_7 may be considered to be a generalization of either Q_3 or Q_5; whereas Q_8 may be considered to be a generalization of either Q_4, Q_6, or Q_7. In a more detailed illustration, the partition function for a grand canonical ensemble may be written as a function of partition functions for canonical ensembles using

$$Q_4(\beta, V, \gamma_i) = \sum_{N_i} Q_2(\beta, V, N_i) \exp\left(-\sum_i \gamma_i N_i\right) \tag{D-1}$$

Note that the symbols Q_2 and Q_4 used in Table 3-1 and in this appendix are equivalent to the symbols Q and Ξ used in other parts of this book.

Alternatively, some of the partition functions listed in Table D-1 may be considered to be degenerations of other partition functions. Degeneration of a given partition function is accomplished by retaining only the maximum term in a series representation of the given partition function in which other partition functions appear as term factors. In a detailed illustration, consider the grand partition function for the simple case in which only one chemical species is present:

$$Q_4(\beta, V, \gamma) = \sum_{N} Q_2(\beta, V, N)\, e^{-\gamma N}$$

The maximum term may be identified by setting the derivative of $Q_2(\beta, V, N)\, e^{-\gamma N}$ with respect to N equal to zero. If an asterisk indicates the N which yields the maximum term, then

$$\ln Q_4(\beta, V, \gamma) = \ln Q_2(\beta, V, N^*) - \gamma N^*$$

or, upon rearranging,

$$\ln Q_2(\beta, V, N^*) = \ln Q_4(\beta, V, \gamma) + \gamma N^* \tag{D-2}$$

Similarly, Q_1 may be related to Q_2 by

$$\ln Q_1(E^*, V, N) = \ln Q_2(\beta, V, N) + \beta E^* \tag{D-3}$$

Combining these two relations, Q_1 (the partition function for a microcanonical ensemble) may be related to Q_4 by

$$\ln Q_1(E^*, V, N^*) = \ln Q_4(\beta, V, \gamma) + \beta E^* + \gamma N^* \tag{D-4}$$

These three relations correspond to the identities

$$-\frac{A}{kT} \equiv \frac{pV}{kT} - \frac{\mu N}{kT} \tag{D-5}$$

$$\frac{S}{k} \equiv -\frac{A}{kT} + \frac{E}{kT} \tag{D-6}$$

$$\frac{S}{k} \equiv \frac{pV}{kT} + \frac{E}{kT} - \frac{\mu N}{kT} \tag{D-7}$$

of classical thermodynamics. Analogous degenerations of the remaining partition functions are possible also.

An examination of the derivative used in the identification of the maximum term gives additional meaning to the maximum-term method. For example, it is seen that, in setting the derivative of $Q_2(\beta, V, N)\, e^{-\gamma N}$ with respect to N equal to zero, one is selecting the value of N for which

$$\gamma = \left(\frac{\partial \ln Q_2(\beta, V, N)}{\partial N}\right)_{\beta, V}$$

which relation is consistent with the second line of Table 3-1.

Most results of interest to thermodynamicists are independent of the nature of the ensemble which is used. Hence, the ensemble type may be chosen frequently for mathematical convenience rather than for physical reasons. Exceptions include (1) variances of fluctuations, (2) the necessary and sufficient condition for thermodynamic equilibrium (see the following paragraph), (3) thermodynamic properties of systems with either small numbers of particles or small energies or small volumes (see Appendix E), and (4) the thermodynamic availability (see Appendix F). If any of these exceptional results are required, then the ensemble type with appropriate independent (nonfluctuating) and dependent (fluctuating) variables must be chosen.

Statistical-thermodynamical interpretations of necessary and sufficient conditions for equilibrium of a thermodynamic system are facilitated by the aforementioned consideration of some partition functions as generalizations of other partition functions. For definiteness, examine a grand canonical ensemble of members (line 4 of Table D-1). If $Q_4(\beta, V, \gamma_i)$ is considered to be a generalization of $Q_1(E, V, N_i)$, one may write

$$Q_4(\beta, V, \gamma_i) = \sum_{E, N_i} \Omega(E, V, N_i) \exp\left(-\beta E - \sum_i \gamma_i N_i\right) \tag{D-8}$$

where the summation is over energy levels E and particle numbers N_i (not over quantum states), and where $\Omega(E, V, N_i)$ is the number of possible member quantum states for a given set of values of E, V, and N_i. A necessary and sufficient condition for a spontaneous change (initiated perhaps by the removal of a restraint) in the thermodynamic state of this system is that, for at least one set of values of E, V, and N_i appearing in the aforementioned summation,

$$\Omega'(E, V, N_i) > \Omega(E, V, N_i) \tag{D-9}$$

where the unprimed and primed symbols refer respectively to the states before and after the spontaneous change. Since $\Omega'(E, V, N_i)$ can never be smaller than $\Omega(E, V, N_i)$, and since every term in the aforementioned summation is positive, it follows that, for every spontaneous change in the thermodynamic state of this system,

$$Q_4'(\beta, V, \gamma_i) > Q_4(\beta, V, \gamma_i) \tag{D-10}$$

or, in the nomenclature of classical thermodynamics,

$$p'(T, V, \mu_i) > p(T, V, \mu_i) \tag{D-10$'$}$$

Hence a necessary and sufficient condition for thermodynamic equilibrium is that the partition function (alternatively, the classical-thermodynamical analog of the logarithm of the partition function) is a maximum for the given values of the independent variables. Using similar arguments, it can be shown that this conclusion applies to all partition functions (excepting Q_8) listed in Table D-1. For example, a necessary and sufficient condition for thermodynamic equilibrium of a system with specified T, p, and N_i is that G is a minimum. It follows from this discussion that anything which can be done to increase the value of the partition function applicable to a given system will increase the stability of that system.

In a typical application of the results of the preceding paragraph, consider a system containing a mixture of several chemical species which are capable of reacting chemically. The equilibrium composition is that composition which maximizes the value of the partition function (or its classical analog) for the given values of the independent variables.

Not all these ensembles require the same level of mathematics. For example, if the member energy E is an independent variable (as in lines 1, 3, 5, and 7 of Table D-1), then the partition function is summed only over those quantum states with member energy E—a difficult summation, in general. Similarly, if the number of member particles N is an independent variable (as in lines 1, 2, 5, and 6 of Table D-1), then the partition function is summed only over those quantum states with number of member particles N—a summation which also requires relatively sophisticated mathematical techniques, in general. Finally, if the independent variables are all intensive (as in line 8 of Table D-1), then the partition function is constrained (and the mathematics is complicated) by the fact that one of the variables β, π, and γ_i is dependent. The only ensemble which avoids all of these complications is the ensemble with independent variables β, V, and γ_i (as in line 4 of Table D-1). This ensemble (the grand canonical ensemble) is used extensively in this book.

An additional advantage of using the grand canonical ensemble is realized in applications to many-body problems (problems in which effects of interparticle forces must be considered). For simplicity, consider a system containing only one chemical species. If one writes

$$\begin{aligned} Q_4(\beta, V, \gamma) &= \sum_N Q_2(\beta, V, N)\, e^{-\gamma N} \\ &= Q_2(\beta, V, 0) + Q_2(\beta, V, 1)\, e^{-\gamma} + Q_2(\beta, V, 2)\, e^{-2\gamma} + \cdots \end{aligned} \tag{D-11}$$

where $Q_4(\beta, V, \gamma)$ (alternatively, Ξ) and $Q_2(\beta, V, N)$ (alternatively, Q) are respectively the grand canonical and canonical partition functions, then the many-body problem may be reduced to a combination of one-body, two-body, etc., problems. Note that in the series given here, the canonical partition functions are coefficients in a series of powers of $e^{-\gamma}$.

Notable exceptions to the general comments of the preceding two paragraphs are provided by the Einstein monatomic crystal, the perfect localized adsorbed gas, and the Debye monatomic crystal. In each of these cases, the fact that the particles or subsystems may be considered to be distinguishable eliminates the primary motivation for avoiding the use of N as an independent variable. Furthermore, in the case of a crystal, the particle force constants and interaction energies depend upon the particle density, which would complicate summing over quantum states of members with identical volumes and different numbers of particles. In the case of a perfect localized adsorbed gas, advantages accrue from using a procedure similar to the procedure used for the Einstein monatomic crystal. Hence canonical ensembles are used in these three cases.

appendix E

entropy according to maximum-term method

The **maximum-term method**, in which only the maximum term in a series representation of the partition function is retained, has been introduced already in Appendix D. In the present appendix, this method is used to provide a simplified statistical-thermodynamical interpretation of entropy and its role in the second and third laws of thermodynamics. Although this method applies in principle only to microcanonical ensembles, it applies in practice to any ensemble of members for which γN, βE, and πV are large in comparison with unity for typical members.

From the first line of Table D-1, one obtains (without use of the maximum-term method) for a microcanonical ensemble

▶ $$\frac{S}{k} \sim \ln \Omega(E, V, N_i) \tag{E-1}$$

From Equations (D-3), (D-4), (D-6), and (D-7), one obtains (with use of the maximum-term method), for a canonical ensemble,

▶ $$\frac{S}{k} \sim \ln \Omega(E^*, V, N_i) \tag{E-2}$$

and for a grand canonical ensemble,

▶ $$\frac{S}{k} \sim \ln \Omega(E^*, V, N_i^*) \tag{E-3}$$

Note that the latter two equations are generalizations of the results of Appendix D in that more than one chemical species may be present. Similar expressions may be written for the other five ensembles of Table D-1; in each case, the fluctuating variables in the group (E, V, N_i) are assigned values associated with the maximum term in the relevant partition function.

A slightly different derivation of these results obtains if one begins with

$$\frac{S}{k} \sim -\sum_j P_j \ln P_j \tag{5-10}$$

and neglects all P_j's except those associated with the maximum term in the relevant partition function. Then the number of P_j's retained equals the number of possible ensemble quantum states for an ensemble of members, each member having the same energy, volume, and number of particles. Since each member quantum state has the same energy, volume, and number of particles, all the retained P_j's have equal values. Consider, for definiteness, a grand canonical ensemble. Then, in the present approximation,

$$P_j = \frac{1}{\Omega\,(E^*, V, N_i^*)} \tag{E-4}$$

where $\Omega\,(E^*, V, N_i^*)$ is the number of possible member quantum states for given values of E^*, V, and N_i^*. If one substitutes from Equation (E-4) into Equation (5-10), then

$$\begin{aligned}\frac{S}{k} &\sim -\,\Omega\,(E^*, V, N_i^*)\frac{1}{\Omega\,(E^*, V, N_i^*)}\ln\frac{1}{\Omega\,(E^*, V, N_i^*)}\\ &\sim \ln\Omega\,(E^*,V,N_i^*)\end{aligned}$$

which is Equation (E-3). Similar derivations may be written for the other ensembles.

Since Ω, the number of possible system quantum states, is a measure of the randomness or disorder in a system, relations such as Equations (E-1) to (E-3) relate clearly the entropy of a system to its randomness or disorder. The dependence of randomness or disorder on the energy, volume, and number of particles of the system is described quantitatively by

$$\langle\beta\rangle = \left(\frac{\partial \ln \Omega}{\partial E}\right)_{V,N_i} \tag{E-5}$$

$$\langle\pi\rangle = \left(\frac{\partial \ln \Omega}{\partial V}\right)_{E,N_i} \tag{E-6}$$

$$\langle\gamma_i\rangle = \left(\frac{\partial \ln \Omega}{\partial N_i}\right)_{E,V,N_i'} \tag{E-7}$$

which follow from the first line of Table 3-1. Since, for normal systems, $\beta\,(\sim 1/kT)$ and $\pi\,(\sim p/kT)$ are always positive, it is seen that increasing either the energy or volume of a normal system with a fixed number of particles always increases Ω; since $\gamma_i\,(\sim -\mu_i/kT)$ may be either positive or negative, it is seen that increasing the number of particles of a system with fixed energy and volume may either increase or decrease Ω, the effect on a given system depending on the values of E, V, and N_i. On the basis of these relations, one might anticipate that the entropy of a given quantity of matter, initially in the solid state, increases monotonically as it is melted, vaporized, dissociated, ionized, and expanded.

An estimate of the order of magnitude of this randomness or disorder may be obtained by inserting a typical value of entropy determined experimentally into Equation (E-1). For systems not too close to 0°K, one finds that typical values of entropy are of the order of Nk. Hence the number of allowed system quantum states Ω is of order e^N, where N is (for a typical macroscopic system) of the order of 10^{20}. It is seen that the randomness or disorder in a typical system is immense.

Now that the correspondence between the degeneracy $\Omega(E, V, N)$ (the number of possible member quantum states for a given set of values of E, V, and N) and the entropy has been established, probabilities of the type indicated in Equation (5-11) and Figure 5-3 may be discussed more quantitatively. Consider, for definiteness and simplicity, a canonical ensemble of members, each member containing N indistinguishable atoms of a perfect monatomic gas; neglect effects of all generalized forces except pressure. In analogy with Equation (5-11), the probability that a member has energy E may be written

$$P_E = \Omega(E, V, N)\frac{e^{-\beta E}}{Q(\beta, V, N)}$$

or, for convenience in calculations to follow,

$$P_E = \Omega(E^*, V, N)\frac{\Omega(E, V, N)}{\Omega(E^*, V, N)}\frac{e^{-\beta E}}{Q(\beta, V, N)} \tag{E-8}$$

From Equation (E-1),

$$\frac{\Omega(E, V, N)}{\Omega(E^*, V, N)} \sim \exp\frac{[S(E, V, N) - S(E^*, V, N)]}{k} \tag{E-9}$$

Combining Equations (8-13), (8-14), and (8-16), one obtains, for a perfect monatomic gas,

$$\frac{S(E, V, N) - S(E^*, V, N)}{k} = N\ln\left(\frac{E}{E^*}\right)^{3/2} = \frac{3}{2}N\ln\frac{E}{E^*} \tag{E-10}$$

Finally, combining Equations (E-8) to (E-10), one may write, for a perfect monatomic gas,

$$P_E = \Omega(E^*, V, N)\left(\frac{E}{E^*}\right)^{3/2\,N}\frac{e^{-\beta E}}{Q(\beta, V, N)} \tag{E-11}$$

The factor $e^{-\beta E}/Q(\beta, V, N)$, which decreases exponentially as E increases, is plotted schematically as a function of E in Figure 5-1; the factor $\Omega(E^*, V, N)(E/E^*)^{3/2\,N}$, which increases rapidly as E increases, is plotted schematically as a function of E in Figure 5-2. Although the form of the latter factor depends on the model being considered, the fact that this factor increases as E increases is a general result, as was shown in Equation (E-5). The fact that P_E attains its maximum value at $E = \langle E\rangle$ may be confirmed by setting the derivative of Equation (E-11) equal to zero. One obtains, for the model being examined,

$$E\,(\text{maximum}\,P_E) = \frac{3}{2}NkT \tag{E-12}$$

so that, by comparison with Equation (8-14), $E\,(\text{maximum}\,P_E) = \langle E \rangle$. The fact that P_E has a gaussian distribution for E near $\langle E \rangle$ may be confirmed by comparing the second derivative of Equation (E-11) with the second derivative of a gaussian curve at $E = \langle E \rangle$. From Equation (E-11),

$$\left.\frac{\partial^2 P_E}{\partial E^2}\right|_{E=\langle E \rangle} = -\frac{P_E(\langle E \rangle)}{\frac{3}{2}N(kT)^2} \tag{E-13}$$

From the results of Problem 8-3, for a canonical ensemble of members, each member containing a perfect monatomic gas,

$$\sigma^2(E) = \frac{3}{2}N(kT)^2 \tag{E-14}$$

Hence

$$\left.\frac{\partial^2 P_E}{\partial E^2}\right|_{E=\langle E \rangle} = -\frac{P_E(E)}{\sigma^2(E)} \tag{E-15}$$

Since one obtains the same result for a gaussian curve (see Appendix B), it is concluded that P_E has a gaussian distribution for E near $\langle E \rangle$.

The established correspondence between the degeneracy and the entropy facilitates also a discussion of the effect, on the degeneracy, of the symmetry restrictions on the quantum-mechanical wave functions. From Problem 6-2

$$\frac{S}{k} \sim -\sum_k [\langle N_k \rangle \ln \langle N_k \rangle - (1 + \langle N_k \rangle) \ln (1 + \langle N_k \rangle)] \qquad \text{Bose-Einstein}$$

$$\sim -\sum_k [\langle N_k \rangle \ln \langle N_k \rangle - \langle N_k \rangle] \qquad \text{Maxwell-Boltzmann}$$

$$\sim -\sum_k [\langle N_k \rangle \ln \langle N_k \rangle + (1 - \langle N_k \rangle) \ln (1 - \langle N_k \rangle)] \qquad \text{Fermi-Dirac}$$

Recall, from Figure 6-1, that, for a given value of $\beta\varepsilon_k + \gamma$,

$$\langle N_k \rangle_{\text{BE}} > \langle N_k \rangle_{\text{MB}} > \langle N_k \rangle_{\text{FD}}$$

Hence, a term-by-term comparison of the three entropy series reveals that

$$S_{\text{BE}} > S_{\text{MB}} > S_{\text{FD}}$$

so that, using Equation (E-1),

$$\Omega_{\text{BE}} > \Omega_{\text{MB}} > \Omega_{\text{FD}}$$

◀

The randomness or disorder is greatest in a Bose-Einstein system and least in a Fermi-Dirac system.

In another application of this statistical-thermodynamical interpretation of entropy, consider the spontaneous process which occurs when a restraint is removed from an isolated system which was in equilibrium initially (see Figure E-1 for a simple example of the removal of a restraint). Represent the entropy and the number of allowed system quantum states of the initial and final equilibrium thermodynamic states by S, Ω, S', and Ω'. As a consequence of the removal of the restraint, the number of possible system quantum states is increased, that is, $\Omega' > \Omega$. Hence the entropy change for this spontaneous process is

$$\frac{S' - S}{k} \sim \ln \frac{\Omega'}{\Omega} > 0 \tag{E-16}$$

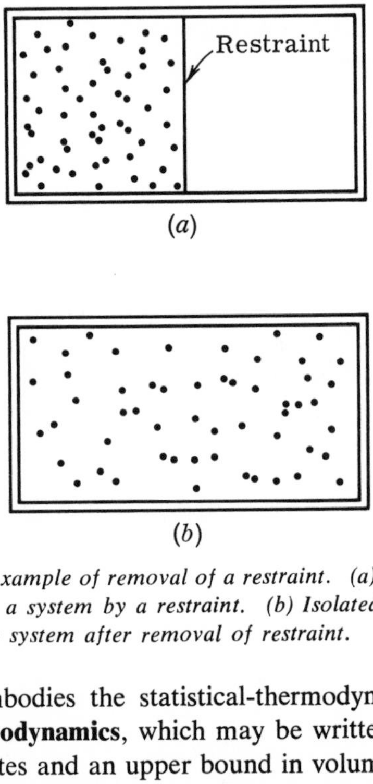

Figure E-1 *A simple example of removal of a restraint. (a) Isolated system with gas confined to one side of a system by a restraint. (b) Isolated system with gas free to move throughout entire system after removal of restraint.*

Equation (E-16) embodies the statistical-thermodynamical analog of the **second law of thermodynamics**, which may be written:[1] "A system having specified allowed states and an upper bound in volume can reach from any given state a stable state and leave no net effect on the environment." Note that Equation (E-16) says nothing about the behavior of an individual member of an ensemble–it describes (as a consequence of the postulates of Chapter 2) only the behavior of the ensemble.

Consider finally the statistical-thermodynamical analog of the third law

[1]G. N. Hatsopoulos and J. H. Keenan, "Principles of General Thermodynamics," p. 34, John Wiley & Sons, Inc., New York, 1965.

of thermodynamics. Adopt an operational viewpoint, and include in Ω only those quantum states which are accessible at elevated temperatures and become inaccessible as the temperature is decreased. (Depending on the system being considered, this viewpoint may exclude quantum states associated with isotope mixing, nuclear ground states, and frozen-in metastabilities.) Then the ground state is nondegenerate and

$$\lim_{T\to 0} \frac{S}{k} \sim \lim_{\beta\to\infty} \ln \Omega = \ln 1 = 0 \qquad \text{(E-17)}$$

Equation (E-17) embodies the statistical-thermodynamical analog of the **third law of thermodynamics**. If one were to adopt an alternative viewpoint, and include in Ω all known quantum states (including, perhaps, some whose accessibility does not change as the system temperature decreases), then the ground state might be degenerate and

$$\lim_{T\to 0} \frac{S}{k} \sim \lim_{\beta\to\infty} \ln \Omega = \ln \Omega_0 \qquad \text{(E-18)}$$

where $\Omega_0 \geqq 1$, that is, the entropy would approach a constant as the temperature approaches zero. Equation (E-18) would provide an equally satisfactory statistical-thermodynamical analog of the third law; the selection of the zero point is arbitrary in both Equation (E-17) and Equation (E-18). (Note that the zero point used in the second equation would change as the accepted model of matter changed, i.e., as the number of "known quantum states" changed.) The important feature of the third law is that the entropy of a system approaches a constant as temperature approaches zero; the value that one chooses to assign to this constant is unimportant.

appendix **F**

probabilities and entropy as functions of availabilities

The purpose of this appendix is to call attention to a simple and useful relation[1] between the probabilities used in statistical thermodynamics and the availabilities used in classical thermodynamics. Using this relation, still another interpretation of the entropy of an ensemble of members is possible.

Consider, for definiteness, a grand canonical ensemble of members in which the only significant generalized force is pressure. The probability P_{E,N_i} that a member has energy E and particle number N_i (not quantum state j) is given by Equation (5-11):

$$P_{E,N_i} = \Omega(E, V, N_i) \frac{\exp(-\beta E - \sum_i \gamma_i N_i)}{\Xi} \qquad (5\text{-}11)$$

whereas the grand partition function Ξ is related to expected values of quantities by Equation 5-9):

$$\ln \Xi = -\beta \langle E \rangle - \sum_i \gamma_i \langle N_i \rangle - \sum_j P_j \ln P_j \qquad (5\text{-}9)$$

If one eliminates Ξ from these two equations, then

$$P_{E,N_i} = \exp[-\beta(E - \langle E \rangle) - \sum_i \gamma_i (N_i - \langle N_i \rangle) + \ln \Omega(E, V, N_i) + \sum_j P_j \ln P_j] \qquad (\text{F-1})$$

or, using the nomenclature of classical thermodynamics in the right-hand side,

$$P_{E,N_i} \sim \exp\left\{-\frac{1}{kT_0}[(E - E_0) - \sum_i \mu_{i0}(N_i - N_{i0}) - T_0(S - S_0)]\right\} \qquad (\text{F-1}')$$

where T_0 and μ_{i0} are, respectively, the temperature and chemical potential of the environment and E_0, N_{i0}, and S_0 are, respectively, the energy, particle

[1]This relation appears to have been derived first by Dr. George N. Hatsopoulos of the Massachusetts Institute of Technology; his generosity in communicating it to the author prior to publication is appreciated.

number, and entropy of the system when in equilibrium with its environment. The maximum useful work effect which can be realized as an open system proceeds (at constant volume) from a state with property values E, V, N_i to a state in equilibrium with its environment is given by

$$\Lambda = (E - E_0) - \sum_i \mu_{i0} (N_i - N_{i0}) - T_0 (S - S_0) \qquad \text{(F-2)}$$

where Λ is **availability**. Combining Equations (F-1′) and (F-2), the probability P_{E,N_i} may be related to the availability Λ by

$$P_{E,N_i} \sim \exp\left(-\frac{\Lambda}{kT_0}\right) \qquad \text{(F-3)}$$

Relations entirely analogous to Equation (F-3) may be written for any type of ensemble; probabilities and availabilities for several types of ensembles are given in Table F-1. Equation (F-3) facilitates calculations of probabilities from experimental data on availabilities. (Calculations for molecular models are not required.)

In order to obtain another interpretation of the entropy of an ensemble of members, a relation similar to Equation (F-3) is required for the probability P_j. The probability P_j that a member of a grand canonical ensemble is in quantum state j is given by Equation (3-15)

$$P_j = \frac{\exp(-\beta E_j - \sum_i \gamma_i N_{ij})}{\Xi} \qquad \text{(3-15)}$$

If one eliminates Ξ from Equation (3-15) and Equation (5-9), then

$$P_j = \exp[-\beta (E_j - \langle E \rangle) - \sum_i \gamma_i (N_{ij} - \langle N_i \rangle) + \sum_j P_j \ln P_j] \qquad \text{(F-4)}$$

The expected value of the maximum useful work effect–which can be realized as a grand canonical ensemble member, initially in its jth quantum state, interacts with its surroundings–is given by

$$\beta \Lambda_j = \beta (E_j - \langle E \rangle) + \sum_i \gamma_i (N_{ij} - \langle N_i \rangle) - \sum_j P_j \ln P_j \qquad \text{(F-5)}$$

where Λ_j is availability. Combining Equations (F-4) and (F-5), one may relate the probability P_j to the availability Λ_j by

$$P_j = e^{-\beta \Lambda_j} \qquad \text{(F-6)}$$

Written in this form, the relation is applicable to any type of ensemble; it indicates that once the quantum state of a member has been identified, a useful work effect,

$$\Lambda_j = -\frac{1}{\beta} \ln P_j \qquad \text{(F-7)}$$

may be realized. From the second law of thermodynamics, however, an interaction with an ensemble which is initially in equilibrium with its en-

Table F-1 Probabilities and availabilities for several ensembles
(All generalized forces except pressure equal zero.)

Independent variables	*Probability*	*Availability*[†] Λ
E, V, N_i	Not relevant	0
β, V, N_i	P_E	$(E - E_0) - T_0 (S - S_0)$
E, V, γ_i	P_{N_i}	$-\sum_i \mu_{i0} (N_i - N_{i0}) - T_0 (S - S_0)$
β, V, γ_i	P_{E, N_i}	$(E - E_0) - \sum_i \mu_{i0} (N_i - N_{i0}) - T_0 (S - S_0)$
E, π, N_i	P_V	$p_0 (V - V_0) - T_0 (S - S_0)$
β, π, N_i	$P_{E, V}$	$(E - E_0) + p_0 (V - V_0) - T_0 (S - S_0)$
E, π, γ_i	P_{V, N_i}	$p_0 (V - V_0) - \sum_i \mu_{i0} (N_i - N_{i0}) - T_0 (S - S_0)$
β, π, γ_i (except one)	P_{E, V, N_i}	$(E - E_0) + p_0 (V - V_0) - \sum_i \mu_{i0} (N_i - N_{i0}) - T_0 (S - S_0)$

[†]The availability given in the last line was used by Gibbs in 1875. See H. A. Bumstead and R. G. Van Name (eds.), "The Collected Works of J. Willard Gibbs," vol. I, p. 77, eq. (54), Yale University Press, New Haven, Conn., 1948. For a recent discussion of the availability given in line 6, see G. N. Hatsopoulos and J. H. Keenan, "Principles of General Thermodynamics," chap. 1, John Wiley & Sons, Inc., New York, 1965.

vironment cannot have, as its sole effect, the performance of useful work by the ensemble. Hence the minimum work of identifying the quantum state of a member of an ensemble must be equal in magnitude and opposite in sign to the maximum useful work which can be obtained from the member once it has been identified. Thus, substituting from Equation (F-7) into Equation (5-10),

$$\frac{S}{k} \sim -\sum_j P_j \ln P_j \tag{5-10}$$

one obtains

$$\frac{S}{k} \sim \beta \sum_j P_j \Lambda_j \tag{F-8}$$ ◀

which states that the entropy of a system is proportional to the average minimum work per member required to identify the quantum states of the members of the ensemble corresponding to the system. This interpretation of entropy supplements the interpretations provided in Chapter 5 and Appendix E.

appendix **G**

generalized coordinates and conjugate momenta

An efficient and generalized discussion of mechanics can be based on the use of generalized coordinates and associated generalized (conjugate) momenta. Hence, since these coordinates and momenta are used in Chapter 7, they are reviewed briefly here for the benefit of the reader who desires such a review. The reader who desires a more complete discussion is referred to a textbook on mechanics.

Consider the general orthogonal curvilinear coordinates $q_1, q_2, \ldots, q_\phi$, where ϕ is the number of degrees of freedom. These coordinates may be, for example, rectangular coordinates, radii, or angles. Since, in general, they are not lengths, one may express arc lengths $ds_1, ds_2, \ldots, ds_\phi$ in the direction of positive $q_1, q_2, \ldots, q_\phi$ by relations of the form

$$\begin{aligned} ds_1 &= h_1\, dq_1 \\ ds_2 &= h_2\, dq_2 \\ &\cdots\cdots \\ ds_\phi &= h_\phi\, dq_\phi \end{aligned} \tag{G-1}$$

The factors $h_1, h_2, \ldots, h_\phi$ are called "scale factors." For rectangular coordinates, these scale factors are unity; for general curvilinear coordinates, they may be functions of the coordinates. Elements of volume and length are given, respectively, by

$$dV = h_1\, dq_1\, h_2\, dq_2 \cdots h_\phi\, dq_\phi \tag{G-2}$$

and

$$(ds)^2 = (h_1\, dq_1)^2 + (h_2\, dq_2)^2 + \cdots + (h_\phi\, dq_\phi)^2 \tag{G-3}$$

Expressions for the scale factors may be obtained by relating the curvilinear coordinates to rectangular coordinates (see Figure G-1). Then

$$(h_1\, dq_1)^2 = \left(\frac{\partial x_1}{h_1\, \partial q_1} h_1\, dq_1\right)^2 + \left(\frac{\partial x_2}{h_1\, \partial q_1} h_1\, dq_1\right)^2 + \cdots + \left(\frac{\partial x_\phi}{h_1\, \partial q_1} h_1\, dq_1\right)^2$$

$$(h_2\,dq_2)^2 = \left(\frac{\partial x_1}{h_2\,\partial q_2}h_2\,dq_2\right)^2 + \left(\frac{\partial x_2}{h_2\,\partial q_2}h_2\,dq_2\right)^2 + \cdots + \left(\frac{\partial x_\phi}{h_2\,\partial q_2}h_2\,dq_2\right)^2$$

. . . .

$$(h_\phi\,dq_\phi)^2 = \left(\frac{\partial x_1}{h_\phi\,\partial q_\phi}h_\phi\,dq_\phi\right)^2 + \left(\frac{\partial x_2}{h_\phi\,\partial q_\phi}h_\phi\,dq_\phi\right)^2 + \cdots + \left(\frac{\partial x_\phi}{h_\phi\,\partial q_\phi}h_\phi\,dq_\phi\right)^2 \tag{G-4}$$

where $x_1, x_2, \ldots, x_\phi$ are rectangular coordinates. Hence, after simplifying,

$$h_1^2 = \left(\frac{\partial x_1}{\partial q_1}\right)^2 + \left(\frac{\partial x_2}{\partial q_1}\right)^2 + \cdots + \left(\frac{\partial x_\phi}{\partial q_1}\right)^2$$

$$h_2^2 = \left(\frac{\partial x_1}{\partial q_2}\right)^2 + \left(\frac{\partial x_2}{\partial q_2}\right)^2 + \cdots + \left(\frac{\partial x_\phi}{\partial q_2}\right)^2 \tag{G-5}$$

. . . .

$$h_\phi^2 = \left(\frac{\partial x_1}{\partial q_\phi}\right)^2 + \left(\frac{\partial x_2}{\partial q_\phi}\right)^2 + \cdots + \left(\frac{\partial x_\phi}{\partial q_\phi}\right)^2$$

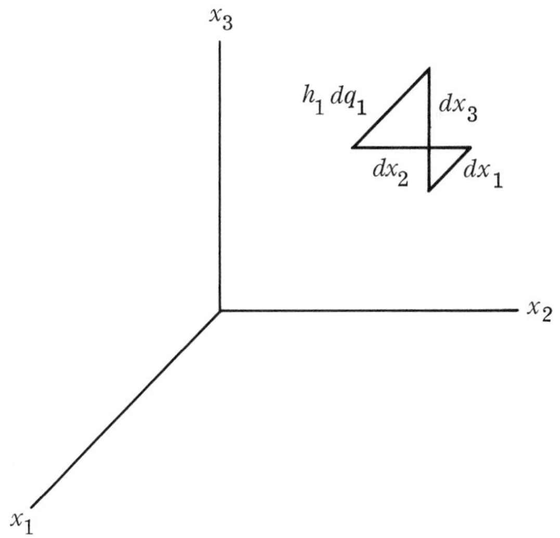

Figure G-1 *The arc length h_1dq_1 related to length elements dx_1, dx_2, and dx_3 for the case in which $\phi = 3$.*

This procedure for obtaining expressions for the scale factors is clarified perhaps by an example.

Example

Consider spherical polar coordinates (see Figure 7-1). Let

$$q_1 = r \qquad q_2 = \theta \qquad q_3 = \phi$$

Then

$$x_1 = r \sin\theta \cos\phi \qquad x_2 = r \sin\theta \sin\phi \qquad x_3 = r\cos\theta$$

$$h_1^2 = (\sin\theta\cos\phi)^2 + (\sin\theta\sin\phi)^2 + (\cos\theta)^2 = 1$$

$$h_2^2 = (r\cos\theta\cos\phi)^2 + (r\cos\theta\sin\phi)^2 + (r\sin\theta)^2 = r^2$$

$$h_3^2 = (r\sin\theta\sin\phi)^2 + (r\sin\theta\cos\phi)^2 + 0 = (r\sin\theta)^2$$

$$(ds)^2 = dr^2 + (r\,d\theta)^2 + (r\sin\theta\,d\phi)^2$$

$$dV = dr\; r\,d\theta\; r\sin\theta\,d\phi$$

These results will be used in a later example involving generalized momenta.

Now consider the generalized momenta associated with these generalized coordinates. For convenience, these momenta are called frequently conjugate momenta. If the potential energy of the system is a function of the generalized coordinates only, one may define the **conjugate momentum** by

$$p_x = \left(\frac{\partial \text{ kinetic energy}}{\partial \dot{q}_x}\right)_{\dot{q}_x', q_x, t} \tag{G-6}$$

where $\dot{q}_x$ is dq_x/dt, t is time, and the subscript $\dot{q}_x'$ means that all $\dot{q}$'s are held constant except $\dot{q}_x$. If the generalized coordinates may be obtained from cartesian coordinates by a transformation which does not contain time explicitly, then the kinetic energy of the system may be written, in terms of the generalized coordinates, in the form

$$\text{Kinetic energy} = \sum_{x=1}^{\phi} \frac{1}{2} m_x (h_x \dot{q}_x)^2 \tag{G-7}$$

where m_x is the effective mass for motion in the q_x direction. Applying Equation (G-6) to Equation (G-7), one obtains

$$p_x = \frac{\partial}{\partial \dot{q}_x} \sum_{x=1}^{\phi} \frac{1}{2} m_x (h_x \dot{q}_x)^2 = m_x h_x^2 \dot{q}_x \tag{G-8}$$

Hence the expression for the kinetic energy may be written, in terms of the conjugate momenta, in the form

$$\text{Kinetic energy} = \sum_{x=1}^{\phi} \frac{(p_x/h_x)^2}{2m_x} \tag{G-9}$$

This form of the expression for kinetic energy is used in Postulate 2 of Chapter 7. These comments concerning conjugate momenta are clarified perhaps by an example.

Example

Consider a particle with mass μ moving, with negligible effects of external fields, in a spherical polar coordinate system, the origin of which coincides with the origin of a cartesian coordinate system. Then, combining the results of the preceding example with Equations (G-7) to (G-9), one obtains

$$\text{Kinetic energy} = \frac{\mu}{2}[\dot{r}^2 + (r\dot{\theta})^2 + (r \sin \theta\dot{\phi})^2]$$

$$p_1 = \mu\dot{r}$$

$$p_2 = \mu r^2 \dot{\theta}$$

$$p_3 = \mu (r \sin \theta)^2 \dot{\phi}$$

$$\text{Kinetic energy} = \frac{1}{2\mu}\left[p_1^2 + \left(\frac{p_2}{r}\right)^2 + \left(\frac{p_3}{r \sin \theta}\right)^2\right]$$

This example illustrates the fact that, in general, the conjugate momenta are not products of mass and velocity.

appendix **H**

center-of-mass coordinate system

Discussions of the rotational and vibrational motions of the diatomic molecule are facilitated by use of a center-of-mass coordinate system (see Chapter 13). Hence a relatively simple motivation for use of a center-of-mass coordinate system is provided here.

For convenience, consider two particles moving in one dimension; take into account the potential energy due to interparticle forces (see Figure 13-2) but neglect potential energies due to external forces. (Although this choice of model requires relatively simple mathematics, it motivates adequately the use of a center-of-mass coordinate system.) Represent the masses and positions of the two particles by m_1, m_2, and x_1 *and* x_2 (see Figure H-1). Applying the methods of Chapter 7, the amplitude (time-independent factor) $\psi(x_1, x_2)$ of the wave function $\Psi(x_1, x_2, t)$ which describes the motion of these two particles must satisfy the time-independent wave equation

$$-\frac{\hbar^2}{2m_1}\frac{\partial^2 \psi(x_1, x_2)}{\partial x_1^2} - \frac{\hbar^2}{2m_2}\frac{\partial^2 \psi(x_1, x_2)}{\partial x_2^2} + U(x_2 - x_1)\,\psi(x_1, x_2) = \varepsilon\psi(x_1, x_2) \tag{H-1}$$

Search for a set of coordinates X and x which replace the coordinates x_1 and x_2 and which facilitate replacing Equation (H-1) by two independent equations–one describing motion of the center of mass and the other describing relative motion of the two particles. Try

$$X = \alpha x_1 + \beta x_2 \qquad x = x_2 - x_1 \tag{H-2}$$

where α and β are factors whose values are to be chosen so that the aforementioned goal is reached. Expressions for the derivatives appearing in Equation (H-1) are required. One obtains

$$\frac{\partial \psi}{\partial x_1} = \frac{\partial \psi}{\partial x}\frac{\partial x}{\partial x_1} + \frac{\partial \psi}{\partial X}\frac{\partial X}{\partial x_1} = -\frac{\partial \psi}{\partial x} + \alpha\frac{\partial \psi}{\partial X}$$

$$\frac{\partial^2 \psi}{\partial x_1^2} = \frac{\partial}{\partial x}\left(\frac{\partial \psi}{\partial x_1}\right)\frac{\partial x}{\partial x_1} + \frac{\partial}{\partial X}\left(\frac{\partial \psi}{\partial x_1}\right)\frac{\partial X}{\partial x_1} = \frac{\partial^2 \psi}{\partial x^2} - 2\alpha\frac{\partial^2 \psi}{\partial x\,\partial X} + \alpha^2\frac{\partial^2 \psi}{\partial X^2}$$

$$\frac{\partial\psi}{\partial x_2} = \frac{\partial\psi}{\partial x}\frac{\partial x}{\partial x_2} + \frac{\partial\psi}{\partial X}\frac{\partial X}{\partial x_2} = \frac{\partial\psi}{\partial x} + \beta\frac{\partial\psi}{\partial X}$$

$$\frac{\partial^2\psi}{\partial x_2{}^2} = \frac{\partial^2\psi}{\partial x^2} + 2\beta\frac{\partial^2\psi}{\partial x\,\partial X} + \beta^2\frac{\partial^2\psi}{\partial X^2}$$

Hence

$$\frac{1}{m_1}\frac{\partial^2\psi}{\partial x_1{}^2} + \frac{1}{m_2}\frac{\partial^2\psi}{\partial x_2{}^2} = \left(\frac{1}{m_1} + \frac{1}{m_2}\right)\frac{\partial^2\psi}{\partial x^2} + \left(\frac{2\beta}{m_2} - \frac{2\alpha}{m_1}\right)\frac{\partial^2\psi}{\partial x\,\partial X} + \left(\frac{\alpha^2}{m_1} + \frac{\beta^2}{m_2}\right)\frac{\partial^2\psi}{\partial X^2}$$

In order to eliminate the mixed derivative $\partial^2\psi/\partial x\partial X$, choose

$$\frac{\beta}{m_2} = \frac{\alpha}{m_1}$$

Then

$$X = \frac{\alpha}{m_1}(m_1 x_1 + m_2 x_2)$$

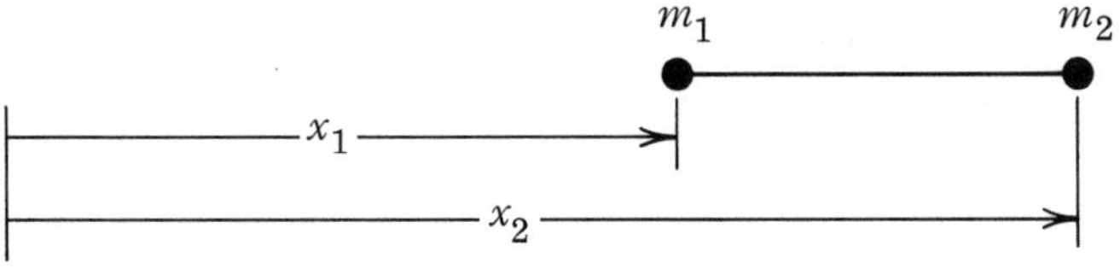

Figure H-1 *Simple model examined in order to motivate use of center-of-mass coordinate system.*

The coordinate X may be used to describe the motion of the center of mass provided that the mass factor appearing in the coefficient of the derivative $\partial^2\psi/\partial X^2$ is equal to $1/(m_1 + m_2)$. Hence, choose

$$\frac{\alpha}{m_1} = \frac{1}{m_1 + m_2}$$

Then

$$X = \frac{m_1 x_1 + m_2 x_2}{m_1 + m_2} \qquad \text{(H-3)}$$

and Equation (H-1) may be written

$$-\frac{\hbar^2}{2\mu}\frac{\partial^2\psi(x, X)}{\partial x^2} - \frac{\hbar^2}{2M}\frac{\partial^2\psi(x, X)}{\partial X^2} + U(x)\,\psi(x, X) = \varepsilon\psi(x, X) \qquad \text{(H-4)}$$

where μ (the **reduced mass**) and M (the **combined mass**) are defined by

$$\frac{1}{\mu} = \frac{1}{m_1} + \frac{1}{m_2} \qquad \text{(H-5)}$$

and

$$M = m_1 + m_2 \qquad \text{(H-6)}$$

In an attempt to separate variables, let $\psi(x, X) = \chi(x)\,\mathbf{X}(X)$. Substitute into Equation (H-4) and divide by $\chi(x)\mathbf{X}(X)$ to obtain

$$\frac{1}{\chi}\left(\frac{\hbar^2}{2\mu}\frac{d^2\chi}{dx^2} - U\chi + \varepsilon\chi\right) = -\frac{1}{\mathbf{X}}\frac{\hbar^2}{2M}\frac{d^2\chi}{dX^2} \tag{H-7}$$

Since the left-hand side is not a function of $\mathbf{X}$ and the right-hand side is not a function of χ, Equation (H-7) can hold only if each side is a function of some constant. If one designates the constant by ε_{tr}, then

$$-\frac{\hbar^2}{2M}\frac{d^2\mathbf{X}}{dX^2} = \varepsilon_{tr}\mathbf{X} \tag{H-8}$$

and

$$-\frac{\hbar^2}{2\mu}\frac{d^2\mathbf{X}}{dX^2} + U\chi = (\varepsilon - \varepsilon_{tr})\chi \tag{H-9}$$

where ε_{tr} is the energy associated with the translational motion of the center of mass. It is seen that $\mathbf{X}(X)$ is the time-independent wave function for a particle with mass M moving (e.g., translating) with negligible effects of external fields, whereas $\chi(x)$ is the time-independent wave function for a particle with mass μ moving (e.g., vibrating) in a field with potential $U(x)$. Hence, by using the **center-of-mass coordinate** X and the **relative coordinate** x, the problem of finding solutions to Equation (H-1) is replaced by the simpler problem of finding solutions to Equations (H-8) and (H-9). Solutions to the latter two equations are given respectively in Problems 7-1 and 7-2.

For convenience in the preceding discussion, the two particles were considered to move in one dimension (i.e., translation and vibration were considered, whereas rotation about the center of mass was neglected). Analogous results obtain if the particles are considered to move in three dimensions; the resulting wave equation for rotation with constant interparticle distance and about the center of mass is given as Equation (13-6).

appendix I

emissions from surfaces

The engineer or scientist is interested frequently in the rate of transfer of particles to or from condensed phases. Detailed analyses of such transfer rates (including, for example, thermal radiation rates, thermionic emission rates, and evaporation rates) require the methods of the discipline known sometimes as physical kinetics. However, many features of these rates may be described by slight extensions of the results of statistical thermodynamics. Hence a brief discussion of these transfer rates (a discussion which leans heavily on the results of Chapters 8, 10, and 11) is presented here.

The approach used is based on the fact that if a condensed phase is in equilibrium with a gas phase, then the gross transfer rate from the condensed phase to the gas phase must equal the gross transfer rate to the condensed phase from the gas phase (the net transfer rate is zero). Hence the relatively difficult calculation of the gross transfer rate from the condensed phase to the gas phase may be replaced, in most applications, by the relatively simple calculation of the gross transfer rate to the condensed phase from a (sometimes hypothetical) gas phase in equilibrium with the condensed phase. This calculation procedure requires (1) the approximation that, for a given state of the condensed phase, the gross transfer rate from the condensed phase to the gas phase is independent of the state of the gas phase, and (2) an experimental determination of the fraction of particles incident on the surface of the condensed phase which enter the condensed phase. The required approximation appears to be in good agreement with experimental observations; the required experimental determination is found to be much more convenient, in practice, than the direct calculation of the gross transfer rate from the condensed phase to the gas phase.

In order to obtain an expression for the number of particles which collide per unit area and per unit time with a surface bounding a gas phase, consider the flux of particles crossing, in one direction, an arbitrary plane in the gas phase. Use a spherical coordinate system with the $\theta = \pi/2$ plane coincident with the aforementioned arbitrary plane (see Figure I-1). The flux of particles crossing this plane and having simultaneously an energy in the range from ε to $\varepsilon + d\varepsilon$ and a direction of motion in the range of solid angle from ω to $\omega + d\omega$ (where $d\omega \equiv \sin\theta\, d\phi\, d\theta$) is given by

$$dJ_N = \frac{1}{V}\frac{d\langle N\rangle}{d\varepsilon}\, d\varepsilon\, \frac{d\omega}{4\pi}\, v\cos\theta \qquad \text{(I-1)}$$

where $(1/V)(d\langle N\rangle/d\varepsilon)\,d\varepsilon$ is the number density of particles in energy range $d\varepsilon$, $d\omega/4\pi$ is the fraction of particles with direction of motion in solid-angle range $d\omega$ (see Figure I-2), and $v\cos\theta$ is the magnitude of the velocity component normal to the given plane. If the "arbitrary plane in the gas phase" is replaced now by the interface between a gas phase and a condensed

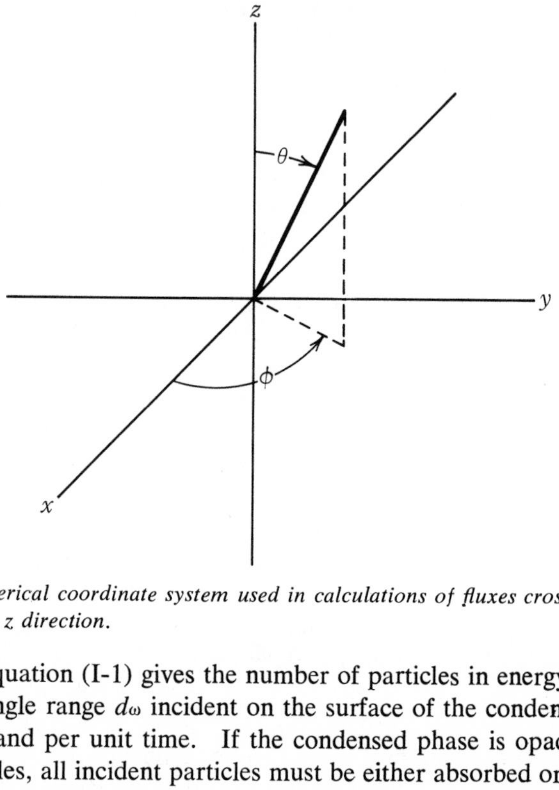

Figure I-1 *Spherical coordinate system used in calculations of fluxes crossing the xy plane in positive z direction.*

phase, then Equation (I-1) gives the number of particles in energy range $d\varepsilon$ and in solid-angle range $d\omega$ incident on the surface of the condensed phase per unit area and per unit time. If the condensed phase is opaque to the incident particles, all incident particles must be either absorbed or reflected. If, in addition, the two phases are in equilibrium, then the rate at which incident particles are absorbed must equal the rate at which particles are emitted by the condensed phase. Hence up to a multiplicative absorption coefficient (which is to be determined experimentally), the flux emitted by a condensed phase may be calculated from considerations of a (sometimes hypothetical) gas phase in equilibrium with the condensed phase and one may write

$$dJ_N'(\varepsilon, \omega) = \alpha \frac{1}{V}\frac{d\langle N\rangle}{d\varepsilon}\, d\varepsilon\, \frac{d\omega}{4\pi}\, v\cos\theta \qquad \text{(I-2)}$$

where $dJ_N'(\varepsilon, \omega)$ is the number of particles in energy range $d\varepsilon$ and in solid-angle range $d\omega$ emitted by the condensed phase per unit area and per unit time, and α is an **absorption coefficient** whose value is to be determined experimentally. (For convenience, the positive z axis is considered to extend into the gas phase. Note that the α used here is not related to the α of Chapter 3.) If α is independent of the angles θ and ϕ, then (since $d\langle N(\varepsilon)\rangle$ and v are independent of θ and ϕ) one may integrate immediately over θ and ϕ (over upper hemisphere only) to obtain

$$dJ_N'(\varepsilon) = \alpha \frac{v}{4\pi V} \frac{d\langle N\rangle}{d\varepsilon} d\varepsilon \int_0^{2\pi} \int_0^{\pi/2} \cos\theta \sin\theta \, d\theta \, d\phi$$

$$= \alpha \frac{v}{4V} \frac{d\langle N\rangle}{d\varepsilon} d\varepsilon \tag{I-3}$$

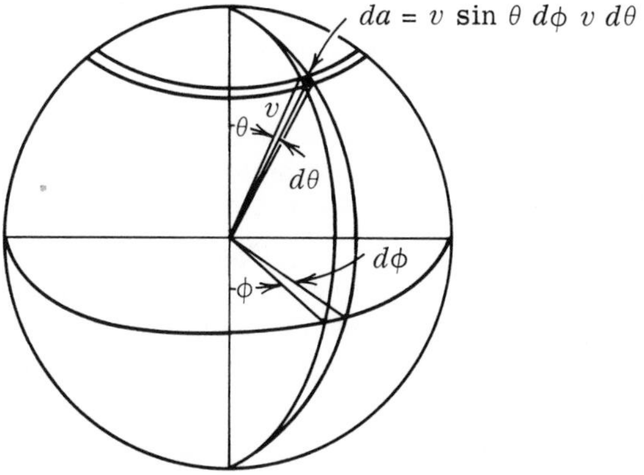

$$\frac{da}{4\pi v^2} = \frac{v \sin\theta \, d\phi \, v \, d\theta}{4\pi v^2} = \frac{\sin\theta \, d\phi \, d\theta}{4\pi} = \frac{d\omega}{4\pi}$$

Figure I-2 *The solid-angle ratio $d\omega/4\pi$ related to the area ratio $d\mathcal{A}/4\pi v^2$. (Associated differential volumes of velocity space are $d\mathcal{A}\, dv$ and $4\pi v^2\, dv$.)*

where $dJ_N'(\varepsilon)$ is the number of particles in energy range $d\varepsilon$ emitted by the condensed phase per unit area and per unit time.

Two special cases are of particular interest. In the case of thermal radiation (Chapter 10),

$$v = c = \text{const}$$

and

$$\frac{d\langle N\rangle}{d\varepsilon} d\varepsilon = \frac{8\pi V}{(\beta hc)^3} \frac{(\beta h\nu)^2}{e^{\beta h\nu} - 1} d(\beta h\nu)$$

where c is the speed of light. Hence, for thermal radiation from a surface,

$$dJ_N'(\nu) = \alpha \frac{2\pi}{(\beta h)^3 c^2} \frac{(\beta h\nu)^2}{e^{\beta h\nu} - 1} d(\beta h\nu) \tag{I-4}$$

In the case of a Maxwell-Boltzmann system of particles with nonzero rest mass,

$$v = \left(\frac{2\varepsilon'}{m}\right)^{1/2}$$

and

$$\frac{d\langle N\rangle}{d\varepsilon}\,d\varepsilon = \langle N\rangle \frac{1}{\langle N\rangle}\frac{d\langle N\rangle}{d\varepsilon'}\,d\varepsilon$$

$$= \langle N\rangle \frac{e^{-\beta\varepsilon'}}{g_e\left(\dfrac{2\pi m}{\beta h^2}\right)^{3/2} V}\,G(\varepsilon')\,d\varepsilon'$$

$$= \langle N\rangle \frac{e^{-\beta\varepsilon'}}{g_e\left(\dfrac{2\pi m}{\beta h^2}\right)^{3/2} V}\,g_e\,2\pi\left(\frac{2m}{h^2}\right)^{3/2} V\varepsilon'^{1/2}\,d\varepsilon'$$

$$= \langle N\rangle \frac{2}{\sqrt{\pi}}\,e^{-\beta\varepsilon'}\,(\beta\varepsilon')^{1/2}\,d(\beta\varepsilon')$$

where the factor $e^{-\beta\varepsilon'}/[g_e(2\pi m/\beta h^2)^{3/2}V]$ is the fraction of particles in a particle quantum state with translational energy level ε' [see Equations (6-11), (8-5), and (8-7)] and $G(\varepsilon')\,d\varepsilon'$ is the number of particle quantum states in the translational energy range from ε' to $\varepsilon' + d\varepsilon'$ (see Chapter 11, keeping in mind that, in Chapter 11, $g_e = 2$). Hence, for the case in which the particles have nonzero rest mass and the Maxwell-Boltzmann approximation may be applied to the gas phase, the emission from the condensed phase may be written

$$dJ_N'(\varepsilon') = \frac{\alpha}{(2\pi m\beta)^{1/2}}\frac{\langle N\rangle}{V}\,e^{-\beta\varepsilon'}\,\beta\varepsilon'\,d(\beta\varepsilon') \tag{I-5}$$

As will be shown later in this appendix, expressions similar to Equations (I-4) and (I-5) may be written for momentum and energy fluxes.

If α is not a function of energy, then Equations (I-3) to (I-5) may be integrated to obtain expressions for the total fluxes. The general expression may be written

$$J_N' = \frac{\alpha}{4V}\int_0^\infty v\,\frac{d\langle N\rangle}{d\varepsilon}\,d\varepsilon = \alpha\frac{\langle N\rangle}{V}\frac{\bar{v}}{4} \tag{I-6}$$

where the average speed is defined by

$$\bar{v} \equiv \frac{1}{\langle N\rangle}\int_0^\infty v\,\frac{d\langle N\rangle}{d\varepsilon}\,d\varepsilon \tag{I-7}$$

For the case of thermal radiation,

$$J_N' = \frac{\alpha}{4}\frac{\langle N\rangle}{V}\,c \sim \alpha\frac{4\pi\zeta(3)\,(kT)^3}{h^3c^2} \tag{I-8}$$

where the latter form follows from Equation (10-16). For the case in which the particles have nonzero rest mass and the Maxwell-Boltzmann approximation may be applied to the gas phase,

$$\bar{v} = \left(\frac{8}{\pi}\frac{1}{m\beta}\right)^{1/2} \int_0^\infty e^{-\beta\varepsilon'}\,\beta\varepsilon'\,d(\beta\varepsilon') = \left(\frac{8}{\pi}\frac{1}{m\beta}\right)^{1/2} \sim \left(\frac{8}{\pi}\frac{kT}{m}\right)^{1/2}$$

and $$J_N' = \frac{\alpha}{4}\frac{\langle N\rangle}{V}\left(\frac{8}{\pi}\frac{1}{m\beta}\right)^{1/2} \sim \frac{\alpha p}{(2\pi mkT)^{1/2}} \tag{I-9}$$

where the latter form follows from the thermal equation of state for a thermally perfect gas.

In the case of thermionic emission, the equilibrium gas-phase electron pressure appearing in Equation (I-9) is replaced frequently by a function of chemical potential and temperature. (A uniform potential in the gas phase may be achieved by considering the gas phase to be a neutral mixture of electrons and positive ions. The pressure appearing in Equation (I-9) would be, nevertheless, only the electron pressure.) Substituting $g_e = 2$ and $\mu = -w$ into Equation (8-5′), one obtains

$$p = 2e^{-w/kT}\left(\frac{2\pi mkT}{h^2}\right)^{3/2} kT \tag{I-10}$$

where p is the gas-phase electron pressure and w is the work function (see Chapter 11). Hence the gross thermionic emission rate may be written

$$J_N' = \alpha\frac{4\pi m}{h^3}(kT)^2 e^{-w/kT} \tag{I-11}$$

When multiplied by the charge per electron, Equation (I-11) gives the gross emission current. This current may be measured by collecting all emitted electrons at an electrode with potential sufficiently positive relative to the potential of the emitting surface. Such measurements have confirmed the temperature dependence predicted by Equation (I-11) and indicate that α is approximately 1/2, whereas w is of the order of several electron volts. (The reported values of α may include, however, effects other than failure of the condensed phase to absorb all incident particles. For example, the reported deviations from $\alpha = 1$ may be due, in part, to a dependence of the work function w on temperature.)

Example

In an application of Equations (I-10) and (I-11), consider thermionic emission from a tungsten filament heated to 2500°K. (The three most practical thermionic emitters are tungsten, thoriated tungsten, and oxide-coated nickel.) For tungsten, the work function w is about 4.5 ev, whereas the absorption coefficient α is about 0.50. Hence, from Equation (I-10), if the electron gas external to the filament is in equilibrium with the electron gas within the filament, then the pressure of the electron gas external to the filament is 1.7×10^{-7} atm; from Equation (I-11), if the electrons external to the filament are removed as fast as they escape from the filament, then the thermionic emission rate is 0.31 amp/cm^2. Attempts to operate two such electrodes with different work functions at different temperatures (the electrode with the lowest work function at the highest temperature) in order to convert heat into electrical work have led to the development of relatively compact **thermionic energy converters** with efficiencies of the order of 10 to 20 percent.

Equations (I-5) and (I-9) to (I-11) depend on use of the Maxwell-Boltzmann approximation. It remains to be shown that this approximation is valid for electrons in a gas phase in equilibrium with free electrons in a metal. As shown in Chapter 8, the condition

$$e^{-\mu/kT} >> 1$$

is sufficient for applicability of the Maxwell-Boltzmann approximation. At equilibrium, the chemical potential of the electrons in the gas phase must equal the chemical potential of the free electrons in the metal. Hence the aforementioned sufficient condition may be written

$$e^{w/kT} >> 1$$

Since w is of the order of several electron volts, this condition is satisfied for all metals at all temperatures at which the metals exist in the solid state. Hence the Maxwell-Boltzmann approximation is valid also for electrons in a gas phase in equilibrium with free electrons in a metal.

In the case of evaporation, the equilibrium gas-phase vapor pressure appearing in Equation (I-9) may be obtained, as a function of temperature for a given substance, either directly from experimental vapor-pressure data or indirectly from phase-change data using the Clausius-Clapeyron equation. When multiplied by the mass per molecule, Equation (I-9) gives the gross evaporation rate in units of mass per unit area per unit time. Experiments indicate that α may approach unity for evaporation from clean surfaces.

Consider now the flux of momentum from an emitting surface. (The resultant force acting on the emitting surface may be interpreted sometimes as a propulsive force and sometimes as a drag force. Since this resultant force is usually small, it is of importance only in situations in which all other forces are even smaller. Such situations may arise, for example, in interplanetary flights in those portions of space where forces due to gravitational fields are very small.) In the case of thermal radiation from a surface, the momentum of a photon with energy $h\nu$ is $h\nu/c$ [see Equations (10-4) and (10-5)]. Hence the momentum component normal to the surface for a photon with energy $h\nu$ moving in a direction with angle θ from the normal to the surface is $(h\nu/c)\cos\theta$. Multiplying Equation (I-2) by this momentum component per photon, one may write

$$dJ_P'(\nu, \omega) = \alpha \frac{1}{V} \frac{d\langle N\rangle}{d\nu} d\nu \frac{d\omega}{4\pi} h\nu \cos^2\theta \tag{I-12}$$

where $dJ_P'(\nu, \omega)$ is the normal-momentum flux due to emission of photons in frequency range $d\nu$ and in solid-angle range $d\omega$. If α is independent of the angles θ and ϕ, one may integrate immediately over θ and ϕ to obtain

$$\begin{aligned} dJ_P'(\nu) &= \alpha \frac{h\nu}{4\pi V} \frac{d\langle N\rangle}{d\nu} d\nu \int_0^{2\pi} \int_0^{\pi/2} \cos^2\theta \sin\theta \, d\theta \, d\phi \\ &= \alpha \frac{h\nu}{6V} \frac{d\langle N\rangle}{d\nu} d\nu \end{aligned} \tag{I-13}$$

where $dJ_P'(\nu)$ is the normal-momentum flux due to emission of photons in frequency range $d\nu$. Substituting for $(d\langle N\rangle/d\nu)\, d\nu$ from

$$\frac{d\langle N\rangle}{d\nu} d\nu = \frac{8\pi V}{(\beta hc)^3} \frac{(\beta h\nu)^2}{e^{\beta h\nu} - 1} d(\beta h\nu)$$

(see Page 103) one may write more explicitly

$$dJ_P'(\nu) = \alpha \frac{4\pi}{3(hc)^3 \beta^4} \frac{(\beta h\nu)^3}{e^{\beta h\nu} - 1} d(\beta h\nu) \tag{I-14}$$

Consider now, in a parallel treatment, the case of emission of particles with nonzero rest mass. Then the momentum component normal to the surface for a particle with translational energy ε' moving in a direction with angle θ from the normal to the surface is $(2m\varepsilon')^{1/2} \cos\theta$. Multiplying Equation (I-2) by this momentum component per particle, one may write

$$dJ_P'(\varepsilon', \omega) = \alpha \frac{1}{V} \frac{d\langle N\rangle}{d\varepsilon'} d\varepsilon' \frac{d\omega}{4\pi} 2\varepsilon' \cos^2\theta \tag{I-15}$$

where $dJ_P'(\varepsilon', \omega)$ is the normal-momentum flux due to emission of particles in translational-energy range $d\varepsilon'$ and in solid-angle range $d\omega$. If α is independent of the angles θ and ϕ, one may integrate immediately over θ and ϕ to obtain

$$dJ_P'(\varepsilon') = \alpha \frac{\varepsilon'}{3V} \frac{d\langle N\rangle}{d\varepsilon'} d\varepsilon' \tag{I-16}$$

where $dJ_P'(\varepsilon')$ is the normal-momentum flux due to emission of particles in translational-energy range $d\varepsilon'$. Substituting for $(d\langle N\rangle/d\varepsilon')\, d\varepsilon'$ from

$$\frac{d\langle N\rangle}{d\varepsilon'} d\varepsilon' = \langle N\rangle \frac{2}{\sqrt{\pi}} e^{-\beta\varepsilon'} (\beta\varepsilon')^{1/2} d(\beta\varepsilon')$$

one may write more explicitly

$$dJ_P'(\varepsilon') = \alpha \frac{2}{3\sqrt{\pi}} \frac{\langle N\rangle}{\beta V} e^{-\beta\varepsilon'} (\beta\varepsilon')^{3/2} d(\beta\varepsilon') \tag{I-17}$$

Momentum-flux equations (I-14) and (I-17) are the analogs of particle-flux equations (I-4) and (I-5).

If α is not a function of energy, Equations (I-14) and (I-17) may be integrated to obtain expressions for the gross normal-momentum flux in the direction away from the surface. For the case of thermal radiation

$$J_P' = \alpha \frac{4\pi}{3\,(hc)^3\,\beta^4} \int_0^\infty \frac{(\beta h\nu)^3}{e^{\beta h\nu} - 1}\, d\,(\beta h\nu)$$

The definite integral appearing here has value $6\zeta\,(4)$, where $\zeta\,(4) = \pi^4/90$. Hence

$$J_P' = \alpha \frac{4\pi^5}{45\,(hc)^3\,\beta^4} = \alpha \frac{\langle p\rangle}{2} \qquad \text{(I-18)}$$

where the latter form follows from Equation (10-13). For the case of emission of particles with nonzero rest mass,

$$J_P' = \alpha \frac{2}{3\sqrt{\pi}} \frac{\langle N\rangle}{\beta V} \int_0^\infty e^{-\beta\varepsilon'}\,(\beta\varepsilon')^{3/2}\, d\,(\beta\varepsilon')$$

The definite integral appearing here has value $\Gamma\,(5/2) = 3\sqrt{\pi}/4$. Hence

$$J_P' = \alpha \frac{\langle N\rangle}{2\beta V} = \alpha \frac{\langle p\rangle}{2} \qquad \text{(I-19)}$$

where the latter form follows from the thermal equation of state for a thermally perfect gas. The $\langle p\rangle$ appearing in Equations (I-18) and (I-19) is the pressure which would exist in a gas phase consisting of emitted particles in equilibrium with the condensed phase. Note that the simple dependence on equilibrium gas-phase pressure obtained in these two equations is realized only if α is independent of θ, ϕ, and the energy of the emitted particle.

Consider finally the flux of translational energy from an emitting surface. Multiplying Equations (I-2) and (I-3) by the translational energy per particle, one obtains, for general α,

$$dJ_E'\,(\varepsilon', \omega) = \alpha \frac{1}{V} \frac{d\,\langle N\rangle}{d\varepsilon'}\, d\varepsilon' \frac{d\omega}{4\pi}\, \varepsilon'\, v \cos\theta \qquad \text{(I-20)}$$

and, for α independent of θ and ϕ,

$$dJ_E'\,(\varepsilon') = \alpha \frac{\varepsilon'\, v}{4V} \frac{d\,\langle N\rangle}{d\varepsilon'}\, d\varepsilon' \qquad \text{(I-21)}$$

where $dJ_E'\,(\varepsilon', \omega)$ is the translational-energy flux in energy range $d\varepsilon'$ and in solid-angle range $d\omega$, and $dJ_E'\,(\varepsilon')$ is the translational-energy flux in energy range $d\varepsilon'$. Substituting for $(d\,\langle N\rangle/d\varepsilon')\, d\varepsilon'$, one obtains for the case of thermal radiation

$$dJ_E'\,(\nu) = \alpha \frac{2\pi}{\beta^4\, h^3\, c^2} \frac{(\beta h\nu)^3}{e^{\beta h\nu} - 1}\, d\,(\beta h\nu) \qquad \text{(I-22)}$$

and for the case of emission of particles with nonzero rest mass

$$dJ_E'(\varepsilon') = \frac{\alpha}{(2\pi m\beta)^{1/2}} \frac{\langle N \rangle}{\beta V} e^{-\beta\varepsilon'} (\beta\varepsilon')^2 \, d(\beta\varepsilon') \tag{I-23}$$

If α is not a function of energy, Equations (I-22) and (I-23) may be integrated to obtain for thermal radiation

$$\begin{aligned} J_E' &= \alpha \frac{2\pi}{\beta^4 h^3 c^2} \int_0^\infty \frac{(\beta h\nu)^3}{e^{\beta h\nu} - 1} d(\beta h\nu) \\ &= \alpha \frac{2\pi}{\beta^4 h^3 c^2} \frac{\pi^4}{15} = \frac{\alpha}{4} \frac{\langle E \rangle}{V} c \\ &= \frac{J_N' \langle E \rangle}{\langle N \rangle} \sim \alpha\sigma T^4 \end{aligned} \tag{I-24}$$

where $\sigma (\equiv 2\pi^5 k^4/15h^3 c^2)$ is the **Stefan-Boltzmann constant** (with value 5.669×10^{-5} (erg/cm^2-sec-°K^4 or 0.1737×10^{-8} Btu/ft^2-hr-°R^4), and for emission of particles with nonzero rest mass,

$$\begin{aligned} J_E' &= \frac{\alpha}{(2\pi m\beta)^{1/2}} \frac{\langle N \rangle}{\beta V} \int_0^\infty e^{-\beta\varepsilon'} (\beta\varepsilon')^2 \, d(\beta\varepsilon') \\ &= \frac{\alpha}{(2\pi m\beta)^{1/2}} \frac{\langle N \rangle}{\beta V} 2 \sim \frac{\alpha}{4} \frac{N}{V} \bar{v}\, 2kT \\ &= J_N' \, 2kT \end{aligned} \tag{I-25}$$

Note that the factor $2kT$ appearing in the final form of Equation (I-25) is greater than E/N; this result is due to the fact that, for particles with nonzero rest mass, the particles with the greatest translational energy have the greatest speed.

The results of these analyses are summarized in Table I-1, where expressions for particle, normal-momentum, and energy-emission fluxes are tabulated for thermal radiation, thermionic emission, and evaporation. The

Table I-1 Gross emissions from surfaces
(α independent of θ, ϕ, and ε')

	J_N'	J_P'	J_E'
General relation	$\alpha \frac{N}{V} \frac{\bar{v}}{4}$	$\alpha \frac{p}{2}$	Not convenient ◀
Thermal radiation ...	$\alpha \frac{4\pi\zeta(3)(kT)^3}{h^3 c^2}$	$\alpha \frac{4\pi^5 (kT)^4}{45 (hc)^3}$	$J_N' \frac{E}{N} = \alpha\sigma T^4$ ◀
Thermionic emission	$\alpha \frac{4\pi m}{h^3} (kT)^2 e^{-w/kT}$	$\alpha \left(\frac{2\pi m}{h^2}\right)^{3/2} (kT)^{5/2} e^{-w/kT}$	$J_N' \, 2kT$ ◀
Evaporation	$\alpha \frac{p}{(2\pi mkT)^{1/2}}$	$\alpha \frac{p}{2}$	$J_N' \, 2kT$ ◀

NOTE: N/V, E/N, and p are for gas phase consisting of emitted particles in equilibrium with condensed phase.

expressions used most frequently by the engineer or scientist are perhaps the expressions for J_E' in the case of thermal radiation and for J_N' in the cases of thermionic emission and evaporation.

If α is set equal to unity, then all expressions written here are applicable to effusion from a small hole in the wall of a cavity (see Figure I-3) for the case in which the presence of the hole causes negligible deviations from thermal equilibrium within the cavity. These expressions indicate that photon effusion is characterized entirely by the cavity temperature; electron effusion is characterized by the cavity temperature and the cavity-wall material; in molecular effusion, if the molecules condense at the cavity temperature (in which case they are produced by vaporization of a source material located within the cavity), then the effusion is characterized by the cavity temperature and the source material; whereas if the molecules

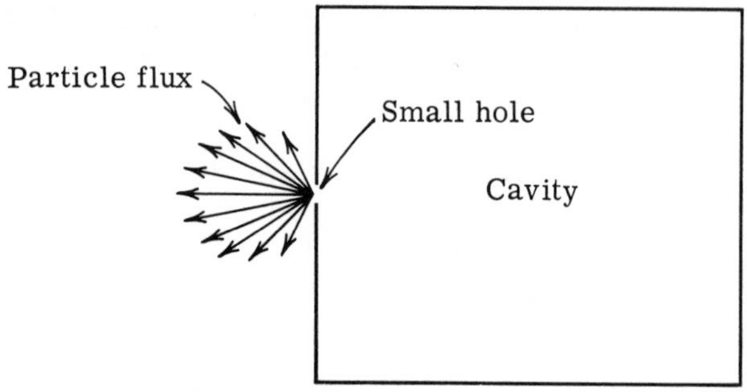

Figure I-3 *Emission from small hole in cavity wall. (The z axis coincides with the orifice axis and is positive outward from the cavity.)*

do not condense at the cavity temperature (in which case they are supplied to the cavity from some external source), then the effusion is characterized by the cavity temperature and the cavity-gas pressure. The thermal equilibrium of the cavity gas is disturbed negligibly if the diameter of the hole is small in comparison with the average distance that a particle moves between collisions. Such effusions are used frequently as blackbody thermal-radiation sources and as molecular-beam sources.

Example

In an application of the methods discussed in this appendix, consider the noise (known frequently as **Johnson noise**) generated in an electrical circuit as a consequence of thermal oscillations of electromagnetic waves in a conducting wire included in this circuit. (Since these "thermal oscillations of electromagnetic waves" have the same nature and origin as the electromagnetic waves of thermal radiation, they also are called photons sometimes.) The thermal-noise power supplied to the circuit by the wire is the rate at which energy associated with these oscillations crosses (in either direction) the points separating the wire from the rest of the circuit. Since the fluxes across these points are one-dimensional, a one-dimensional counterpart to Equation (I-21) is required. One may write

$$2\,dJ_E'(\varepsilon') = \frac{\varepsilon' c}{l}\frac{d\langle N\rangle}{d\varepsilon'}\,d\varepsilon' \tag{I-26}$$

where $dJ_E'(\varepsilon')$ is the translational-energy flux in one direction, $(1/l)(d\langle N\rangle/d\varepsilon')\,d\varepsilon'$ is the number of particles (photons) per unit length in energy range $d\varepsilon'$, l is the length of the wire, and the coefficient α is equated to unity since the circuit is continuous at the ends of the wire. Since the electromagnetic waves in the wire are one-dimensional, one-dimensional counterparts to the appropriate equa-

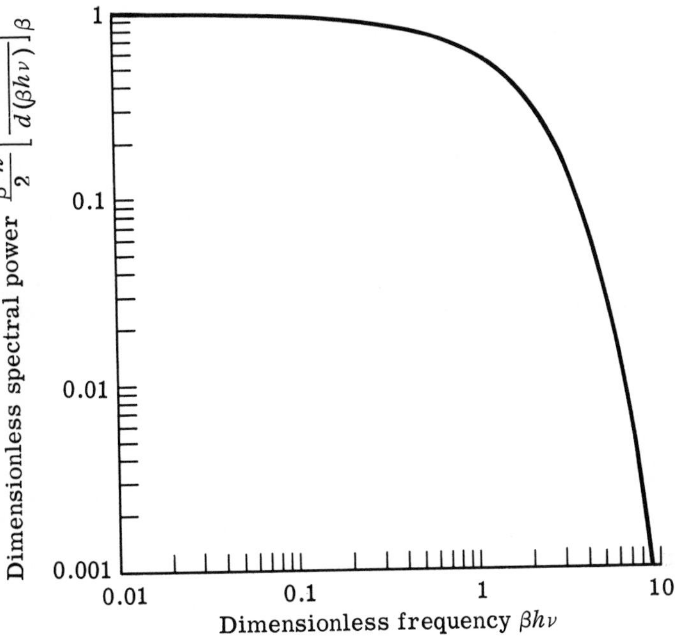

Figure I-4 *Spectral thermal-noise power as a function of frequency.*

tions of Chapter 10 are required also. The allowed frequencies ν_k are related to the quantum numbers k by

$$\nu_k = \frac{ck}{2l} \tag{I-27}$$

so that the number of quantum states with frequencies between ν and $\nu + d\nu$ is given by

$$G(\nu)\,d\nu = \frac{4l}{c}\,d\nu \tag{I-28}$$

whereas the number of particles (photons) in energy range $d\varepsilon'$ is given by

$$\frac{d\langle N\rangle}{d\varepsilon'}\,d\varepsilon' = \frac{4l}{\beta hc}\frac{1}{e^{\beta h\nu} - 1}\,d(\beta h\nu) \tag{I-29}$$

Substituting from Equation (I-29) into Equation (I-26), one obtains

$$2\, dJ_E'(\nu) = \frac{4}{\beta^2 h} \frac{\beta h\nu}{e^{\beta h\nu} - 1}\, d(\beta h\nu) \tag{I-30}$$

for the thermal-noise power supplied in the frequency range between ν and $\nu + d\nu$. If $\beta h\nu << 1$, then (in the nomenclature of classical thermodynamics)

$$2\, dJ_E'(\nu) \approx 4kT\, d\nu \tag{I-31}$$

that is, the noise is **white noise** (independent of frequency). If $\beta h\nu >> 1$, then

$$2\, dJ_E'(\nu) \approx \frac{4}{\beta^2 h} \frac{\beta h\nu}{e^{\beta h\nu}}\, d(\beta h\nu) \tag{I-32}$$

that is, the noise power decreases rapidly as frequency increases (see Figure I-4).

These results have important implications for electronic circuits which transmit or amplify signals; they indicate that the signal-to-noise ratio is increased if the temperature of the circuit components is decreased, the bandwidth $\Delta\nu$ within which the signal is transmitted or amplified is decreased, and the lowest passed frequency is increased. Since, at 300°K, $1/\beta h$ is about 6×10^8 cycles/sec, it is seen that microwave amplifiers (for which the lowest frequencies are of the order of 10^9 cycles/sec) can operate under conditions for which the noise power is relatively small.

appendix J

maxwell-boltzmann velocity distribution

In the derivation of Equation (I-5), the fraction of particles with translational energy between ε' and $\varepsilon' + d\varepsilon'$ was found (for a Maxwell-Boltzmann system of particles with nonzero mass) to be

$$\frac{1}{\langle N \rangle}\frac{d\langle N \rangle}{d\varepsilon'}\,d\varepsilon' = \frac{2}{\sqrt{\pi}}e^{-\beta\varepsilon'}\,(\beta\varepsilon')^{1/2}\,d\,(\beta\varepsilon')$$

If one is interested in the fraction of particles with speed between v and $v + dv$, one might substitute for ε' from $\varepsilon' = mv^2/2$ to obtain

$$\frac{1}{\langle N \rangle}\frac{d\langle N \rangle}{dv}\,dv = \left(\frac{\beta m}{2\pi}\right)^{3/2} e^{-\beta mv^2/2}\,4\pi v^2\,dv \qquad \text{(J-1)}$$

If one is interested in the fraction of particles in velocity-range $v^2\,d\omega\,dv$, one might multiply the right-hand side of Equation (J-1) by $d\omega/4\pi$ (see Figure I-2) to obtain

$$\frac{1}{\langle N \rangle}\frac{d\langle N \rangle}{v^2\,d\omega\,dv}\,v^2\,d\omega\,dv = \left(\frac{\beta m}{2\pi}\right)^{3/2} e^{-\beta mv^2/2}\,v^2\,d\omega\,dv \qquad \text{(J-2)}$$

or, in terms of rectangular coordinates,

$$\frac{1}{\langle N \rangle}\frac{d\langle N \rangle}{dv_x\,dv_y\,dv_z}\,dv_x\,dv_y\,dv_z$$

$$= \left(\frac{\beta m}{2\pi}\right)^{3/2} \exp\left[-\frac{\beta m\,(v_x^2 + v_y^2 + v_z^2)}{2}\right] dv_x\,dv_y\,dv_z \qquad \text{(J-2')}$$

where v_x, v_y, and v_z are, respectively, the x-, y-, and z-velocity components. The distributions described by Equations (J-1) and (J-2) are known as the **Maxwell-Boltzmann speed distribution** and the **Maxwell-Boltzmann velocity distribution**, respectively. They apply to polyatomic gases as well as to monatomic gases, and are used frequently in the kinetic theory of gases.

appendix **K**

natural constants[†]

Quantity	*Value (cgs units)*	*Value (mksa units)*
Avogadro's constant N_A....	6.02252×10^{23}/mole	6.02252×10^{23}/mole
Boltzmann's constant k.....	1.38054×10^{-16} erg/°K	1.38054×10^{-23} joule/°K
Electron rest mass m_e......	9.1091×10^{-28} g	9.1091×10^{-31} kg
Electronic charge e.........	4.80298×10^{-10} esu	1.60210×10^{-19} coulomb
Newton constant g_n.........	9.80665×10^{2} cm/sec^2	9.80665 m/sec^2
Planck's constant h.........	6.6256×10^{-27} erg-sec	6.6256×10^{-34} joule-sec
Stefan-Boltzmann constant σ...............	5.6697×10^{-5} erg/cm^2-°K^4-sec	5.6697×10^{-8} watt/m^2-°K^4
Gas constant $R\,(=N_A k)$....	8.3143×10^{7} erg/mole-°K	8.3143 joules/mole-°K
Atomic mass unit $u\,(=1/N_A)$..............	1.66043×10^{-24} g	1.66043×10^{-27} kg
Speed of light $c\,(=\sqrt{2\pi^5 k^4/15h^3\sigma})$	2.997925×10^{10} cm/sec	2.997925×10^{8} m/sec

† SOURCE: New Values for the Physical Constants, *Phys. Today*, vol. 17, pp. 48–49, February, 1964.

appendix **L**

conversion factors

Length	1 cm	$= 10^{-2}$ m
		$= 10^{8}$ A
		$= 3.9370 \times 10^{-1}$ in.
Mass	1 g	$= 10^{-3}$ kg
		$= 6.02252 \times 10^{23}$ atomic mass units
		$= 2.20462 \times 10^{-3}$ lb_m
Force	1 dyne	$= 1$ g-cm/sec^2
		$= 10^{-5}$ newton
		$= 10^{-5}$ kg-m/sec^2
		$= 2.2481 \times 10^{-6}$ lb_f
Energy	1 erg	$= 1$ dyne-cm
		$= 10^{-7}$ joule
		$= 10^{-7}$ newton-m
		$= 2.390 \times 10^{-8}$ calorie
		$= 6.2418 \times 10^{11}$ ev
		$= 9.481 \times 10^{-11}$ Btu
Pressure	1 atm	$= 7.60 \times 10^{2}$ torrs
		$= 1.01325 \times 10^{6}$ dynes/cm^2
		$= 1.01325 \times 10^{5}$ newtons/m^2
		$= 1.4696 \times 10$ lb_f/in.^{2}
Temperature†	1°K	= 1°C
		= 1.8°R
		= 1.8°F

†0°C corresponds to 273.15°K, 491.67°R, and 32°F.

list of symbols

- a — Force constant for harmonic oscillator
- A — Helmholtz function ($\equiv E - TS$)
- $\mathcal{A}$ — Area
- b — Force constant for harmonic oscillator
- B — Magnitude of potential barriers encountered by adsorbed particle as it moves parallel to adsorbing surface (Figure 12-2); also band spectral constant ($\equiv h/8\pi^2 I_e c$) (Chapter 13)
- c — Speed of light; also a constant (Chapter 7)
- c_l — Speed of longitudinal wave (Chapter 14)
- c_t — Speed of transverse wave (Chapter 14)
- C — Heat capacity
- D — Debye function [Equation (14-19)]
- D_e — Negative of potential energy of diatomic molecules at equilibrium distance r_e for case of no electron excitations
- D_0 — Dissociation energy of diatomic molecule at 0°K ($\equiv D_e - h\nu/2$)
- e — Base of natural system of logarithms
- E — Energy of system (called internal energy if effects of surface-tension and field forces are negligible)
- F_c — Generalized force [$\equiv -(\partial E/\partial X_c)_{X_{c'}, s}$] exerted by a system on its surroundings
- g_e — Number of allowed internal quantum states of particle or subsystem with given internal energy level (If no additional subscripts are used, the internal energy level is the lowest possible level and the particle or subsystem is in its ground state.)
- G — Gibbs function ($\equiv H - TS$)
- $G_{\varepsilon'}$ — Number of quantum states with energy ε'
- G_ν — Number of quantum states with frequency ν (Chapter 10); also number of oscillators with frequency ν (Chapter 14)
- $G(\varepsilon')\,d\varepsilon'$ — Number of quantum states with energies between ε' and $\varepsilon' + d\varepsilon'$

$G(\nu)\,d\nu$	Number of quantum states with frequencies between ν and $\nu + d\nu$ (Chapter 10); also number of oscillators with frequencies between ν and $\nu + d\nu$ (Chapter 14)
h	Planck's constant
$\hbar$	Planck's constant divided by 2π
h_x	Scale factor selected so that $h_x\,dq_x$ represents actual displacement in direction q_x
H	Enthalpy ($\equiv E + pV$)
i	$\sqrt{-1}$
I_e	Moment of inertia about center of mass ($\equiv \mu r_e^2$)
j	Ensemble-member quantum state
J_E	Energy flux
J_N	Particle flux
J_P	Momentum flux
k'	A constant
k	Boltzmann's constant; also quantum number for translation
K	Number of different types of particles
K_p	Equilibrium constant [$\equiv \prod_i (p_i/p^o)^{\nu_i}$]
l	Length of edge of box; also quantum number for vibration
L	Total angular momentum
L_z	Angular momentum about z axis
m	Mass of particle or subsystem
m_x	Mass associated with generalized coordinate q_x
M	Number of sites available for "localized" adsorption
n_j	Number of ensemble members in their jth quantum state
n_j^*	Most probable number of ensemble members in their jth quantum state
n	Number of members in ensemble
N	Number of particles in system
N_A	Avogadro's constant
p	Pressure
p^o	Arbitrary constant with units of pressure
p_x	Momentum conjugate to generalized coordinate q_x
P_j	Probability ($\equiv n_j^*/n$) that an ensemble member is in its jth quantum state
P_k	Fraction of particles which are in their kth quantum state
q_x	Generalized coordinate
q_n	Partition function for nth harmonic oscillator
Q	Heat added to system; also partition function for canonical ensemble
Q_z	Partition function

r Radius (Figure 7-1); also distance between nuclei (Figures 13-1 and 13-2)
r_e Equilibrium distance between nuclei
R Gas constant ($\equiv N_A k$)
s Length of arc
S Entropy of system
t Time
T Temperature
U Potential energy
v Magnitude of velocity
V Volume of system
w Work required to remove an electron from a metal
W Work done by system
x One of three orthogonal rectangular coordinates; also $e^{-\beta\varepsilon_{ik}-\gamma_i}$ (Chapter 6); also dummy integration variable (Chapters 8 and 14); also mole fraction (Chapter 13); also distance between two particles (Appendix H)
X Coordinate of center of mass
X_c Generalized displacement
y One of three orthogonal rectangular coordinates
z One of three orthogonal rectangular coordinates
α Lagrangian multiplier; also $2\pi(\nu m/h)^{1/2}$ (harmonic oscillator); also directional angle (Chapter 14); also absorption coefficient (Appendix I)
β Lagrangian multiplier related to E
γ_i Lagrangian multiplier related to N_i
ε Energy of particle or subsystem
η Dummy summation index
θ Colatitudinal angle (Figures 7-1, 13-1, and I-1)
θ_D Debye temperature ($\equiv h\nu_m/k$)
θ_E Einstein temperature ($\equiv h\nu/k$)
θ_r Characteristic temperature for rotation ($\equiv \hbar^2/2I_e k$)
θ_V Characteristic temperature for vibration ($\equiv h\nu/k$)
Θ θ-dependent wave function
λ Wavelength
Λ Thermal de Broglie wavelength [$\equiv (h^2/2\pi mkT)^{1/2}$]; also availability (Appendix F)
μ Chemical potential; also reduced mass
μ^o $\mu - kT \ln p/p^o$
ν Frequency of vibration of harmonic oscillator; also wave frequency
ν_i Stoichiometric coefficient for ith type of particle
Ξ Grand partition function

π Lagrangian multiplier related to V; also ratio of circumference of a circle to its diameter

Π Continued product over dummy index

$\sigma^2(A)$ Variance $[\equiv\langle(A - \langle A\rangle)\rangle]$ of quantity A

σ Symmetry number (= 1 for distinguishable nuclei, = 2 for indistinguishable nuclei); also Stefan-Boltzmann constant (Appendix I)

Σ Summation over indicated dummy index

ϕ Number of degrees of freedom of system; also longitudinal angle (Figures 7-1, 13-1, and I-1); also coordinate-independent wave function (Chapter 7)

Φ ϕ-dependent wave function; also generalized force conjugate to number of adsorption sites (Chapter 12)

$\Phi^\dagger$ Generalized force conjugate to area (Chapter 12)

$\chi(T)$ Pressure-independent parameter appearing in isotherm for perfect localized adsorbed gas [Equation (12-21)]

$\chi^\dagger(T)$ Pressure-independent parameter appearing in isotherm for perfect mobile adsorbed gas [Equation (12-35)]

$\chi(x)$ Time-independent wave function for a particle with reduced mass moving relative to center of mass

$\mathbf{X}(X)$ Time-independent wave function for a particle with combined mass moving with center of mass

ψ Time-independent wave function

Ψ Total wave function

ω Wave number ($\equiv \varepsilon/hc$); also solid angle (Appendix I)

$\Omega(E, X_c, N_i)$ Number of possible ensemble-member quantum states for given set of values of E, X_c, N_i

Ω Number of possible quantum states of ensemble of members

Ω_R Number of possible quantum states of reservoir

Ω_t Total number of possible quantum states of ensemble of members and reservoir

$\langle\ \rangle$ Expected value

$\sim$ Is in correspondence with

A dot over a symbol indicates the derivative with respect to time; a bar over a symbol indicates the average value.

Subscripts

a Harmonic oscillator with force constant a

ad Adiabatic process

b Harmonic oscillator with force constant b

BE Bose-Einstein

E A given value of energy

FD	Fermi-Dirac
i	Type of particle
j	Ensemble-member quantum state; also total-angular-momentum quantum state (Chapter 13)
k	Particle quantum state
m	Azimuthal quantum state; also maximum (Chapter 14)
MB	Maxwell-Boltzmann
n	nth harmonic oscillator
N	Given values of particle numbers
p	Constant pressure
r	Reversible process
rot	Rotational
R	Reservoir
t	Total for ensemble of members and reservoir
tr	Translational
V	Constant volume
vib	Vibrational
x	x coordinate
y	y coordinate
z	z coordinate
0	0°K; also equilibrium position (Chapters 9 and 12); also environment (Appendix F)

Superscripts

*	Complex conjugate (formed by replacing each i by $-i$); also value of parameter which yields maximum term in series representation of partition function (Appendixes D and E)
′	A set with specified member omitted; also functions containing only contributions of translational degrees of freedom (Chapter 11 and Appendix I); also final state (Appendix E); also emissions with absorption coefficient less than unity (Appendix I)

index

Boldface page numbers indicate the page on which the term is defined.